COMPUTER MODELING and SIMULATION

COMPUTER MODELING and SIMULATION

FRANCIS F. MARTIN
Hughes Ground Systems
Formerly Booz. Allen Applied Research, Inc.

JOHN WILEY & SONS, INC., New York · London · Sydney

Library of Congress Catalog Card Number: 67-28948
GB 471 57352X
Printed in the United States of America

To Peg

PREFACE

Watching the development of computer modeling and simulation from its infancy more than a decade ago to its present form has been an exciting experience and being involved in this development has been equally exciting. The early attempts may appear simple and naïve in comparison with the present highly sophisticated forms, but this impression is somewhat misleading because the pioneering work during the early developmental stages was just as challenging and demanding as present-day applications. We often forget that pioneering work is necessary as the genesis of any tool or technique.

The development of computer modeling and simulation has paralleled the evolution of electronic digital computers in their successive generations of development. This is plausible, for the two are so closely related. As digital computers evolved into today's highly sophisticated devices from the simple computers of the 1940's, their basic features have remained the same: all computers have memory devices, arithmetic units, control units, and input/output devices and, similarly, certain basic elements in computer modeling and simulation also remained unchanged; for example, all computer simulations consist of mathematical computations, logic flows, deterministic or nondeterministic elements, or both. We have used the technique in new applications, we have added refinements, and we have developed new and efficient simulation languages, but the basic features remain the same.

This does not deny that breakthroughs in the technique will occur in the future, breakthroughs that may completely alter our present concepts and applications. On the contrary, we must expect and should anticipate many changes and new applications. Computer modeling and simulation has application to the solution of problems in engineering, the physical and biological sciences, operations research, systems analysis, business and commerce, industry, national defense, education, social sciences, government, and many others.

Because the technique has grown so rapidly in so many diverse areas, there is a need to summarize the highlights and to articulate the rationale and methodologies in computer modeling and simulation. There is also a need to plan and organize the materials so that the student or beginner can learn the technique and the professional can refer to the materials easily. For some time I have recognized and anticipated these needs and have been interested in writing a book on the technique. It is the purpose of this book to provide an introductory background for the student as well as reference material for the professional.

Computer Modeling and Simulation provides a broad overview of methods, tools, and techniques, such as statistical methods and computer programming, but without attempting complete coverage of these disciplines. It discusses procedures of model construction, starting with the inception of the problem statement, and carries on through to completion of the problem solution with a look at over-all procedures that have general application and appear technically sound. Specific problems, which naturally require specialized attention, are used only for illustration purposes. I make no attempt to trace through the development of a model in any particular area of application, such as business or transportation.

A set of problems is included at the end of each chapter. They are designed as practical exercises for the student or beginner in the use of the technique, and several are intended to stimulate creative thinking. The appendices include a glossary of terms applicable to the technique, an example of a model, a set of commonly used formulas, tables, and graphs of select functions, and a comprehensive bibliography. The references are listed by several specific categories, such as simulation techniques and simulation languages. Numbers appearing in brackets throughout the text apply to references in the bibliography that will give the reader additional sources on the technique and its related areas.

I gratefully acknowledge the encouragement and assistance given by my colleagues and friends. Thanks are due especially to Dr. George H. Shortley for his suggestions on the manuscript, to Edward G. Loges, John Newman, and Thomas R. Shaw for their valuable comments, and to Paul Devine Jr. for proofreading the mathematical equations.

Francis F. Martin

Bethesda, Maryland
September 1967

CONTENTS

COMPUTER MODELING and SIMULATION

PART ONE

Introduction

1

INTRODUCTION

Computer modeling and simulation is a powerful technique with a broad range of applications in all research and analysis activities. The technique has had a remarkable development, and speculations about its future applications are equally impressive. The meaning of computer modeling and simulation seems to depend on whoever comments upon the technique, whether layman or specialist.

The layman may understand very little about computer modeling and simulation, so that he may view the entire process with some apprehension and skepticism. His viewpoint may be well justified, especially because of the manner in which computers produce results at electronic speeds. The process is quite complicated for laymen to understand fully because it cuts across several disciplines, such as probability and statistics, mathematics, and computer programming. Yet regardless of the layman's view, laymen are the principal users of computer modeling and simulation results.

The statistician may view the technique as a synthetic experiment with flexibilities never experienced before in laboratory or field experimentation. With the technique he can design experiments and test concepts unlike anything previously possible. The statistician, however, is fully aware that, for any experimentation device, what comes *out* is only as good as what goes *in* the experiment. He treats the results with certain quantitative restraints by assigning statistical confidence measures to the results.

The mathematician may view computer modeling and simulation as a tool of mathematical logic and computation. The technique is one of several at his command for problem solution. He views the technique as a mathematical device which he applies when it is the most appropriate and expedient tool. For him mathematical modeling is as old as mathematics itself, and it is the application of electronic computers to modeling that is recent.

Systems analysts, operations analysts, and business analysts may view computer modeling and simulation as one of several simulation techniques available; for example, simulation includes the use of analog devices, laboratory models, and "test-bed" sites. Computer modeling and simulation is a tool to provide analysts with answers to questions that arise in systems and operations analysis. Analysts use the technique whenever its use is appropriate. They view the use of the computer as one feature of the broader simulation technique.

Computer programmers may view computer modeling and simulation as an interesting and challenging programming problem. It is a problem to which programmers direct their resources and talents to produce an efficient computer program. Their interests are usually in methods and means of producing results on the computer rather than in the end results themselves. Computer programmers have developed a storehouse of programming skills which can be effectively applied to computer modeling and simulation.

Actually the definition of computer modeling and simulation includes all these viewpoints. It is a *synthetic experiment, a mathematical tool,* a *simulation technique,* and a *programming problem.* Even though the layman's view may be the most spurious, he usually provides the questions that the specialists answer by application of the technique. The layman may not know that computer modeling and simulation is the appropriate technique to apply to his problem, and he may not even

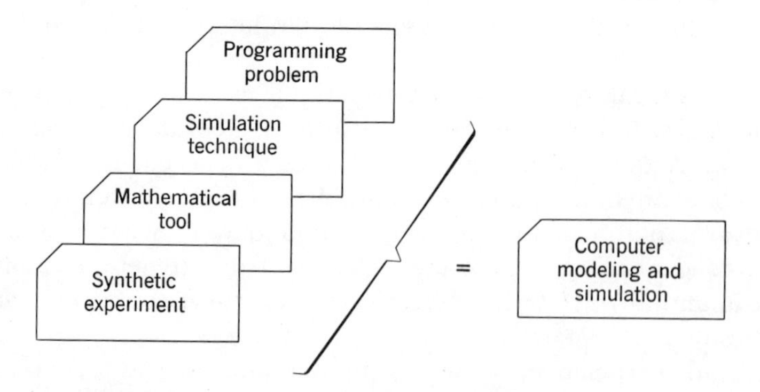

Fig. 1.1 Definition of computer modeling and simulation.

be aware of the technique. But he places his confidence in the specialists just as the patient places his confidence in the medical doctor (Fig. 1.1).

As model builders we have three main responsibilities. First, we must understand what computer modeling and simulation is. Second, we must know how to apply the technique. Third, we must be able to provide meaningful results from the model. We must bear in mind that it is usually laymen who will be making decisions on the basis of model results. Therefore results should be presented in terms that laymen can understand and apply in decision making.

It is our purpose to devote our attention to these responsibilities in the discussion of computer modeling and simulation. In this chapter we define the scope of the book and some of the basic terms. We present a brief history of the technique and also list several of its advantages.

DEFINITIONS

A *computer simulation model* is a logical-mathematical representation of a concept, system, or operation programmed for solution on a high-speed electronic computer.

A *deterministic model* is an analytical representation of a concept, system, or operation in which there are unique outcomes for a given set of inputs.

A *nondeterministic* or *stochastic model* is one in which the functional relationships depend on chance parameters. The outcomes for a given set of inputs can be predicted only in a probabilistic context.

An *expected value model* is one in which the expected values (or means) are assigned to the chance parameters.

A computer simulation model may contain all or some of the features of deterministic, nondeterministic, or expected value models.

HISTORY

Let us trace briefly the ancestry of computer modeling and simulation. Man's ingenuity and capacity for invention has no bounds, and his skill in devising or combining elements leads him to new technical achievements. Given two elements, *computers* and *modeling,* he created a new compound, *computer modeling and simulation.*

We consider first the history of electronic digital computers. It is very brief in terms of years, yet very broad in terms of accomplishments. The theoretical basis for computers developed scarcely over a century ago. Research in computer design was started after 1930, and the actual implementation of computers was only started after World War II.

The theoretical basis for computer technology is Boolean algebra, which was developed by the English mathematician George Boole around 1850. Boolean algebra has applications to logic, set theory, and probability theory, and it provides the concepts for the study of switching problems in computer design.

Switching theory, which has direct Boolean algebra application, uses Boolean symbols, terms, and expressions. Switching theory includes the theory of circuits and networks and is concerned with circuits that can be in two or more discrete states. The bulk of switching theory, however, is primarily concerned with two states, or "on-off" binary devices. It is these binary devices that are fundamental to computer implementation. The two circuit states are distinguished by high or low voltages and are represented by two binary digits (bits), 0 or 1, which is the binary number system.

Binary representation forms the basis for the logical design of digital computers. Internal logic structure is designed according to Boolean logic using AND, OR, and NOT functions. The internal number system, the internal arithmetic, and the storage of information in computer memory are always in binary form. For example, a 36-bit computer word contains a serial arrangement of 36 zeros and ones which can be interpreted numerically or logically by the computer. Computer technology is a direct outgrowth of Boolean algebra and switching theory. If these two disciplines had not been developed, the present-day mechanization of electronic digital computers would never have been possible. At least, the mechanization would have been quite different.

The earliest example of an electronic digital computer is the ENIAC, which stands for Electronic Numerical Integrator and Computer. The ENIAC, a general-purpose computer with fixed-point operation, was built in 1946 at the Moore School of Engineering, University of Pennsylvania, for the U.S. Army Ballistics Research Laboratories at Aberdeen, Maryland. Other examples of noncommercial computers built since World War II include the following:

ADEC, built by Harvard University for the U.S. Naval Proving Grounds, Dahlgren, Virginia.

ILLIAC, built by the University of Illinois.

SWAC and SEAC, both built by the National Bureau of Standards.

CALDIC, built by the University of California at Berkeley.

JOHNNIAC, built by Rand Corporation.

LEPRECHAUN, built by the Bell Telephone Laboratories for the U.S. Air Force.

Some outstanding scientists associated with early computer development include Babbage, Turing, Aiken, von Neumann, Weiner, Phister, and Korn.

Since mid-twentieth century many commercial computers have been built for scientific and business applications. If we compiled a complete list of computer lines and peripheral equipment built in the United States, our list would contain several hundred entries. Today there are an estimated 25,000 computers in operation in the United States, in comparison to less than 100 in 1950. Some, but not all, of the industries that produce commercial computers include Burroughs Corporation, Control Data Corporation, General Electric Company, Honeywell Incorporated, International Business Machines Corporation, National Cash Register Company, Radio Corporation of America, and Sperry Rand Corporation. These industries alone have produced more than 100 major computer lines in addition to smaller computers and peripheral equipment [206].

In the short period since their early development electronic digital computers have developed from rather simple electronic devices in the beginning to the highly sophisticated computers of today. This development has taken place within two decades. Early computers had operation speeds measured in seconds and milliseconds. We now measure operation speeds in microseconds and even nanoseconds. Early computers had bit storage capacities numbering in the hundreds. We now have computers with bit storage capacities numbering in the millions. Early computers had restrictive command structures. We now have computers with flexible command structures numbering in the hundreds. The operation of early computers was rather rigid in comparison to the extreme flexibility of operation in present-day computers.

We have seen a trend toward microminiaturization of computer components in effort to reduce the size of computers. We have seen drum memory replaced almost entirely by ferrite core memory for faster access and vacuum tubes replaced by solid-state transistors to decrease size and heat generation and increase switching speeds. We have seen the introduction of sophisticated peripheral equipment, such as high-speed printers and high-speed tape drives. With these and many other advances going on in computer technology, transformations and innovations in computers will certainly result. What computers of the future will look like and what their capabilities will be is certainly interesting speculation [200, 205].

Let us consider next the history of mathematical and analog modeling. We can trace mathematical models to the early beginnings of mathematics. The earliest example of an explicit mathematical model is the Pythagorean theorem, which dates from the sixth century B.C. in Greece.

The Pythagorean theorem heads a long list of classic examples of mathematical models, which include such examples as Newton's "laws of motion" discovered in the seventeenth century, Euler's "polynomials" derived in the eighteenth century, Dalton's "law of additive pressures" formulated in the nineteenth century, Maxwell's "wave equations" derived in the nineteenth century, and Einstein's "theory of relativity" discovered in the twentieth century.

Probability and statistics form the basis for the nondeterministic models in computer modeling and simulation. We mention only a few prominent figures in history whose contributions directly apply to the technique. These include Bernoulli, a Swiss who wrote a treatise on probability in 1713 and derived the binomial probability distribution; Gauss, a nineteenth-century German who developed the method of least squares and derived the normal probability distribution; Poisson, a nineteenth-century Frenchman who derived the Poisson probability distribution; and Pearson, a nineteenth-century Britisher who derived the Pearson distributions and Pearson coefficients.

Besides mathematical models, we can trace analog models as far as we can trace the graphic and plastic arts back to early civilizations. Classic examples of analog models include world globes, relief maps, solar system models, molecular structure models, and supersonic wind tunnels. Analog models represent physical or scientific phenomena by analog representation, such as physical models. Mathematical models represent physical or scientific phenomena by abstract mathematical representation.

In the early development of electronic digital computers it became apparent that mathematical and analog models could be programmed for solution on high-speed computers. This is a significant feature in the history of computer modeling and simulation. At first the applications were restricted to small, simple models because of the limitations of early computer technology, but as computers increased in flexibility of operation, speed, and memory capacity it became feasible to apply them more frequently to models of larger scope.

Let us consider a transition example during the early development of computers. In the early 1950s an air battle analog simulator device was constructed at Johns Hopkins University. This analog device consisted of hardware designed to simulate mechanically an air battle between two opposing forces. Each game was played manually by several participants and took approximately three hours per game run. The outcomes, however, were determined by chance elements and not by player skill. Later this same game was formulated on a mathematical model and programmed for solution on the UNIVAC 1103A computer.

A completely automated game run on the computer took approximately one second of computer time. Roughly, this is a time compression ratio of 10,000:1 in making the transition from an analog simulator to a computer simulation model. The implications of the new technique were phenomenal.

In the above example the significance of the time compression lies in the fact that it had become possible to implement models for digital computer simulation that previously were prohibitive to simulate by analog method or by manual calculations. The fact that thousands of runs could be made is incidental.

Applications of computer modeling and simulation in the two decades following World War II were heavily oriented toward military problems such as war gaming, military systems analysis, and military operations research. Consequently, several large-scale war games have been computerized to study and experiment with military tactics and strategy. Increasingly larger numbers of applications are being made, however, in commercial, scientific, and other nonmilitary problems as well. An even greater increase of computer modeling and simulation applications can be expected in the future in the nonscientific and nonmilitary disciplines.

The technique has tremendous potential in all disciplines. Its greatest impact has been in the physical sciences, mathematics, engineering, operations research, operations analysis, systems analysis, probability and statistics, military sciences, and business administration. Computer modeling and simulation can be applied to virtually every discipline in which phenomena can be quantified and represented by mathematical models. This means that disciplines such as medicine, law, library sciences, social sciences, and life sciences can find some applications of the technique for problem solution. We seek to expand the applications of the technique and to apply the technique wherever its application is useful and can produce meaningful results.

Several institutions and agencies have contributed to the progress of computer modeling and simulation. Some of the major contributions include the University of Michigan, Johns Hopkins University, Case Institute of Technology, Ohio State University, University of California, Massachusetts Institute of Technology, Rand Corporation, Office of Naval Research, U.S. Army Research and Development Laboratory, Ballistics Research Laboratories, and White Sands Proving Grounds. In addition, many private industries and research and development firms have contributed to the progress of the technique.

In summary we illustrate the genealogy of computer modeling and simulation in Fig. 1.2.

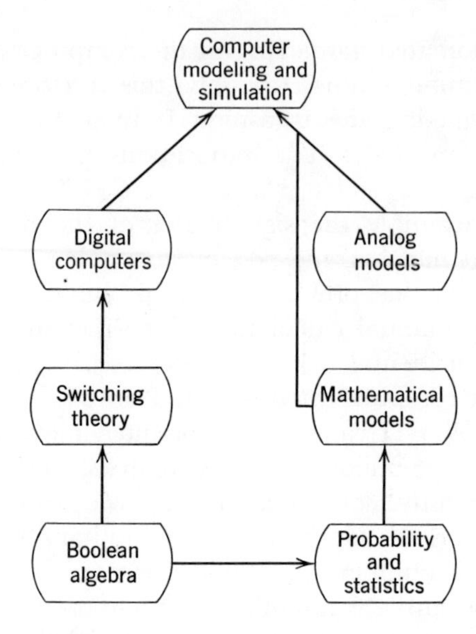

Fig. 1.2 Genealogy of computer modeling and simulation.

ADVANTAGES

Let us examine some of the advantages of applying computer modeling and simulation to research and analysis problems. Specific questions about a system which may be in its conceptual phase, in a phase of development and testing, or already built often can only be answered by computer modeling and simulation. Assuming that the model is valid, in that it accurately simulates the system or operation functions and measures what it is supposed to measure, then the model is an inexpensive, efficient, rapid device to analyze and evaluate systems or operations.

We list some of the advantages of the technique that apply to systems or operations:

1. Decisions concerning future systems in a conceptual stage can be easily made. Many answers can be obtained on a conceptual system prior to design and development phases. It is not necessary to build the system to obtain answers; thus costly trial-and-error methods can be reduced or eliminated.

2. System performance can be simulated and observed under all conceivable conditions. System and environmental parameters can be easily changed to simulate any desired condition, and we can explore conditions that cannot be controlled in the natural environment. It is not necessary to depend so completely upon laboratory or field testing of a system.

3. Results of field system performance can be extrapolated on a computer simulation model for purposes of prediction. Given field performance data, we can expand the interpretation of the data in a probabilistic context.

4. System trials can be speeded up by incredible orders of magnitude. Real-world performance times can be compressed to electronic speeds, so that a real-world process that takes hours or months to perform can be simulated in the computer in fractional seconds or minutes. Our only limitation is the capability of the computer itself.

5. Artificial, yet realistic data on a system can be provided quickly and in large quantities without having to exercise the real-world system. Most real-world systems are expensive to exercise and are not always accessible. Exercise is not always practical or feasible, and results are often inconclusive. A computer model is not restricted by these real-world constraints of system exercise.

6. Chance elements associated with a system can be gamed by Monte Carlo method to determine system outcomes in a probabilistic context. Chance element parameters can be controlled in order to study their effects on system performance. The user has complete control over the probabilistic parameters and can select any desired combinations of parameters to exercise the model.

7. A model is an extremely flexible device and is adaptable to almost any reasonable application. We can study real-world situations as well as hypothetical situations, as there are no real-world constraints on the inputs selected.

8. The model of a conceptual system is useful in forecasting success or failure. A model that forecasts system failure is less expensive than a system that is built and fails. There is also a saving of manpower and resources and a saving to the society that is spared the building of the unsuccessful system.

9. Computer modeling and simulation is often the only feasible technique to analyze and evaluate a system. Certain very complex systems defy analysis by standard analytic techniques. Certain systems defy evaluation by laboratory or field test experimentation. Sometimes modeling and simulation is the only practical approach for our problem solution.

SCOPE

We now summarize the scope of the book. First we list criteria for application of the technique. We describe a few examples of military and nonmilitary computer simulation models. We explore potential applications of the technique in the present and future.

Next we review methods, techniques and tools applicable to computer modeling and simulation. Specific attention is given to Monte Carlo, probability distributions, generation of random statistical variates, data collection, data generation, data reduction, data analysis, experimental design, response surface, curve fitting, flow charting, computer programming, simulation languages, and model validation. The review discusses only salient features applicable to computer modeling and simulation. It is not intended to be a comprehensive treatment of the subjects.

Finally we discuss some of the procedures and tasks in model construction. We consider "what to do and how to do it" in model construction. The tasks are organized into three phases: (a) conceptualization, (b) implementation, and (c) results. We give helpful suggestions and several illustrations for each phase. In summary we illustrate the tasks with a "bubble" flow chart showing the gross flow and interactions of tasks in model construction.

The appendices contain a glossary, an example of a model, equations, tables, graphs, and references all applicable to computer modeling and simulation technique.

PART TWO

Applications

2

APPLICATIONS

CRITERIA FOR APPLICATION

Even though computer simulation is a powerful tool in problem solution, we should apply the technique discriminately and wisely. There are many classes of problems in which computer simulation is a highly appropriate technique. There are also many problems in which other methods are more efficient than computer simulation. The technique is a powerful tool when applied correctly, but incorrect application is wasteful and displays poor judgment. The distinction between when to simulate and when not to simulate is usually clear if we understand the technique and apply criteria for application. Much of the decision, however, depends on the specific problem, the urgency of the solution, and the resources available.

We can follow general guidelines and apply certain broad criteria to a given problem to determine the appropriate tool to select. First, let us consider when it is appropriate to simulate.

We should apply the technique on the basis of the following criteria:

1. We should apply computer modeling and simulation technique whenever analytical tools are unavailable or inappropriate for the problem solution. Whenever there are problems demanding solution and no convenient analytical tools for their solution exist, then another approach, such as simulation, must be considered. Problems and the appropriate analytical tools for their solution do not necessarily exist side by side concurrently.

2. We should apply computer simulation when we have reasonable assurance that the concept, system, or operation can be successfully simu-

lated. We must be able to obtain sufficient data and information on the system to give realism to the model and make a successful simulation possible.

3. We should apply computer modeling and simulation whenever there is a horrendously large volume of computations necessary. Some problems cannot be solved manually because of the sheer size of computational requirements alone. The application of high-speed computers has made it feasible to solve huge, complex problems that would otherwise be impossible to solve in a reasonable length of time.

4. We should apply computer simulation whenever all other approaches have been investigated and are considered inappropriate.

5. We should apply computer simulation whenever the mere process of constructing a simulation of a system can in itself be a beneficial learning experience of the system processes. This process can provide an experience that cannot be gained in any other way.

Example 2.1. An electronics firm wanted to investigate the feasibility of a conceptual electronics system to generate flight paths in real time on the basis of several specified criteria. The system consists primarily of a computing device that operates on aircraft characteristics parameters, airborne traffic data, and prohibited zones data, and minimizes flight time and collision danger. The output is a programmed flight plan that assigns each aircraft the appropriate flight path parameters.

A systems analysis was initiated to analyze the flight path programmer, and it was immediately apparent that the best approach to the problem was a computer simulation model of the conceptual system. It was possible to duplicate exactly every system computation and logic process in order to determine system reaction under every conceivable situation. It was possible to determine when the system was at or near saturation and to examine the effects on the air traffic.

A simulation was applied because the system could be successfully simulated. A simulation was applied because an extremely large volume of computations was necessary in the analysis.

A simulation was applied primarily because of criteria 2 and 3.

Once we have determined that a given problem is amenable to solution by computer modeling and simulation, we should then determine the degree of automation to apply. Various degrees of automation are possible within the combination of the computer, man, and the simulated system. A *fully automatic simulation* is one in which the process is completely automated for the computer, and there is no human intervention in the model processes. A *semiautomatic simulation* is one in which humans play an integral part in the model processes. An *integrated simulation* is one in which a hardware system is integrated with the computer, and the system uses simulated inputs generated on the computer. The computer may also be used in other processes, such as analysis of system outputs.

For a given problem we select the degree of automation on the basis of the following criteria:

1. We should apply a *fully automatic simulation* whenever the system is fully automatic and is primarily quantitative in nature, and when human roles have little effect in the internal processes of the system.

2. We should apply a *semiautomatic simulation* whenever the system is semiautomatic, the system requires many complex decisions to be made by humans, and human intervention in system processes affects the outcomes. In a semiautomatic simulation the model processes are halted at critical points, and humans introduce intermediate inputs which are relevant to the model processes.

3. We should apply an *integrated simulation* whenever it is desirable to exercise the system with controlled inputs, such as the use of the system for a training device or for laboratory testing.

Example 2.2. The computer simulation model of the flight path programmer mentioned in Example 2.1 is an example of a fully automatic simulation. The conceptual system was planned to be fully automatic. Humans provide inputs and receive outputs, which can be accepted or rejected, but they do not participate in the internal system processes. Therefore a fully automatic simulation model was appropriate to analyze the system.

Computerized business games are examples of semiautomatic simulation models. Participants in the game make critical decisions during the simulation which affect model outputs. Computerized teaching machines are examples of integrated simulations. Participants make responses to programmed inquiries during the learning process.

We should consider the interactions of man and machine on the basis of the following criteria:

1. Computers are more efficient than humans for tedious, involved computations. Therefore we should apply computers in tasks which involve tedious computations.

2. Computers can make simple logical decisions based on calculations faster and more accurately than can humans.

3. Humans can perform certain higher order perceptive thinking processes which cannot be programmed on computers in the present state of the art. Therefore the application of the computer may not be too helpful for tasks that are predominantly perceptive in nature.

4. The human capability of making judicious decisions can be greatly enhanced by using a computer to give accurate, up-to-date information relevant to the decision-making process.

5. Certain critical decisions should always rest with the human evaluator. These decisions cannot be programmed for the computer.

Example 2.3. Several major airline companies use computers to handle tedious tasks, such as the bookkeeping involved with reservations. With many daily flights extending over a long period of time and with several requestors throughout the nation, the problem of making, checking, and canceling reservations has become a very large search problem in information retrieval. Thus the problem is unmanageable for humans to handle manually. The tedium of such a task has been greatly reduced by the use of the computer.

EXAMPLES OF COMPUTER SIMULATION MODELS

We now describe some examples of computer simulation models which have been built by various agencies, universities, industries, and research and consulting firms since 1950. These examples have been chosen because they show a variety of applications of the technique, but we have not attempted an exhaustive treatment of all models built during this period.

1. The operations research department of a large midwestern university constructed a computer simulation model of an air defense system in order to evaluate the over-all system performance. This model was built and programmed for solution on a large digital computer in the late 1950s.

The air-defense system is characterized by a time history of events beginning with target detection and terminating with target kill, in which these events are simulated in the computer program. The probability of an event E occurring is determined in the model by comparing the probability P_E with a uniform random number. The simulated event occurs whenever the probability is greater than or equal to the random number. If an event occurs, the time interval from that event to a logical subsequent event is computed by sampling from a probability distribution.*

In this model all probability distributions are generated from functions derived from empirical data obtained in field testing of the system. The following probability distributions are applied: (a) the probability of occurrence of an event follows the Bernoulli distribution; (b) the time intervals between related events follow the log normal distribution, in which the mean and variance are determined from functions; (c) the two-dimensional errors in azimuth and distance measurement from sensor to target follow the circular normal distribution.

* Probability distributions are discussed in Chapter 3.

The model operates on a time status record, which is an event-processing technique using a designated section of computer memory for storage of events. The event associated with the earliest time is picked from the time status record. The event is processed uniquely, updated, and returned to the time status record unless it is a terminal event. This procedure is repeated for the next earliest time, and the procedure is repeated over and over until all events have been completely processed in the time history of events, and there are no unprocessed events left in the time status record.

The model inputs consist of the design of an enemy airborne threat against a specific air defense system. The model outputs consist of a summary of system performance plus selected details, such as number of missiles fired. The effectiveness of the system is computed for any given raid configuration simulated against the system. The model was operational for several years, and at a later date the original model was revised and more sophisticated procedures were designed into the model.

2. Let us consider an example of an integrated simulation, which is a different approach from the above example. A large-scale simulation was implemented at a West Coast electronics firm in the early 1960s to evaluate the effectiveness of an air defense system. An integrated simulation between test-bed site and a large digital computer was designed to evaluate the man-machine complex of sensors, trackers, and weapons.

Various tests were designed to determine over-all system evaluation, in which each test was designed to evaluate a specific system function, such as target tracking, in which the system traces the target path and predicts target coordinates on the basis of positional and velocity measurements. The evaluation process was divided into major tasks as follows: generation of synthetic data inputs, actual test exercise, data reduction, data analysis, and test evaluation. A large-scale digital computer was used in connection with several task phases.

Three large-scale computer programs were written to integrate the evaluation process of the air defense system. A target generation program was used to generate simulated system inputs. A data reduction program was used to reduce the test output data, which were recorded on magnetic tape during test exercise. Finally, a correlation and analysis program was used to analyze test results by correlating inputs with outputs and computing statistics of the deviations.

The target generation program accepts target and raid input parameters, and it performs the computations on the path of motion equations and outputs synthetic target kinematic data for system exercise. The program outputs three magnetic tapes: (a) true raid tape, (b), simulator tape, and (c) data link simulator tape. A computer subroutine is used to perturb the flight path data according to the normal probability distribution on the radar simulator tape and the data link simulator tape. The true raid tape contains the actual unperturbed flight path parameters for each aircraft target. The radar simulator tape contains simulated radar returns of the perturbed flight path. The data link simulator tape contains coordinates of the perturbed flight path in simulated message formats being received by the system from external sources.

The actual test exercise was conducted with two inputs: simulated radar returns and simulated data link messages. Internal system processes of target tracking during the test exercise were recorded on output tapes. These tapes were used as inputs for the data reduction program, which reconstructed all the detailed history of the raid flown against the system. However, the reconstructed raid really represents the system's interpretation of the threat situation and is not necessarily an accurate representation. A typical raid produces hundreds of thousands of data information items. The data reduction program tries to determine target characteristics and the times of occurrence of certain significant system events, such as initial target detection.

The correlation and analysis program traces the actual history of each target course path and correlates this path with the history of the air defense system target track as interpreted by the system. The actual course path is input from the true raid tape, and the system target track is input from the data reduction program outputs.

The correlation and analysis program mathematically constructs a box of volume V about the actual target coordinates at time T. Each current target track being processed by the system is compared with the box about the actual target location XYZ. Whenever a processed target track falls inside the box of volume V over a brief time period, the target track and actual target are assumed to correlate in position.

The deviations in XYZ, the squares of the deviations, and the cross-products of the deviations are computed at increments in time. The cumulative frequencies of these values are stored for each combination of target track and actual target. At the end of the computer run the mean, variance, and correlation coefficients for each combination are printed in the computer printout. From these output data over-all system tracking capability is evaluated.

3. A terminal air traffic control system in a metropolitan airport was modeled at a midwestern university laboratory for the purpose of simulating terminal control of incoming aircraft only. The model was first operational on a large computer around 1960.

Only certain key events in the terminal control process are watched from the time an aircraft enters the system until it lands on the runway. These events include the following: the aircraft arrives at a designated point *A*, arrives at the outer fix, and departs from the outer fix; altitude is cleared; the craft arrives at the inner fix, departs from the inner fix, and lands on the runway. The time history of events is processed by the time status record technique, which we explained earlier.

A Gaussian distribution of errors was assumed for the generation of the event time intervals. As an aircraft enters the system an estimated time of arrival at the runway is computed, landing priorities are established, and an approach path to the runway is determined.

The computer model performs certain operations normally performed by a human operator. The interpretation of the human controller function is simulated in terms of distributions of errors around the estimated time of arrival at successive points. This model is used to predict how an actual system will perform in terms of landing rates and controller work load under varied conditions.

4. A simulation of a communication network study was performed in a laboratory of an East Coast engineering school in the late 1950s. This simulation was programmed for a large computer to simulate four characteristics of a communications network: discrete messages, random routing, decentralized control, and state of flux.

The inputs are network tables and probability tables. The printout contains statistical information on specific communications, including the number of messages in the network, the proportion of messages delivered and lost, and the transit times of the messages delivered. The means and variances, maxima and minima of the number of messages, transit time, and histogram of transit times are all printed in the output.

Time is simulated by choosing a unit interval, called a cycle, so short that not more than one event may occur at any one mode during a unit interval. Events happening in the network during a cycle are ordered by assigning to each a uniform random number and considering the events in the order of magnitudes of the numbers. Random numbers are supplied from a magnetic tape that contains a list of random numbers previously generated by a multiplicative technique.

5. The problem of airplane optimization was approached in a twofold manner at the operations division of a large West Coast aircraft company. The airplane was optimized in a simple commercial airline model, and an additional computer program was developed to evaluate the optimum airplane in competition with current aircraft.

Information was obtained from the model on the number of seats, design speed, and design range of the optimum airplane. These outputs were used to present graphic results of direct operating costs per seat mile as a function of flight distance. This model was first operational in the late 1950s.

6. A computerized system to aid decision making by managers of research and development operations was simulated at a research firm. This simulation enables the system designer to test system hypotheses, determine system problem areas, suggest solutions, determine system managerial difficulties, and simplify explanation of the proposed system to managers.

7. In the mid-1960s a government agency designed a model to simulate intercity traffic flows. The model is modular in form, and it generates traffic according to a definite set of rules. The model selects the origin and determines the best route. It selects the destination city and the type of traveler. It computes the number of travelers and assigns the mode of travel. The model computes the time in transit and periodically prints out summary data. When all travelers have been assigned appropriate routes for each origin-destination pair, the time of day is advanced and the procedure is repeated.

8. A model was developed by an eastern consulting firm that attempts to recreate a total baseball game in its lifelike form. The model operates upon the interactions among pitching, batting, fielding, and strategy components of play. Outputs include evaluation of alternative batting lineups, in-game strategies, trade of players, and team-to-team competition. A preplay of an entire season from historical performance data is also possible.

9. In the 1960s a consulting firm constructed a simulation of corporate financial operations. The model simulates a manufacturing firm having three interrelated product lines. It simulates the response of the company to the marketplace during a time period. By feedback loop the model adjusts following time periods accordingly. The model ties together operational plans, effects of engineering and research expenditures, and the company response to marketplace. The model also takes into account the lag between engineering expenditures and their effects, marketing expenditures and their effects, and advertising expenditures and their effects. The results are measured in terms of return on revenue and assets, asset turnover, and unused borrowing.

10. In the 1960s a computer simulation of the operation of a fleet of berth liners was developed for use as a planning tool. The simulation, which was developed for a government agency, has applications in vessel replacement programs, trade-route reviews, effects of competitive service, and evaluation of advanced systems, cargo or revenue pools, rules, and rates.

The simulation consists of two major functional parts: a program, which controls the activities of simulated ships, and a schedule generator, which assigns sailing dates and services. The ship is considered the sole active element, and the effects of scheduling, cargo, and port characteristics are all measured in terms of ship performance. The simulation is a critical events model in which five chronologically discrete events are simulated: at sea, port entry, on berth, layup, and port exit.

The following ship activities are determined by stochastic (or random) processes: choice of next port, outbound cargo load, added cargo destinations, lost time on berth, delays due to tide, and speed at sea. The schedule generator generates a set of sailing schedules and itineraries. Next an assignment routine matches particular ships with sailing dates and subservices.

Simulation inputs include parameter values and data tables. These are inputs relating to speeds, cargo classes, ports, and ship space. A postprocessor was implemented to fulfill user requirements for output analysis. Voyage logs are printed out to show the operations of each ship on each voyage. Selective printouts are possible, and a large number of three-dimensional tables, such as cargo tonnage and revenues, can also be printed out.

A test was run against actual historical data from an Atlantic trade route, and computer results showed good agreement with actual results. A comparison of simulated outputs and actual outputs confirmed the realism of the simulation.

11. A research corporation and an eastern university developed a digital computer simulation of an urban renewal decision model. The impacts of urban renewal, such as clearance or nonurban renewal, are represented. The model basically contains several subsystems. Several of the submodels include population, employment, land use, social indices, housing types, and industrial location submodels. The data requirements for the model are enormous. Data banks were developed for the running of the model, and an experimental design for maximizing the informational content was developed.

12. Since the mid-1950s a very large number of models of computer-assisted war games and fully computerized war games have been designed and developed. These games represent all types of land, sea, and air warfare in all levels of intensity, including cold war, limited war, counterinsurgency, and global war conflicts. A few examples of operational war games include ADVAL, ATOM, CASCADE, LEGION, SIM, STAGE, SWIM, TACS, and THEATERSPIEL. However, none of these models will be described here. War games that are in development or are operational are generally classified, and their

documentation is not available to the public. The reader is referred to the bibliography, Section I, for references on war games.

In Appendix B we describe a model of demand for movement more fully than any of the above examples.

POTENTIAL APPLICATIONS

We now explore some potential applications of computer modeling and simulation. The potentials are great and may very well extend to the imaginativeness of those who seek to apply the simulation technique. Computer modeling and simulation is a powerful and useful technique and its potential seems unlimited for problems amenable to quantification. Only the future will disclose how much of the technique has been fully utilized.

Many of these applications have been and are being explored, but we mention them because more expansion and progress is still possible in these areas. This list is not intended to be exhaustive or to identify all the problem areas in the various disciplines but only to suggest some possible applications. The reader should expand this list on the basis of his own experiences.

Some potential applications of computer modeling and simulation include the following:

1. To analyze and evaluate electronic, mechanical, or electromechanical systems that are in a conceptual phase or developmental phase. To test and evaluate operational systems and expand their applications. To analyze and evaluate the operations of automatic, semiautomatic, or manual systems.
2. To study problems in electronic systems design and circuit design. To analyze and evaluate logical design of electronic systems. To determine optimum wiring diagrams. To analyze experimental circuit designs. To optimize electronic packaging and evaluate packaging techniques. To study and analyze equipment problems.
3. To analyze and evaluate operations. To analyze the procedures and the integration of men and systems in operations. To analyze the effects of human decisions made in the operations.
4. To study and analyze transportation and traffic problems. To select optimum routing. To select appropriate roadways, seaways, or airways. To analyze and evaluate road and expressway designs. To analyze and evaluate traffic control systems. To assist in transportation planning. To analyze demands for travel. To analyze the effects of demands on air, land, or sea transportation facilities: road networks, airport runways,

and sea-lanes. To analyze the effects of traffic delays, rerouting, and perturbation of arterial flow in transportation networks.

5. To assist in business games and to evaluate business strategies. To analyze business and market trends. To apply cost reduction to business operations. To administer inventory control. To allocate resources and to analyze product and market distribution.

6. To study educational problems, such as problems in administration and instruction. To analyze and evaluate computerized teaching theories and practices. To evaluate testing techniques. To assist in educational administration problems. To determine optimum class scheduling. To analyze and evaluate education budgets. To analyze, evaluate, or generate school bus-route selection and scheduling. To assist in novel and exotic applications in extracurricular activities, such as design of marching band routines, athletic contest strategies, and sports half-time activities. To analyze the effects of movement flows of students within the educational plant. To determine effective pupil placement.

7. To assist in personnel administration. To determine job placement and optimum job assignment. To evaluate potential assignments with job requirements. To match employee capabilities with job demands.

8. To study problems in the biological sciences. To analyze the effects of chance of mutation, heredity, and environment. To analyze environmental adaptation and growth phenomena. To study life and death processes. To analyze evolutionary processes. To analyze the effects of random processes in nature.

9. To study problems in the physical sciences. To analyze random processes in mechanical, electrical, acoustical, and optical systems. To simulate laboratory experiments. To analyze and evaluate physical phenomena. To analyze and evaluate applications of the physical sciences.

10. To analyze the effects of meteorological changes. To model weather and climate. To study weather forecasting. To analyze the effects of random processes in meteorology. To predict weather front movements. To select optimum air, land, and sea routes under existing weather patterns. To analyze the behavior of hurricanes, typhoons, and tornados.

11. To apply to all types of forecasting techniques, such as predictions of national and local elections, business trends, weather, sports outcomes, demographic changes, and population growth.

12. To design computerized war games and computer-assisted war games for land, sea, and air warfare. To analyze and evaluate doctrine, strategy, tactics, and resources in land, sea, and air engagements. To analyze the effects of environment and enemy threats on military and naval operations. To study counterinsurgency problems. To optimize deployments of military machines and personnel. To analyze and eval-

uate military and naval systems under simulated field environment. To analyze and evaluate military and naval systems in conceptual or developmental phases. To study problems in logistics, communications, and command and control.

13. To evaluate systems in their conceptual phase. To evaluate postulated or projected postal systems, transportation systems, space systems, communications systems, marine systems, sanitation systems, and irrigation systems.

14. To assist in hospital administration problems. To evaluate patient record retrieval procedures. To apply cost reduction to hospital procedures. To study optimum staff scheduling and personnel assignment. To study hospital inventory control procedures.

15. To analyze and evaluate problems in the engineering sciences. To study the effects of alternate designs in civil engineering projects, electrical and electronic systems, and mechanical systems. To analyze effects and evaluate proposed dam sites, road beds, power lines, locks, transportation terminals, fuel supply lines, and utilities. To analyze the sociological, political, and economic effects of proposed engineering projects.

16. To assist in demographic studies. To analyze the effects of population growth and population shift. To predict the effects and impacts of population growth. To integrate demographic problems with economics, community planning, zoning, marketing outlets, resources allocations, and urban renewal. To analyze the effects of population changes on composition of age groups and ethnic groups.

17. To study information retrieval procedures and systems for legal, medical, and other library systems. To assist in retrieval of legal case histories, court decisions, medical case histories, and social welfare case histories.

18. To simulate space travel. To analyze space vehicle trajectories. To analyze effects of space phenomena on vehicular performance. To analyze effects of space travel on electromechanical systems. To study effects of random processes on space travel. To analyze launch techniques. To analyze terminal techniques, such as landing, personnel removal, and cargo removal. To analyze effects of space travel on human behavior and sociological patterns.

19. To analyze the effects of demands on communications channels. To study the effects of alternate communications routing. To study the effects of random processes, garbling, signal attenuation, and environmental perturbations on communications links. To analyze the effects of failures in communications networks.

20. To test strategy and tactics in business, sports, politics, and human relations. To study worth and value in social relations. To study

strategy and tactics in human behavior. To study success and failure in individuals. To study success and failure in social groups.

21. To determine effects of alternate flight paths. To analyze flight-planning techniques. To determine optimum flight paths and to study effects of weather and congestion on flight control.

22. To study the effects of investment behavior. To study the interactions that take place between broker and trader. To test the processes of portfolio selection. To test the price-setting mechanism.

23. To analyze the competitive conditions in overseas or domestic markets. To analyze the results of decision-making tools. To study the production capacity of entire industries or segments of industries.

24. To analyze a wide variety of urban problems, such as land use and transportation. To demonstrate to decision makers the consequences of alternate decisions. To study the effects of metropolitan growth patterns.

25. To study the effects of failures in networks, such as power, telephone, and television. To analyze the effects of alternate routing in communications and power networks.

26. To study the interactions in social, political, military, or economic hierarchical structures. To analyze the effects of failures in social, political, military, or economic hierarchical structures.

27. To apply to the study of musical analysis. To study the effects of variations in musical form and sequence. To study the effects of random change in musical composition. To study the effects of musical acoustics. To analyze bore-to-length ratio in wind instrument design. To analyze specifications of musical instrument design. To analyze acoustic effects of architectural design.

PROBLEMS

2.1 A client requests a proposal for an analysis of a conceptual electronic system which automatically performs inventory control at several warehouse locations throughout a given region. What investigation of the problem would be necessary to determine the appropriateness for a simulation?

2.2 We have been asked to analyze a conceptual English grammar-teaching machine in which the student makes simple decisions from several alternatives. If we were asked to model the conceptual system, what degree of automation (fully automatic or semiautomatic) should be selected? Why?

2.3 From the following list of decisions or processes, indicate which processes can be automated and the degree of automation practical, and indicate which processes cannot be automated. State the reasons why.

It is decided to widen the main street.

It is determined that message *A* will arrive before *C* in a given communications system.

How to route 1000 railroad cars over a multinodal railroad network.
Whether to build a satellite-tracking system.

2.4 Select an example of a computer simulation model described in this chapter. Prepare a list of specific inputs that appear reasonable for the model.

2.5 Select a range of input values that appear reasonable in 2.4.

2.6 Select examples of potential applications described in this chapter. What problems might be handled with a fully automatic simulation? Semiautomatic simulation? Integrated simulation?

2.7 Prepare your own supplemental list of potential applications of computer modeling and simulation.

2.8 A government agency client desires to determine the effects of alternate flight paths. How would we determine the appropriateness for simulation?

2.9 Select a current local, state, or national problem. Discuss the problem briefly in terms of appropriateness of solution by computer simulation.

2.10 Consider the advisability of solving any of the following problems by computer simulation. Discuss advantages and disadvantages.

Predicting weather front movement.
Devising a system to control the circulation of library books.
Tracing incoming and outgoing vehicular traffic flows to and from the central business district.
Predicting stock market trends, given historical data of stock market activity.
Selecting freight movement that maximizes speed and minimizes cost.
Studying ground clutter effects in radar video returns.
Devising a legal case history retrieval system.
Studying the migratory patterns of starlings.
Controlling intersection traffic signals by computer.

2.11 Write a very brief essay expressing your views on potential applications of computer simulation.

2.12 The planning commission is attempting to predict future residential, industrial, and business expansions. How could computer simulation be utilized in making these predictions?

2.13 Suppose you have decided on an objective basis that a computer simulation is the appropriate technique for a particular problem. How would you convince your client? State the approach you would take.

2.14 Within your own experience, cite an example of a system that is unsuccessful or has failed and might never have been built if the conceptual system had been analyzed by computer simulation.

2.15 Given the dichotomy: models and computers. Speculate as to which area of the two will require greater progress to meet potential applications of computer modeling and simulation in the future.

2.16 If the parameters of a problem cannot be easily quantified, does this rule out a solution by computer simulation? Explain.

PART THREE

Methods, Techniques, and Tools

In the next four chapters we discuss methods, techniques, and tools applicable to computer modeling and simulation. The purpose of these chapters is to give specific attention to salient features especially appropriate and necessary to the simulation technique. The content of the discussions is selective rather than an exhaustive or definitive treatment of each topic. Such treatment is not possible in a book of this scope. In our effort at being selective we realize the risk of overlooking or giving insufficient attention to some important aspect. Therefore we refer the reader to the bibliography for definitive references.

Bibliography Sections A, C, D, and E contain references especially applicable to Chapters 3 and 4. Bibliography Sections A and B are especially useful for Chapter 5, and Sections J, K, L, and M are applicable to Chapter 6.

In the four chapters we discuss 14 topics arranged in sequential order. The order chosen, however, has no relation to the relative importance of the various topics. We discuss the topics in the following order: Monte Carlo, probability distributions, generation of random statistical variates, data collection, data generation, data reduction, data analysis, experimental design, response surface, curve fitting, flow charting, computer programming, simulation languages, and model validation.

In Chapter 3 we focus our attention on the stochastic features of modeling. Nondeterministic characteristics play an important role in model building, and we open the chapter with a brief discussion of Monte Carlo. We discuss characteristic features of discrete and continuous probability distributions.

We give some examples and illustrations of commonly used probability distributions. Finally, we discuss uniform and nonuniform random number generation techniques useful in stochastic modeling.

In Chapter 4 we discuss four topics: data collection, data generation, data reduction, and data analysis. These are manipulative and analytical data-handling techniques that are frequently used in some phase of model construction. These data-handling techniques can be handled internal to the model, or they can be handled external to the model.

In Chapter 5 we briefly discuss a few techniques of mathematical statistics. We discuss experimental design, response surface, and curve fitting primarily to acquaint the reader with these techniques. We strongly recommend perusing some of the references in Sections A and B of the bibliography. These sections list several references which treat the topics comprehensively.

In Chapter 6 we discuss tools and techniques in the modeling procedure. We discuss flow charting, computer programming, simulation languages, and model validation. Flow charting is an indispensable tool in the implementation of the model; it would be an impossible task to construct a large model without flow charting. We discuss various aspects of computer "hardware" and "software," and we present a brief summary of select simulation languages available at the present time.

We include model validation in the discussion in Chapter 6 because of its extreme importance in computer modeling and simulation. We realize that the value of the model depends upon proper validation. Unless the validity of the model is established and can be demonstrated as well, the model is of questionable value to the potential user.

The materials in the four chapters are presented as background information for Part 4 which deals with model construction and in which we give definite procedures that are useful in the construction of a computer-simulation model.

3

STOCHASTIC FEATURES

MONTE CARLO

Monte Carlo is a "game of chance" technique that we can apply to solve certain problems. In the Monte Carlo method we apply random sampling to determine a solution rather than solving the problem analytically or by another method. Later we will discover how powerful the Monte Carlo method is when properly applied.

First, we illustrate Monte Carlo by the following trivial example. Suppose it is required to evaluate the definite integral

$$y = \int_0^1 x \, dx. \tag{3.1}$$

Normally, we could solve the integral by one of the following methods:

1. Analytically and obtain an exact solution.
2. Numerically or by approximation method, such as Simpson's rule, and obtain an approximate solution.
3. Graphically with the aid of a mechanical device, such as a planimeter for measuring area under a curve.

Or we could apply the less conventional Monte Carlo method as follows. Select N samples of pairs of uniform random numbers, in which for each number there is an equal chance of selecting any value between zero and one. Let each of the pairs of numbers represent a point in the XY plane in which the first number is the abscissa (or X value) and the second number is the ordinate (or Y value). Find the percentage of points in the N samples which fall under the curve of the function

$$f(x) = x \tag{3.2}$$

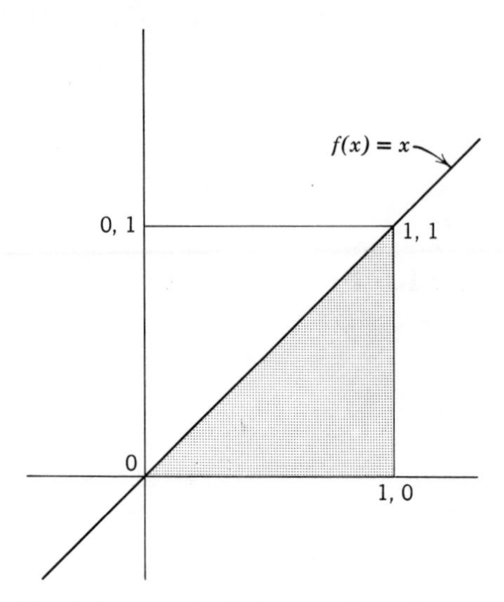

Fig. 3.1 Graph of the function $f(x) = x$.

(which is the derivative of the integral in 3.1) and within the boundaries 0,0; 1,0; 1,1; 0,1. This percentage gives the approximate value of the definite integral (Fig. 3.1).

Using the uniform random number table in Appendix D, or any other series of random numbers, and arbitrarily selecting a sample size of 80 points, we find from the series we used that 41 out of 80 fall under the curve of the function in (3.2). Thus the estimated value of the integral by Monte Carlo method is 0.5125 as compared to the exact value determined by analytical method of 0.5.

Monte Carlo is a nonanalytical technique to obtain approximate solutions of functional equations of various types, such as the definite integral in (3.1), and it is a numerical method of solving nondeterministic (stochastic) models. Monte Carlo has frequent application in computer modeling and simulation, and it can be applied to solve complex systems without determination of the complicated analytical representations of the system. Monte Carlo is especially applicable to systems which are characterized by complicated probability equations. In addition, Monte Carlo is useful to solve definite integrals as shown above, to solve integrodifferential equations, and to solve systems of linear equations.

In the solution of complex systems or operations, often the case is such that analytical models of the system cannot be derived. For example, this may be due to lack of necessary information or data about the system. Yet the requirements for a solution may be imminent, and in many instances Monte Carlo method is the only approach in the solution of the system. Or, even if an analytical model is available, the Monte Carlo method is often the more feasible approach.

In the Monte Carlo solution of complex systems the deterministic and random features of the system processes are imitated step by step. In the random features of the model one or more of the functional relations depend upon chance parameters, whose values are selected from a probability distribution. For example, a given communications system is activated by the arrival of a message, which occurs at random according to a probability distribution. Therefore, the outcomes in a Monte Carlo model may differ for repeated runs with the same input values. For example, if we flip a coin twice, there are four possible outcomes: head-head, tail-tail, head-tail, tail-head. Thus to produce statistically significant results in a Monte Carlo solution, repeated runs (or replications) are required with the same inputs and using values from probability distributions in the stochastic functions.

The heart of any Monte Carlo procedure is the determination of outcomes at random at critical decision points in a stochastic process. The simplest type is a "yes-no" decision point, such as a situation where there are only two possible outcomes. Suppose that E_1 and E_2 are the only possible outcomes of a particular trial, and the probability that E_1 occurs is p_1 and the probability that E_2 occurs is p_2, where $p_2 = 1 - p_1$.

Thus to determine whether E_1 or E_2 occurs in a given trial, we generate a uniform random number U between the interval zero and one, and we perform a test. E_1 occurs if $U \leq p_1$; otherwise E_2 occurs.

Another type of decision that must be made is an extension of the simple "yes-no" type. In this type there are several possible outcomes with given probabilities of occurrence of each. Suppose that $E_1, E_2, E_3, \ldots, E_n$ are the possible outcomes of a particular trial, and the probability that each occurs is $p_1, p_2, p_3, \ldots, p_n$, respectively, and $p_1 + p_2 + p_3 + \cdots + p_n = 1$.

Thus to determine whether $E_1, E_2, E_3, \cdots, E_n$ occurs in a given trial, we generate a uniform random number U between the interval zero and one, and we perform a test. E_1 occurs if $U \leq p_1$. E_2 occurs if $p_1 < U \leq p_1 + p_2$. E_3 occurs if $p_1 + p_2 < U \leq p_1 + p_2 + p_3$. Ej occurs if

$$\sum_{i=1}^{j-1} p_i < U \leq \sum_{i=1}^{j} p_i, \qquad (j = 2, 3, \ldots, n) \tag{3.3}$$

Another type of decision is that of determining at random a number from a distribution whose parameters, such as mean and variance, are known. For example, this type of decision is involved in determining a linear measurement whose measurement error follows the normal probability distribution. Suppose that a given error is normally distributed with mean μ and variance σ^2. Thus to determine the measurement in one trial, we generate a normal random number R and compute the measurement X by

$$X = \mu + R\sigma. \tag{3.4}$$

We now illustrate another important and useful application of Monte Carlo in stochastic modeling. Suppose we seek to determine the probability distribution function C and its mean μ and variance σ^2 parameters. Suppose the dependent variable C is presently given by the function

$$C = f(\alpha, \beta, \gamma, \ldots), \tag{3.5}$$

where $\alpha, \beta, \gamma, \ldots$ are random variables whose individual distribution functions are known. That is, for each random variable $\alpha, \beta, \gamma, \ldots$ we know its mean μ_i and variance σ_i^2. This type of problem is typical.

We solve this problem as follows:

1. For each random variable $\alpha, \beta, \gamma, \ldots$ we sample from its distribution function for given μ_i, σ_i^2 and calculate the value of the ith variable.
2. We repeat the step above for the next random variable until we have calculated values for all the random variables $\alpha, \beta, \gamma, \ldots$.
3. Next we compute a specific value for C in (3.5), using the values of the random variables $\alpha, \beta, \gamma, \ldots$ calculated in Steps 1 and 2 above.
4. We repeat the above process in Steps 1, 2, and 3 until we have N values of C.
5. For the N values of C we determine the probability frequency function and compute the mean μ and variance σ^2 for C. We now express the function C as

$$C = f(\mu, \sigma^2), \tag{3.6}$$

where μ,σ^2 are given as functions of input variables or parameters. Calculation procedures are given in the next section.

Example 3.1. Suppose we are simulating the operation of a simple system which consists of a series of events $E_1E_2E_3$, where the events are related as follows: Events $E_1E_2E_3$ occur in that order and are measurements in X, Y, Z, respectively, where

$$X = 1 - e^{-\lambda},$$

$$Y = 1 - e^{-\phi},$$

$$Z = (X^2 + Y^2)^{1/2},$$

and λ and ϕ are random variables. The mean and variances of λ and ϕ are $\bar{\lambda}$ and $\sigma_\lambda{}^2$ and $\bar{\phi}$ $\sigma_\phi{}^2$, respectively, and are given.

Our objective is to determine the mean and variance of Z, so we determine the outcome by Monte Carlo in the following steps:

1. Generate a normal random number R_1.
2. Compute

$$\lambda = \bar{\lambda} + R_1\sigma_\lambda.$$

3. Compute

$$X = 1 - e^{-\lambda}$$

and retain the value of X.

4. Generate a normal random number R_2.
5. Compute

$$\phi = \bar{\phi} + R_2\sigma_\phi.$$

6. Compute

$$Y = 1 - e^{-\phi}$$

and retain the value of Y.

7. Compute

$$Z = (X^2 + Y^2)^{1/2}$$

and retain the value of Z.

8. Replicate Steps 1 through 7 N times.
9. Compute the mean and variance of Z by

$$\bar{Z} = \frac{1}{N}\sum_{i=1}^{N} Z_i$$

$$S_Z{}^2 = \frac{1}{N}\sum_{i=1}^{N} Z_i{}^2 - \bar{Z}^2,$$

respectively.

In summary, Monte Carlo samples from probability distributions to determine specific outcomes. Monte Carlo involves (a) probability distributions, (b) random number generation, and (c) sampling techniques. These three items are discussed in subsequent sections of the book. In Chapters 8, 9, and 10 we illustrate the use of Monte Carlo in the solution of systems or operations.

PROBABILITY DISTRIBUTIONS

Probability is a quantitative measure of the chance or likelihood of an event occurring. This may be a chance event, such as the probability that it will rain on a given day or the probability that a surveillance radar will detect an airborne vehicle at a given range. Or it may be the probability that a dimensional measurement does not exceed a given amount or the probability that one or more aircraft demand the use of a runway at an airport in an interval of time.

Probability is expressed by a quantity P, given by

$$P = \frac{m}{n}, \tag{3.7}$$

where m is the number of favorable possibilities (or successes) and n is the total number of equal likely events. The value of P always ranges between zero and unity, as we can see that only the inequality

$$0 \leq m \leq n \tag{3.8}$$

can exist. From the definition of m and n above it is obvious that $m > n$ cannot exist. The probability of an impossible event is zero. The probability of an event that is certain is one.

Whenever there are events that cannot occur together, such as tossing both a head and a tail in a single toss of a coin, these events are said to be mutually exclusive. And the probabilities of these events are calculated by the *theorem of addition of probabilities*. The theorem states that the probability that one of n mutually exclusive events occurs is equal to the sum of their separate probabilities and is expressed by

$$P(A_1 + A_2 + \cdots + A_n) = P(A_1) + P(A_2) + \cdots + P(A_n) = \sum_{i=1}^{n} P(A_i). \tag{3.9}$$

Further, if one of the events must occur, then

$$P(A_1 + A_2 + \cdots + A_n) = 1. \tag{3.10}$$

Example 3.2. Suppose aircraft A can be in only one of the following states:

E_1 = on the ground.
E_2 = climbing.
E_3 = in cruise altitude.
E_4 = descending.

The associated probabilities of being in any one of the states E are the following:

p_1 = probability of being in state E_1 (on ground).
p_2 = probability of being in state E_2 (climbing).
p_3 = probability of being in state E_3 (cruise altitude).
p_4 = probability of being in state E_4 (descending).

The four states are examples of mutually exclusive events, since aircraft A can be in only *one* state at any one time, and it must be in one of the states E. Therefore, from the theorem of addition of probabilities, the following relationship applies:

$$p_1 + p_2 + p_3 + p_4 = 1.$$

Whenever there are stochastically independent events, the probabilities of combinations of these events are calculated by the *multiplication formula*, which states that the probability that stochastically independent events occur together equals the product of the probabilities of occurrence of each event and is expressed by

$$P(A_1A_2 \cdots A_n) = P(A_1)P(A_2) \cdots P(A_n) = \prod_{i=1}^{n} P(A_i). \tag{3.11}$$

Example 3.3. Suppose p_a is the probability that aircraft A is in the air, p_v is the probability there is 10 miles visibility, and p_b is the probability that aircraft B is in the air. These are all probabilities associated with stochastically independent events. Therefore the probability that aircraft A and aircraft B are both in the air and that there is 10 miles visibility is determined by the multiplication formula

$$P = p_a p_b p_v.$$

We define a *probability distribution* as a systematic arrangement of numerical data. We illustrate it by a graph of frequency of measurement versus measurement, and we express it by a mathematical function. We may plot the raw scores on a test, or we may plot the measurement accuracies of a given radar. For one variable, the frequency is measured along the ordinate (vertical axis) and the measurement x is read along the abscissa (horizontal axis). A smooth curve of the plot is known as the *probability density function* $f(x)$ or the *probability frequency function* $f(x)$ of the random variable x_i. The terms frequency function and density function are interchangeable.

The integral (or the cumulative) of the frequency function $f(x)$ is the *probability distribution function* $F(X)$. The probability density graph is a graph of the first derivative of the probability distribution function graph. Thus $f(x)$ is the first derivative of $F(X)$, and, conversely, $F(X)$

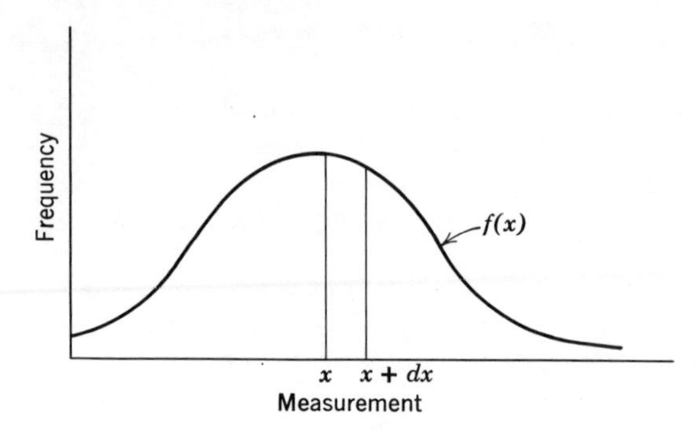

Fig. 3.2 Probability density (or frequency) function curve.

is the integral of $f(x)$. We express the relationship in mathematical symbology as follows:

$$\frac{dF(X)}{dx} = f(x) \tag{3.12}$$

$$F(X) = \int_a^X f(x)\,dx. \tag{3.13}$$

The total area under the density function curve is always represented as unity. The area (given in percentage or decimal) under a portion of the probability density function curve is the probability P of a random measurement x_i lying between the two corresponding abscissa values, x and $x + dx$. In probability symbology this is represented by

$$P(x < x_i < x + dx) \tag{3.14}$$

and is illustrated in Fig. 3.2, in which the curve is the density function $f(x)$ and x_i lies between x and $x + dx$. The random variable x_i may occur with the frequency given by the ordinate value on the smooth curve of $f(x)$. We can convert this frequency of occurrence into a probability value by using a functional relationship.

The cumulative form or the probability distribution function $F(X)$ is illustrated in Fig. 3.3, in which the probability that a random measurement x_i is less than or equal to x is given by the corresponding ordinate value, in which probability is expressed in percentage or decimal. In probability symbology this is expressed by

$$P(x_i \leq x). \tag{3.15}$$

The relationship between the probability distribution function $F(X)$ and the probability frequency function $f(x)$ (Fig. 3.4) is

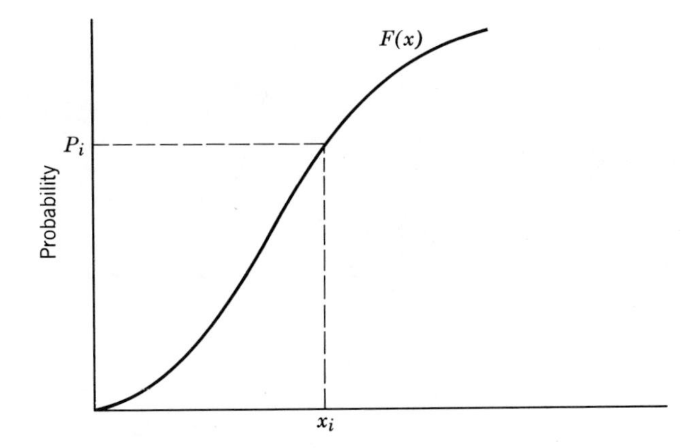

Fig. 3.3 Probability distribution function curve.

expressed in (3.13) for a continuous distribution or by

$$F(X) = \sum_{X_1}^{X_2} f(x) \tag{3.16}$$

for a discrete distribution. Probability distributions may be continuous, such as men's heights or measurement errors. Probability distributions may be discrete, such as number of children or number of demands upon a runway.

Example 3.4. The following are additional examples of continuous distributions:

Thickness of a wire.
Error in the heading of an aircraft.
Error in the speed of an automobile.
Biological life span.
Random failure patterns.
Fatigue tests.
Event time intervals.
Tide measurements.

The following are additional examples of discrete distributions:

Mortality rate.
Transmission failures.
Customer arrivals.
Business failures.
Demands at a service counter.
Number of defective relays.
Number of trees per acre.

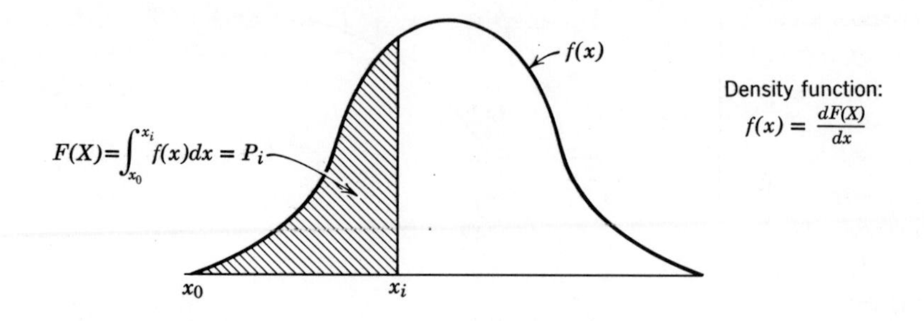

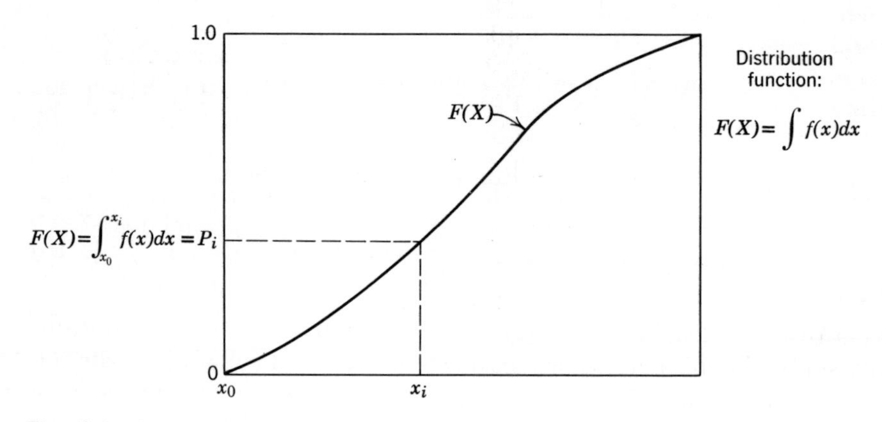

Fig. 3.4 Graphic illustration of the relationship of the density function $f(x)$ and the distribution function $F(X)$.

MEASURES OF PROBABILITY FREQUENCY FUNCTION CHARACTERISTICS

We measure characteristic features or statistical parameters of the probability frequency $f(x)$ by computing the first, second, third, and fourth moments. The moments of continuous probability distributions are given by integrals, whereas the summation sign (Σ) replaces the integral for the moments of discrete distributions. We define the moments as follows:

First Moment

The expected value of x represented by $E(x)$ or mean μ of a random variable x_i is defined as the first moment (or center of gravity) about zero measurement on the frequency function curve $f(x)$. The first moment is also known as the average, the moment of central tendency, or the centroid. For a continuous distribution this moment of central tendency is given by the mean

$$\mu = \int_{-\infty}^{\infty} xf(x)\, dx, \tag{3.17}$$

and for a discrete distribution it is given by

$$\mu = \sum_{-\infty}^{\infty} xf(x). \tag{3.18}$$

The mean can be thought of as a point on the horizontal axis in the middle of the probability frequency function curve. The torque on the left side of the point is equal to the torque on the right side of the point. For a distribution of unlimited range this is represented by

$$\int_{-\infty}^{\mu} (\mu - x) f(x)\, dx = \int_{\mu}^{\infty} (x - \mu) f(x)\, dx \tag{3.19}$$

or

$$\sum_{-\infty}^{\mu} (\mu - x) f(x) = \sum_{\mu}^{\infty} (x - \mu) f(x) \tag{3.20}$$

for continuous and discrete distributions, respectively.

Second Moment

The second moment is the dispersion or spread about the mean. The second moment, or moment of inertia, is called the variance σ^2 or spread or mean square deviation. The square root of the variance is called the root mean square or the standard deviation σ. The variance or moment of dispersion is given by

$$\sigma^2 = \int_{-\infty}^{\infty} (x - \mu)^2 f(x)\, dx = \int_{-\infty}^{\infty} x^2 f(x)\, dx - \mu^2 \tag{3.21}$$

for a continuous distribution or by

$$\sigma^2 = \sum_{-\infty}^{\infty} (x - \mu)^2 f(x) = \sum_{-\infty}^{\infty} x^2 f(x) - \mu^2 \tag{3.22}$$

for a discrete distribution.

For a given probability distribution a specified percentage of all cases falls within given σ limits. We will specify some of these limits when we discuss certain examples of probability distributions later in this section.

Third Moment

The third moment about the mean characterizes the skewness of the distribution and is a measure of symmetry. The third moment is given by

$$M_3 = \int_{-\infty}^{\infty} (x - \mu)^3 f(x)\, dx \tag{3.23}$$

for a continuous distribution or by

$$M_3 = \sum_{-\infty}^{\infty} (x - \mu)^3 f(x) \tag{3.24}$$

for a discrete distribution.

If the third moment is greater than zero the frequency distribution curve is asymmetrical and positively skewed, or it peaks to the left. When the third moment is equal to zero the frequency curve is symmetrical and has no skewness. When the third moment is less than zero, the frequency curve is asymmetrical and negatively skewed, or it peaks to the right. Positively skewed, symmetrical, and negatively skewed curves are illustrated in Fig. 3.5.

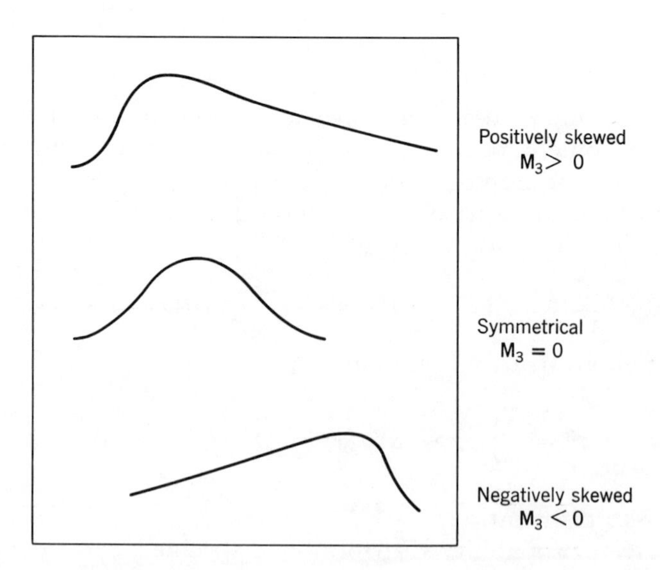

Fig. 3.5 Skewness of probability density function.

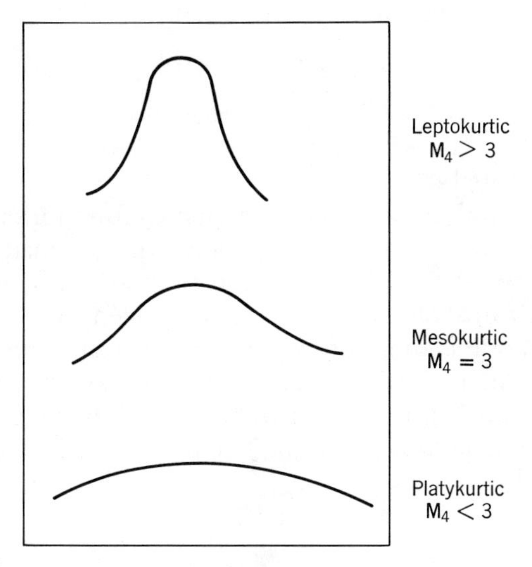

Fig. 3.6 Kurtosis of probability density function: ($\sigma = 1$).

Fourth Moment

The fourth moment about the mean is a measure of kurtosis, or the flatedness or peakedness of the curve. The fourth moment is given by

$$M_4 = \int_{-\infty}^{\infty} (x - \mu)^4 f(x)\, dx \tag{3.25}$$

for a continuous distribution or by

$$M_4 = \sum_{-\infty}^{\infty} (x - \mu)^4 f(x) \tag{3.26}$$

for a discrete distribution.

If $\sigma = 1$ and the fourth moment is greater than 3 the frequency curve is leptokurtic (tall and thin). When the fourth moment is equal to 3 the frequency curve is mesokurtic (medium). When the fourth moment is less than 3 the frequency curve is platykurtic (flat). Leptokurtic, mesokurtic, and platykurtic curves are illustrated in Fig. 3.6.

nth Moment

The nth moment is given by

$$M_n = \int_{-\infty}^{\infty} (x - \mu)^n f(x)\, dx \tag{3.27}$$

for a continuous distribution or by

$$M_n = \sum_{-\infty}^{\infty} (x - \mu)^n f(x) \tag{3.28}$$

for a discrete distribution.

We have shown that probability frequency functions may be characterized by the mean or average, variance or standard deviation, the skewness, and the kurtosis. In addition to these characteristics, probability frequency functions may be characterized by the mode and the median. The mode is the number in the horizontal measurement that occurs most frequently; thus a unimodal frequency curve peaks only once. The median is the number in the horizontal measurement that occupies the 50 percentile position. The mean, mode, and median may be coincidental depending upon the type of distribution.

	Probability Frequency (or density)		Probability Distribution	
	Function	Graph	Function	Graph
Continuous	$P(x < x_i < x + dx) = f(x)$ $f(x)$ is the first derivative of $F(X)$	Frequency versus measurement 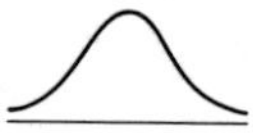	$P(x_i \leq x) = F(X)$ $F(X) = \int_a^b f(x)\,dx$ $F(X)$ is the integral of $f(x)$.	Cumulative percentage 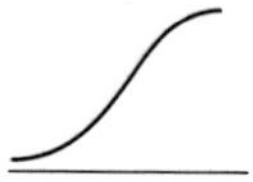
Discrete	$P(x < x_i < x + \Delta x) = f(x)$ $f(x)$ is term of $F(X)$	Frequency versus measurement 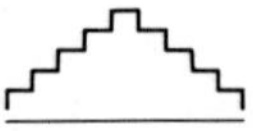	$P(x_i \leq x) = F(X)$ $F(X) = \sum_{b}^{a} f(x)$ $F(X)$ is the summation of $f(x)$.	Cumulative percentage 

Fig. 3.7 Characteristics

We can extend our discussion of univariate probability distributions to apply to the bivariate and multivariate distributions. We apply the *multiplication formula* in measuring the characteristic features of probability distributions whenever there is stochastic independence in each dimension. For example, in the bivariate distribution, in which x and y are stochastically independent, the probability frequency function $f(x, y)$ is given by

$$f(x, y) = f(x)f(y) \tag{3.29}$$

by application of the multiplication formula and is represented by a surface. The probability distribution function $F(X, Y)$ is given by

$$F(X, Y) = \int^{X}\int^{Y} f(x, y)\, dx\, dy \tag{3.30}$$

In the multivariate distribution with variables $x_1, x_2, \ldots, x_n$, the relationship of the probability frequency function $f(x_1, x_2, \ldots, x_n)$

First Moment (mean)	Second Moment (variance)	Third Moment (skewness)	Fourth Moment (kurtosis)
$\mu = \int_{-\infty}^{\infty} x f(x)\, dx$ $\bar{x} = \frac{1}{N}\sum x$	$\sigma^2 = \int_{-\infty}^{\infty} (x - \mu)^2 f(x)\, dx$ $S^2 = \frac{1}{N-1}\sum x^2 - \bar{x}^2$	$M_3 = \int_{-\infty}^{\infty} (x - \mu)^3 f(x)\, dx$	$M_4 = \int_{-\infty}^{\infty} (x - \mu)^4 f(x)\, dx$
$\mu = \sum_{-\infty}^{\infty} x f(x)$ $\bar{x} = \frac{1}{N}\sum x$	$\sigma^2 = \sum_{-\infty}^{\infty} (x - \mu)^2 f(x)$ $S^2 = \frac{1}{N-1}\sum x^2 - \bar{x}^2$	$M_3 = \sum_{-\infty}^{\infty} (x - \mu)^3 f(x)$	$M_4 = \sum_{-\infty}^{\infty} (x - \mu)^4 f(x)$

of probability distributions.

and the probability distribution function $F(X_1, X_2, \ldots, X_n)$ is given by

$$F(X_1, X_2, \ldots, X_n) = \int X_1, X_2, \ldots, X_n \int f(x_1, x_2, \ldots, x_n)\, dx_1\, dx_2 \cdots dx_n, \quad (3.31)$$

where

$$f(x_1, x_2, \ldots, x_n) = f(x_1)f(x_2) \cdots f(x_n) = \prod_{i=1}^{n} f(x_i). \quad (3.32)$$

As in the case of the univariate distribution, the integrals are used for the continuous distributions, and summation signs replace the integrals in the discrete distributions. In each case there are as many integral signs and differentials in the continuous distributions or summation signs in the discrete distributions as there are variables.

The first and second moments in any dimension may be computed for N sample measurements X_i by the following moment estimators:

$$\bar{X} = \frac{1}{N} \sum_{i=1}^{N} X_i, \qquad (i = 1, 2, \ldots, N) \quad (3.33)$$

$$S^2 = \frac{1}{N} \sum_{i=1}^{N} (X_i - \bar{X})^2 = \frac{1}{N} \sum_{i=1}^{N} X_i^2 - \bar{X}^2, \quad (3.34)$$

respectively.

In Fig. 3.7 we summarized the characteristics of continuous and discrete probability distributions for univariate distributions.

Examples of Probability Distributions

There are several probability distributions that are applicable in computer modeling and simulation. From the previous discussion we know that probability distributions may be continuous or discrete. We know that probability distributions may be univariate, bivariate, or multivariate. In Table 3.1 we list representative examples of distributions in the above categories.

We describe various examples of probability distributions below in which we discuss major characteristics of each distribution. We begin with the uniform distribution because it is very simple and is a basic distribution in stochastic modeling. Following this description we discuss several nonuniform probability distributions.

Uniform or Rectangular Distribution. A uniform or rectangular distribution is a symmetrical, continuous probability distribution that is

Table 3.1 Categories of Probability Distributions

Category	Continuous	Discrete
Univariate (one-dimensional)	Uniform Normal (Gaussian) Exponential Pearson types Weibull Log normal γ β χ^2 Student (or t) F Triangular	Binomial (Bernoulli) Poisson Hypergeometric Geometric
Bivariate (two-dimensional)	Bivariate uniform Bivariate normal Circular normal Rayleigh	Bivariate binomial Bivariate Poisson Bivariate hypergeometric
Multivariate (multi-dimensional)	Multivariate uniform Multivariate normal Spherical normal	Multivariate binomial Multivariate Poisson Multivariate hypergeometric

widely applied in computer modeling and simulation. First we describe the univariate, uniform distribution. It is a flat distribution in which the frequency function is usually given by

$$f(x) = 1 \qquad 0 \leq x \leq 1 \tag{3.35}$$

and the probability distribution function is given by

$$F(X) = \int_0^X dx. \tag{3.36}$$

There is an equal likelihood of any measurement occurring at any point along the abscissa of the frequency function. The uniform distribution is the only distribution with this characteristic. For the probability distribution function between the interval zero and one, the mean and variance are given by

$$\mu = \int_0^1 x\, dx = 0.5 \tag{3.37}$$

$$\sigma^2 = \int_0^1 (x - 0.5)^2\, dx = 0.0833, \tag{3.38}$$

respectively. The standard deviation σ is 0.2887.

The third and fourth moments about the mean are given by

$$M_3 = \int_0^1 (x - 0.5)^3 \, dx = 0 \tag{3.39}$$

$$M_4 = \int_0^1 (x - 0.5)^4 \, dx = 0.0125, \tag{3.40}$$

respectively.

Approximately 57.74% of all measurements fall within the $\pm 1\sigma$ limits. The univariate, uniform distribution is primarily applicable in the generation of uniform random numbers, which we explain in a later section. By a transformation of variables, the univariate, uniform distribution is always necessary first in the generation of nonuniform random numbers. We also explain this in a later section.

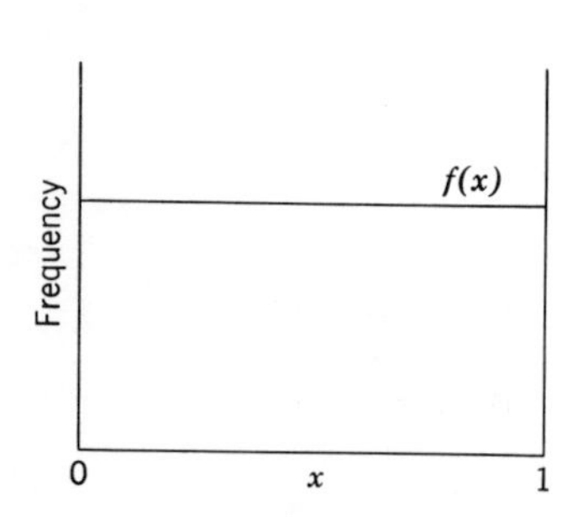

Fig. 3.8 Uniform probability density function.

In Fig. 3.8 we show a graph of the uniform frequency function $f(x)$. We can easily see that the frequency function is a straight-line segment parallel to the x axis. The frequency function can be extended over a wider range. Thus we would extend the limits of integration in computing the first, second, third, and fourth moments. The range from zero to one, however, is the most frequently applied [89].

The bivariate, uniform probability frequency function $f(x, y)$ is given by the multiplication formula

$$f(x, y) = f(x)f(y) = 1 \qquad \begin{cases} 0 \leq x \leq 1 \\ 0 \leq y \leq 1 \end{cases} \tag{3.41}$$

and the bivariate, uniform probability distribution function $F(X, Y)$ is given by

$$F(X, Y) = \int_0^X \int_0^Y dx \, dy = 1. \tag{3.42}$$

There is an equal likelihood of any point x, y occurring within the unit square bounded by the points 0,0; 1,0; 1,1; 0,1. The means and variances in each dimension for the bivariate case are given by

$$\mu = \int_0^1 \int_0^1 xy \, dx \, dy \begin{cases} \mu_x = 0.5 \\ \mu_y = 0.5 \end{cases} \tag{3.43}$$

$$\sigma^2 = \int_0^1 \int_0^1 (x - 0.5)^2 (y - 0.5)^2 \, dx \, dy \begin{cases} \sigma_x{}^2 = 0.0833 \\ \sigma_y{}^2 = 0.0833 \end{cases} \tag{3.44}$$

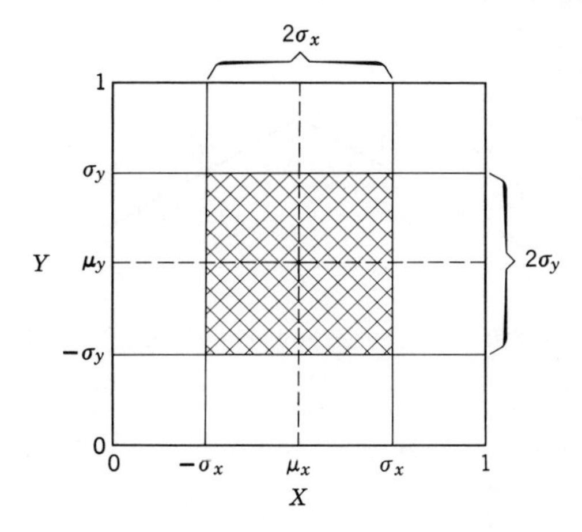

Fig. 3.9 Bivariate uniform probability density function.

The standard deviation σ_x is 0.2887 and σ_y is 0.2887. Approximately one-third of all measurements fall within the $\pm 1\sigma_x$ and $\pm 1\sigma_y$ limits. This is shown in the shaded area in Fig. 3.9.

The mean, variance, and third and fourth moments for the multivariate, uniform probability distribution are computed by an extension of the above formulas. We can see that for limits of integration from zero to one the mean, variance, and third and fourth moments in one variable are always the same as the mean, variance, and third and fourth moments, respectively, in every other variable.

There are probably no physical phenomena that can be described by the uniform distribution. This is due to the fact that variabilities in nature are usually nonuniformly distributed. However, whenever there are purely random choices to be made among several alternatives, the uniform distribution is frequently applied. For example, if an individual has four destinations to select from, he may choose any one purely at random. If his pattern of choices is not known, selection on a uniform basis is valid. It has been common practice to assume uniformity when little is known about the distribution.

Triangular Distribution [62]. The triangular distribution is a continuous distribution in which the probability frequency function is given by

$$f_1(x) = \frac{2}{a(a+b)}(a+x) \qquad -a \leq x \leq 0 \tag{3.45}$$

$$f_2(x) = \frac{2}{b(a+b)}(b-x) \qquad 0 \leq x \leq b \tag{3.46}$$

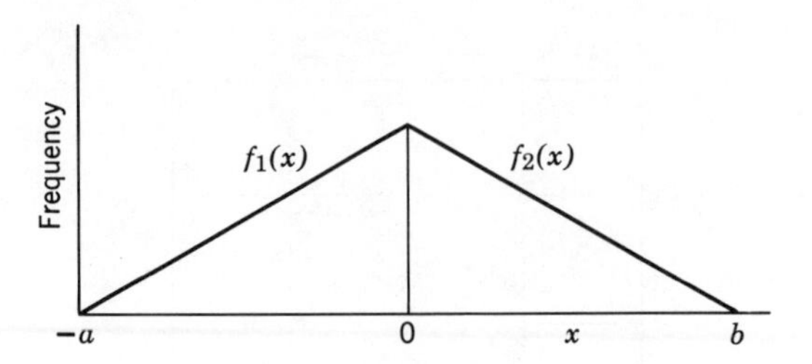

Fig. 3.10 Triangular probability density function.

and the probability distribution function is given by

$$F(X) = \begin{cases} \dfrac{2}{a(a+b)} \displaystyle\int_{-a}^{X} (a+x)\,dx \quad \text{if} \quad -a \leq X \leq 0 \\ \dfrac{2}{a(a+b)} \displaystyle\int_{-a}^{0} (a+x)\,dx + \dfrac{2}{b(a+b)} \displaystyle\int_{0}^{X} (b-x)\,dx \\ \qquad \text{if} \quad 0 \leq X \leq b \end{cases} \tag{3.47}$$

The mean and variance are given by

$$\mu = (b - a)/\overline{3} \tag{3.48}$$

$$\sigma^2 = (a^2 + ab + b^2)/\overline{18} \tag{3.49}$$

respectively. A graph of the frequency function is shown in Fig. 3.10.

Binomial Distribution. The binomial probability distribution derived by Bernoulli is a discrete distribution in which the outcome of an event is but one of two ways: either a success or failure, heads or tails, life or death, go or no-go, effective or noneffective, occurrence or nonoccurrence.

The probability of getting s successes in n trials of an experiment, where p is the probability of success of any trial, is given by the probability frequency function

$$f(s) = \frac{n!}{s!(n-s)!} p^s (1-p)^{n-s}. \tag{3.50}$$

The probability distribution function is given by

$$F(k) = \sum_{0}^{s=k} \frac{n!}{s!(n-s)!} p^s (1-p)^{n-s}, \qquad (k = 0, 1, \ldots, n) \tag{3.51}$$

Use of (3.18), (3.22), (3.24), and (3.26) gives the mean, variance, and third and fourth moments of the binomial distribution as

$$\mu = np \tag{3.52}$$

$$\sigma^2 = np(1 - p) = npq \tag{3.53}$$

$$M_3 = npq(q - p) \tag{3.54}$$

$$M_4 = npq[1 + 3pq(n - 2)], \tag{3.55}$$

respectively, where the probability of failure q of an event is given by

$$q = 1 - p. \tag{3.56}$$

The standard deviation is given by

$$\sigma = (npq)^{1/2}. \tag{3.57}$$

The multinomial distribution is a discrete generalization of the binomial probability distribution with k variables. The density function of the multinomial distribution is given by the multiplication formula

$$f(s_1, s_2, \ldots, s_{k-1}) = n! \prod_{i=1}^{k} \left\{ \frac{p_i^{s_i}}{s_i!} \right\} \tag{3.58}$$

and the distribution function is given by

$$F(s_1, s_2, \ldots, s_{k-1}) = \sum_{0}^{m} n! \prod_{i=1}^{k} \left\{ \frac{p_i^{s_i}}{s_i!} \right\}. \tag{3.59}$$

We apply the binominal distribution in a stochastic computer simulation whenever the probability of an event occurring follows the Bernoulli distribution. Applications of this distribution are shown in Part 4. Methods of generating binomial random variates s given n and p are shown later.

Example 3.5. Tables of the binomial probability distribution are given in *Standard Mathematical Tables*, fourteenth edition, Chemical Rubber Co., Cleveland, Ohio, 1965. Individual terms in the density function to four decimal places are given in the tables on pages 437–443. The tables give $f(x)$ versus x, n, p, where $0 \leq x \leq 20$, $1 \leq n \leq 20$, $0.05 \leq p \leq 0.50$. Tables of the cumulative binomial function are given on pages 444–450. The tables are calculated to four decimal places and have the same range of values as in the density function tables.

Binomial probability distribution tables have also been published by Harvard University, National Bureau of Standards, Office of Technical Services, and H. G. Romig.

Poisson Distribution. If we let s in the binomial probability distribution remain finite for a large number of trials as n approaches infinity and p approaches zero in such a manner that the product np remains constant, then (3.50) becomes

$$f(s) = \frac{(np)^s}{s!} e^{-np}, \tag{3.60}$$

which is known as the Poisson distribution, where $e = 2.71828$. This is a discrete distribution that describes the distribution of rare event occurrences or events over periods of time. The Poisson is the limit of the binomial distribution.

The following are some examples which are known to follow the Poisson distribution:

1. The number of α-particles that enter a prescribed region during a prescribed interval of time.
2. The number of defects of a manufactured article.
3. The number of accidents, such as railroad, automobile, or airplane accidents, in some unit of time.
4. The number of insurance claims in some unit of time.
5. The number of incoming calls at a switchboard in some unit of time.
6. The demands upon a runway at an airport.
7. The demands on berthing facilities at a port.
8. The arrival of customers at a service station, toll bridge, or retail store.
9. Arrivals or departures of travelers at a specified point.

For given n and p we can determine the probability of obtaining no successes by the function

$$Q_{(s=0)} = e^{-np}, \tag{3.61}$$

where the exponent np is the mean or expected number of successes.* If Q is the probability of no successes, then the probability of one or more successes, which must be some finite number, is given by the complement of Q as

$$P_{(s\geq 1)} = 1 - Q = 1 - e^{-np}. \tag{3.62}$$

The probability of just one success is given by

$$P_{(s=1)} = npe^{-np}. \tag{3.63}$$

and the probability of two successes is given by

$$P_{(s=2)} = \tfrac{1}{2}(np)^2 e^{-np}; \tag{3.64}$$

* Note that $(np)^{\circ}/0! = 1$.

for example, given $np = 1.0$, the probability of no successes is 0.37, of one or more successes, 0.63, of only one success, 0.37, and of only two successes, 0.18. A graph of the probability of at least one success in n trials for given probability p of success for an individual trial in which $p = 0.05, 0.1, 0.3, 0.5, 0.7, 0.9$ is shown in Fig. 3.11.

Example 3.6. Tables of the Poisson probability distribution are given in *Standard Mathematical Tables*, 14th edition, Chemical Rubber Co., Cleveland, Ohio, 1965. Individual terms in the Poisson density function to four decimal places are given in the tables on pages 451–457. The tables give $f(x)$ as functions of x, m, where $m = np$, $0 \leq x \leq 39$, $0.1 \leq m \leq 20$. Tables of the cumulative function are given on pages 458–464. The tables are to four decimal places and with the same range of values as the density tables.

Poisson probability distribution tables have also been published by H. O. Hartley and E. S. Pearson and T. Kitagawa.

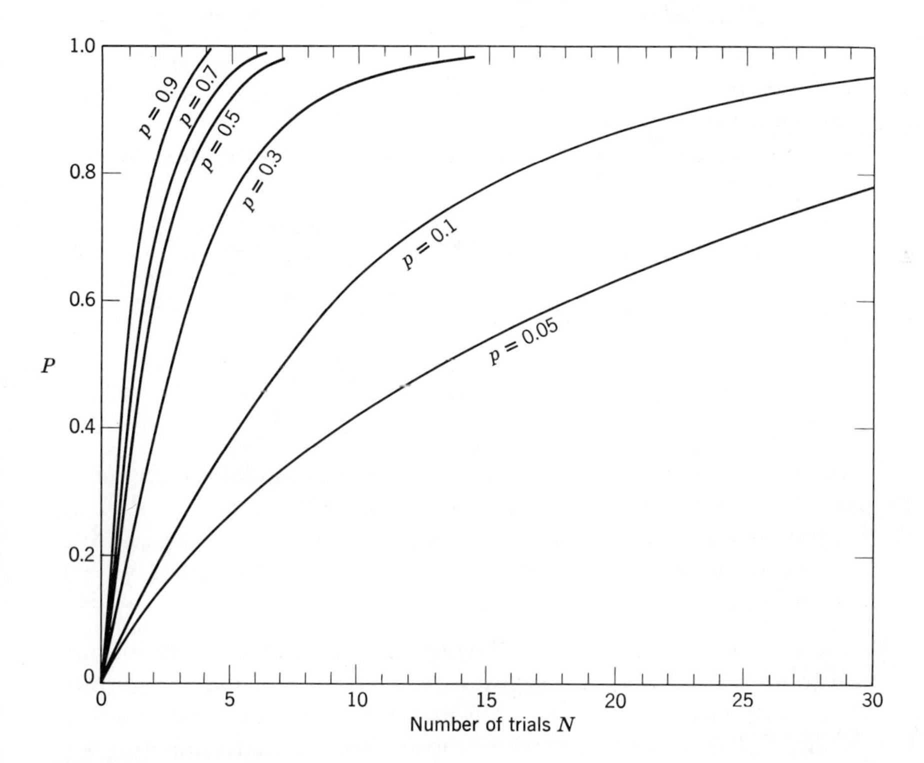

Fig. 3.11 Probability of at least one success in N trials for given probability p of success for an individual trial.

The mean and variance of the Poisson distribution are given by the expressions

$$\mu = np \tag{3.65}$$

$$\sigma^2 = np, \tag{3.66}$$

respectively. The standard deviation is given by

$$\sigma = \sqrt{np}. \tag{3.67}$$

The third and fourth moments are given by

$$M_3 = np \tag{3.68}$$

$$M_4 = 3np(np + \tfrac{1}{3}), \tag{3.69}$$

respectively.

The probability distribution function is given by

$$F_{(m)} = \sum_{s=0}^{m} f(s) = \sum_{s=0}^{m} \frac{(np)^s}{s!} e^{-np}, \tag{3.70}$$

where $F(s)$ is the probability that m or fewer successes will occur when the average number of successes is np.

The multivariable Poisson density function is given by the multiplication formula

$$f(s_1, s_2, \ldots, s_k) = e^{-(n_1p_1+n_2p_2+\cdots)} \prod_{i=1}^{k} \frac{(n_ik_i)^{s_i}}{(s_i)!} \tag{3.71}$$

and the distribution function is given by

$$F(m_1, m_2 \ldots m_k) = \prod_{i=1}^{k} \left[e^{n_ik_i} \sum_{s_i=0}^{m_i} \frac{(n_ik_i)^{s_i}}{(s_i)!} \right]. \tag{3.72}$$

The Poisson distribution is applied in stochastic modeling whenever the probability of events occurring over a period of time are Poisson distributed. Applications of the Poisson distribution in modeling and methods of generating Poisson random variates s for given np are shown later.

Normal or Gaussian Distribution. The normal or Gaussian distribution is a continuous, symmetrical distribution, with the mean at the origin, which is frequently applied in computer modeling and simulation. The normal distribution describes most measurement phenomena. Examples of phenomena that follow the normal distribution include the following:

Measurement error in angular or in linear dimensions.
Measurement error in angular or in linear velocity components.
Diameters of a hole made by a drill press.
Scores on a test.
Yield of produce on a plot of ground.
Heights or weights of men, women, or children.

Both the binomial and Poisson distributions approach the normal as their means approach infinity. This feature is explained in most books on probability.

The normal probability frequency function $f(x)$ in one variable with mean μ and variance σ^2 or the univariate normal is given by

$$f(x) = \frac{1}{\sigma(2\pi)^{1/2}} \exp\left[\frac{-(x-\mu)^2}{2\sigma^2}\right] \tag{3.73}$$

and the probability distribution function $F(X)$ is given by

$$F(X) = \int_{-\infty}^{X} f(x)\,dx = \frac{1}{\sigma(2\pi)^{1/2}} \int_{-\infty}^{X} \exp\left[\frac{-(x-\mu)^2}{2\sigma^2}\right] dx, \tag{3.74}$$

where $1/(2\pi)^{1/2} = 0.3989$.

The graphs of the frequency and distribution functions in one variable are shown in Figs. 3.12 and 3.13, respectively. These are graphs of the standard normal probability distribution in which the first, second, third, and fourth moments are given by

$$\mu = 0 \tag{3.75}$$

$$\sigma^2 = 1 \tag{3.76}$$

$$M_3 = 0 \tag{3.77}$$

$$M_4 = 3, \tag{3.78}$$

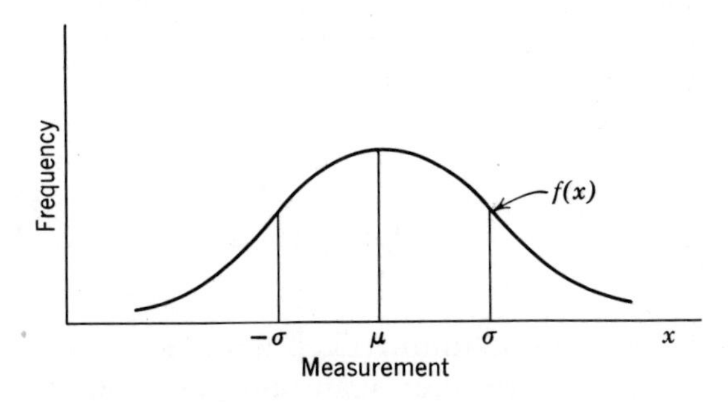

Fig. 3.12 Normal probability frequency (or density) function.

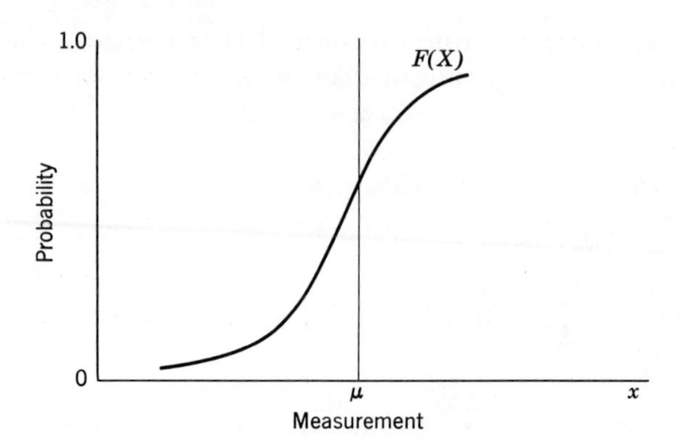

Fig. 3.13 Normal probability distribution function.

respectively. We characterize the standard normal frequency function as unimodal, symmetrical, mesokurtic, and with the origin at the mean.

The mean μ and variance σ^2 of the normal distribution are computed from (3.17) and (3.21), respectively. However, for a finite set of n samples of measurements X_i we compute the mean $\bar{X}$ and variance S^2 by

$$\bar{X} = \frac{1}{n} \sum_{1}^{n} X_i \tag{3.79}$$

$$S^2 = \frac{1}{n} \sum_{1}^{n} (X_i - \bar{X})^2 = \frac{1}{n} \sum_{1}^{n} X_i^2 - \bar{X}^2, \tag{3.80}$$

respectively. The standard deviation S (or root mean square) is given by the square root of the variance. The unbiased standard deviation observed in the sample is given by

$$S = \left[\frac{1}{n-1} \sum_{1}^{n} (X_i - \bar{X})^2\right]^{1/2} = \left[\frac{1}{n-1} \left(\sum_{1}^{n} X_i^2 - n\bar{X}^2\right)\right]^{1/2}. \tag{3.81}$$

Equation (3.81) is the maximum likelihood estimator. These same equations apply to compute the mean and variance in other dimensions as well.

In the one variable normal probability frequency function the approximate spread about the mean in σ units is as follows:

$\pm 1\sigma$ includes about 68.3% of all cases.
$\pm 2\sigma$ includes about 95.5% of all cases.
$\pm 3\sigma$ includes about 99.7% of all cases.

Thus it is apparent that beyond the 3σ limits only 0.3% of the cases occur; that is, three out of 1000 measurements fall outside the 3σ limits.

We also refer to probable error (PE) and mean absolute error (MAE) in addition to σ. Their relationships are as follows:

PE includes 50% of all cases.
$\text{PE} = 0.6745\sigma$.
$\text{MAE} = 0.7979\sigma$.
$\sigma = 1.4826\ \text{PE} = 1.2533\ \text{MAE}$.

Example 3.7. There are many published tables of the normal probability distribution. *Tables of Normal Probability Functions*, National Bureau of Standards, Washington, D.C., 1953, contains 343 pages of tables to 15 decimal places. The volume contains tabular values of the density function and the distribution function, in which the arguments range is $0 \leq x \leq 10$. Tables of the density function, distribution function, and the first through sixth derivatives are given in Cramer, *Mathematical Methods of Statistics*, Princeton University Press, Princeton, N.J., 1963. These are tables to five decimal places and are given on page 557.

Normal probability tables have also been published by Chemical Rubber Co., National Bureau of Standards, Harvard University, R. S. Burington and D. C. May, and H. D. Young.

The Cramer [38] reference contains a table of the probability that an observed normally distributed variable ξ differs from the mean m in either direction by more than λ times σ. This is expressed in mathematical symbology by

$$P = p(|\xi - m| > \lambda\sigma),$$

where $0.01 \leq p \leq 100$; p is a function of λ, and $0 \leq \lambda \leq 4$. This table appears on page 558 of [38].

The bivariate normal or the normal probability density function $f(x, y)$ describing stochastically independent phenomena in two dimensions is determined by using the multiplication formula and is given by

$$f(x, y) = f(x)f(y) = \frac{1}{2\pi\sigma_x\sigma_y} \exp\left[-\frac{(x - \mu_x)^2}{2\sigma_x^2} - \frac{(y - \mu_y)^2}{2\sigma_y^2}\right]. \tag{3.82}$$

The probability distribution function $F(X, Y)$ is given by

$$F(X, Y) = \iint_{-\infty}^{XY} f(x, y)\, dx\, dy$$

$$= \frac{1}{2\pi\sigma_x\sigma_y} \iint_{-\infty}^{XY} \exp\left[-\frac{(x-\mu_x)^2}{2\sigma_x^2} - \frac{(y-\mu_y)^2}{2\sigma_y^2}\right] dx\, dy, \quad (3.83)$$

where $1/2\pi = 0.1592$.

The general case is called the elliptical normal distribution. However, if the variance in x and the variance in y are equal and the correlation coefficient ρ is zero, we have a special bivariate case, called the circular normal distribution, in which the frequency function $f(x, y)$ in rectangular coordinates is given by

$$f(x, y) = \frac{1}{2\pi\sigma^2} \exp\left[-\frac{(x-\mu_x)^2 + (y-\mu_y)^2}{2\sigma^2}\right], \quad (3.84)$$

where $\sigma = \sigma_x = \sigma_y$, $\rho = 0$, and the distribution function $F(X, Y)$ is given by

$$F(X, Y) = \iint_{-\infty}^{XY} f(x, y)\, dx\, dy$$

$$= \frac{1}{2\pi\sigma^2} \iint_{-\infty}^{XY} \exp\left[-\frac{(x-\mu_x)^2 + (y-\mu_y)^2}{2\sigma^2}\right] dx\, dy. \quad (3.85)$$

In the circular normal distribution $f(x, y)$ and $F(X, Y)$ can be transformed from rectangular to polar coordinates in which the frequency and distribution functions are given by

$$f(r) = \frac{r}{\sigma^2} e^{-r^2/2\sigma^2} \quad (3.86)$$

$$F(R) = \int_0^R f(r)\, dr = \frac{1}{\sigma^2} \int_0^R r e^{-r^2/2\sigma^2}\, dr, \quad (3.87)$$

respectively, where $r = [(x-\mu_x)^2 + (y-\mu_y)^2]^{1/2}$. This form is often referred to as the Rayleigh distribution.

The approximate spread about the origin or center (mean zero in x and y) in σ units is as follows:

1σ includes about 39.5% of all cases.
2σ includes about 86.5% of all cases.
3σ includes about 98.5% of all cases.

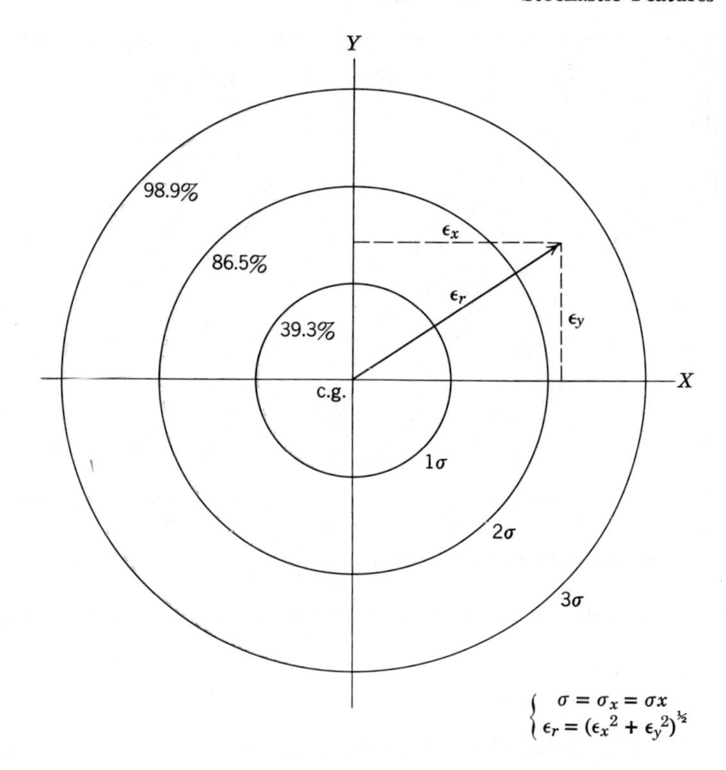

$$P = \frac{1}{2\pi\sigma^2} \int_0^R e^{-r^2/2\sigma^2}\, dr = 1 - e^{-R^2/2\sigma^2} \quad \text{(Probability distribution function)}$$

Fig. 3.14 Circular normal (or Rayleigh) probability distribution.

This dispersion about the origin is illustrated in Fig. 3.14. The probability of a two-dimensional error being less than a given amount for a given σ, where σ ranges from 25 to 3000 units in discrete increments, is shown in Fig. 3.15 [82, 83].

We also refer to circular probable error (CPE) and mean radial error (MRE) in addition to σ. Their relationships are as follows:

CPE includes 50% of all cases.

$$\text{CPE} = 1.177\sigma.$$

$$\text{MRE} = 1.253\sigma = 1.065\ \text{CPE}.$$

$$\sigma = 0.8493\ \text{CPE} = 0.7979\ \text{MRE}.$$

Example 3.8. Tables of the bivariate normal probability distribution have been published by Bell Aircraft Corporation (Report No. 02-949-106), 1956, National Bureau of Standards, Applied Mathematics Series 50, 1959, Office of Technical Services, and C. Nicholson.

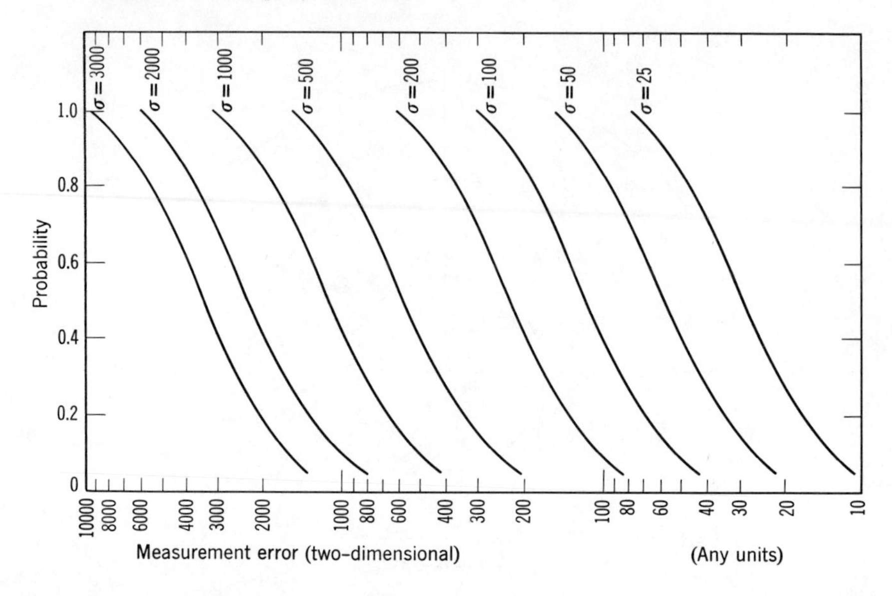

Fig. 3.15 Probability of two-dimensional error being less than given amount (circular normal).

The normal probability frequency function $f(x, y, z)$ that describes measurement phenomena in three dimensions in which x, y, z are stochastically independent is given by the general expression for the trivariate normal:

$$f(x, y, z) = \frac{1}{(2\pi)^{3/2}\sigma_x\sigma_y\sigma_z} \exp\left[-\frac{(x-\mu_x)^2}{2\sigma_x^2} - \frac{(y-\mu_y)^2}{2\sigma_y^2} - \frac{(z-\mu_z)^2}{2\sigma_z^2} \right] \tag{3.88}$$

and the probability distribution function $F(X, Y, Z)$ is given by

$$F(X, Y, Z) = \frac{1}{(2\pi)^{3/2}\sigma_x\sigma_y\sigma_z} \iiint_{-\infty}^{XYZ} \exp\left[-\frac{(x-\mu_x)^2}{2\sigma_x^2} - \frac{(y-\mu_y)^2}{2\sigma_y^2} - \frac{(z-\mu_z)^2}{2\sigma_z^2} \right] dx\, dy\, dz, \tag{3.89}$$

where $1/(2\pi)^{3/2} = 0.0635$.

The general trivariate case is the ellipsoidal normal distribution; however, if the variances in x, y, z, respectively, are all equal and the correlation coefficients are all zero, we have a special case called the spherical normal distribution, in which the frequency function $f(x, y, z)$ is given by

$$f(x, y, z) = \frac{1}{(2\pi)^{3/2}\sigma^3} \exp\left[-\frac{(x-\mu_x)^2 + (y-\mu_y)^2 + (z-\mu_z)^2}{2\sigma^2}\right] \tag{3.90}$$

and the distribution function $F(X, Y, Z)$ is given by

$$F(Z, Y, Z) = \frac{1}{(2\pi)^{3/2}\sigma^3} \iiint_{-\infty}^{XYZ} \exp\left[-\frac{(x-\mu_x)^2 + (y-\mu_y)^2 + (z-\mu_z)^2}{2\sigma^2}\right] dx\, dy\, dz. \tag{3.91}$$

The spherical normal distribution can be illustrated by generating a sphere by rotation of the circular normal distribution.

The approximate spread about the center of density function sphere (mean zero in x, y, and z) in σ units is as follows:

1σ includes about 19.5% of all cases.
2σ includes about 74% of all cases.
3σ includes about 97% of all cases.

We also refer to spherical probable error (SPE) and mean spherical radial error (MSRE) in addition to σ. Their relationships are as follows:

SPE includes 50% of all cases.
SPE $= 1.5382\sigma = 0.9639$ MSRE.
MSRE $= 1.5958\sigma$.
$\sigma = 0.6501$ SPE $= 0.6267$ MSRE.

The fractional space about the origin, beginning with $\sigma = 0$ and increasing the σ value symmetrically about zero, under the one-variable, circular, and spherical normal frequency function curves, is given in Table D.2.

A graph of the cumulative dispersion about the origin for one-variable, circular, and spherical normal distribution functions is shown in Fig. 3.16 and the table of the graph is given in Table D.3.

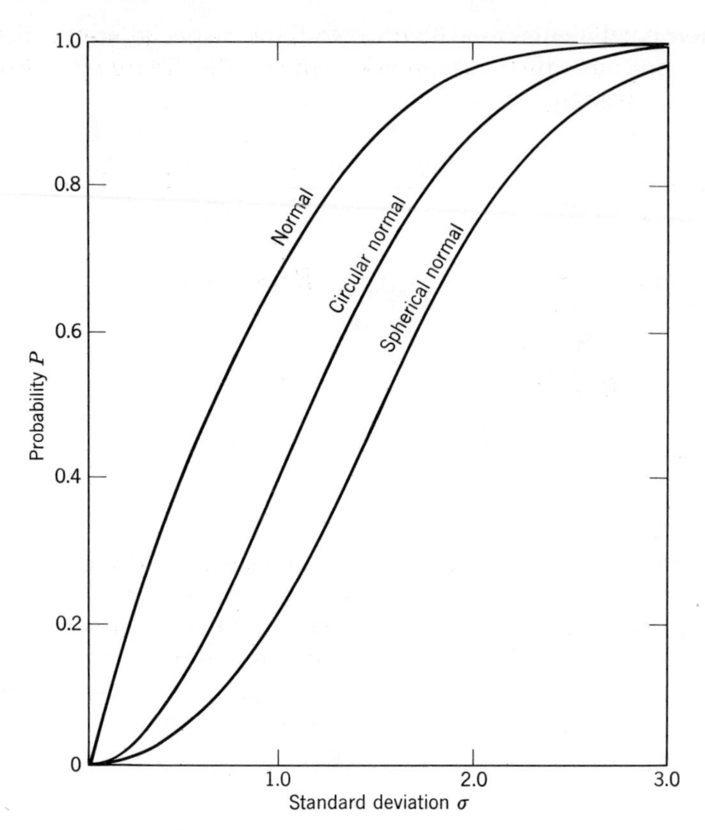

Fig. 3.16 Cumulative dispersion about the origin for the normal, circular normal, and spherical normal probability distributions.

Estimates of the statistical parameters (mean and variance) for the jth dimension in the multidimensional normal probability distribution are given by

$$\bar{X}_j = \frac{1}{m} \sum_{i=1}^{n} X_i \simeq \mu_j \tag{3.92}$$

$$S_j^2 = \frac{1}{m-1} \sum_{i=1}^{n} (X_i - \bar{X}_j)^2 \simeq \sigma_j^2, \tag{3.93}$$

where $i = 1, 2, 3, \ldots, n$ and $j = 1, 2, 3, \ldots, m$.

A table of the cumulative normal probability distribution in one variable is given in Table D.5. The table contains 128 divisions in which the arguments are in octal number system and the tabular values are in decimal. We have arranged the table in this manner for ease in computer application. We explain this feature later.

The normal probability distribution, whether it is univariate or multivariate, is applied in stochastic modeling whenever measurement phenomena are normally distributed. Applications of the normal distribution and methods of generating normal random variates are explained later.

Let us next illustrate procedures to determine the normalcy and parameters of a discrete set of empirical measurement data X_i. We show graphical and computational methods and χ^2 test below.

Graphical Method. Tabulate the raw data X_i in a frequency and cumulative table, in which the frequency of occurrence, cumulative frequency, and cumulative percentage are tabulated for grouped intervals of equal spacing as shown in Table 3.2. The *frequency of*

Table 3.2 Example of a Frequency and Cumulative Table

Interval	Frequency	Cumulative Frequency	Cumulative Percentage
0–5	0	0	0
5–10	2	2	1
10–15	2	4	2
15–20	6	10	5
20–25	10	20	10
25–30	20	40	20
30–35	28	68	34
35–40	32	100	50
40–45	32	132	66
45–50	28	160	80
50–55	18	178	89
55–60	12	190	95
60–65	6	196	98
65–70	4	200	100
70–75	0	200	100

occurrence is the number of data points which fall within given Δx intervals as x increases. The *cumulative frequency* is the running summation of the frequencies of occurrence for each interval. The *cumulative percentage* is the cumulative frequency expressed in percentage.

Test the data by the χ^2 test to determine normalcy and closeness of fit.

If the data are normal plot the tabular points from the cumulative percentage column on normal probability graph paper in which the mid-Δx intervals are the ordinate and the cumulative percentage points are the abscissa.

Draw a "best fit" straight line for the above data points.

Read the mean $\bar{X}$ off the ordinate. The mean is at the intersection of the best fit straight line and the 50 percentile.

Determine the standard deviation. Read the 84.5 percentile off the ordinate and subtract the mean. The difference is the 1σ standard deviation.

An example of a plot on normal probability graph paper is shown in Fig. 3.17.

Computional Method. Tabulate the raw data X_i in a frequency table.

Test the data by the χ^2 test to determine normalcy and closeness of fit.

If the data are normal, compute the mean $\bar{X}$ and standard deviation S by

$$\bar{X} = \frac{1}{N} \sum_{1}^{N} X_i \tag{3.94}$$

$$S = \left[\frac{1}{N-1}\left(\sum_{1}^{N} X_i^2 - N\bar{X}^2\right)\right]^{1/2}, \tag{3.95}$$

respectively.

χ^2 *Test* [79]. Tabulate the raw data X_i in a frequency table.

Count the observed frequencies θ_i in each of k categories. Denote by $\theta_1, \theta_2, \theta_3 \cdots \theta_k$, where $\Sigma_1^k \theta_i = N$ must exist.

Determine the expected (or theoretical) frequencies $\hat{\theta}_i$ in each category, according to the theoretical normal probability density function, in which

$$\sum_{1}^{k} \hat{\theta}_i = N \tag{3.96}$$

and $\hat{\theta}_i \geq 5$ must exist. The values of $\hat{\theta}$ are determined from a table of the normal frequency function.

Compute the statistic

$$\chi^2 = \sum_{1}^{k} \frac{(\theta_i - \hat{\theta}_i)^2}{\theta_i}. \tag{3.97}$$

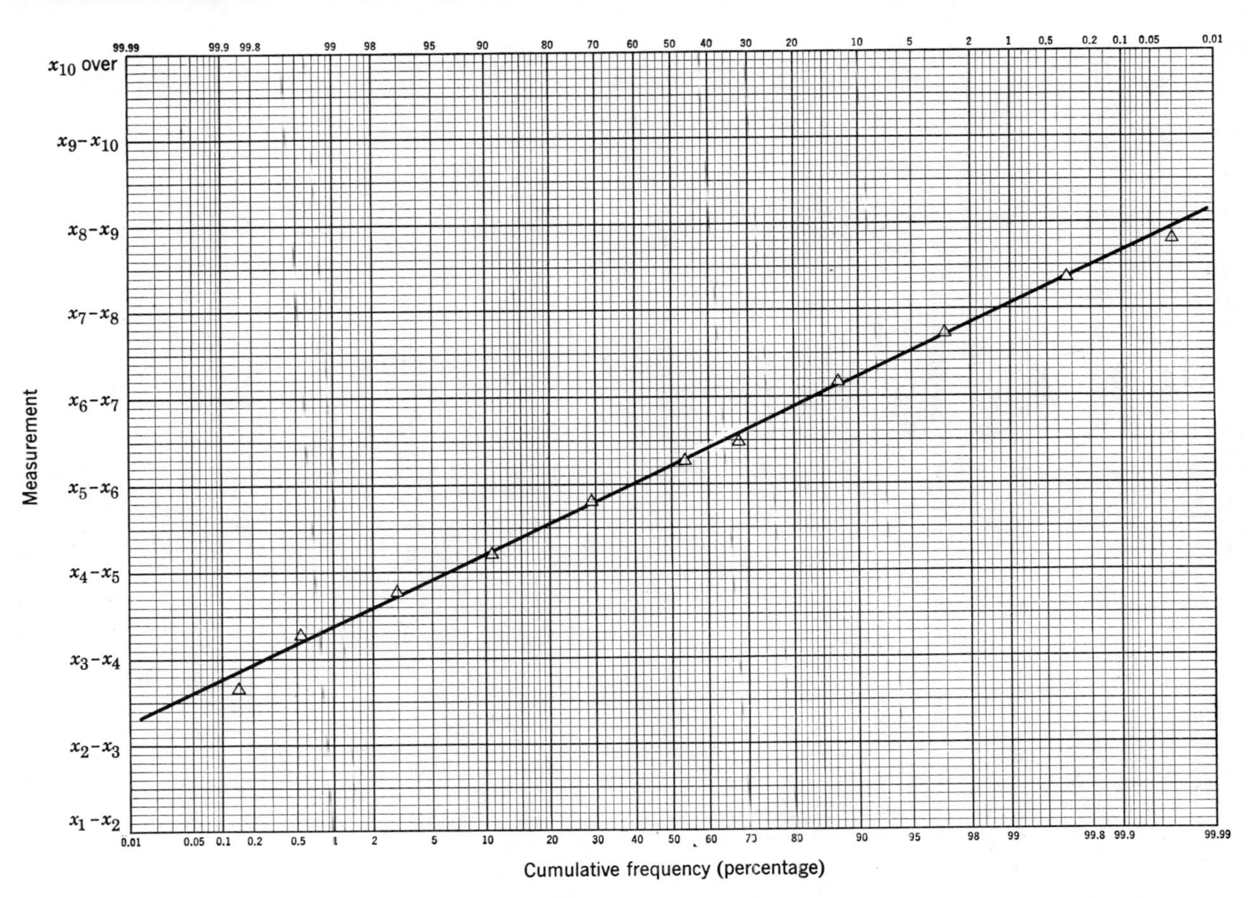

Fig. 3.17 Normal probability graph.

Compare the χ^2 value with published χ_0^2 tables. Locate the χ_0^2 value in the table for the appropriate degrees of freedom (df) row, in which df $= k - 1$. The percentile at the top of the column is the probability of χ^2 being less than the χ_0^2 value. If $\chi^2 \leq \chi_0^2$ is found, the sample is considered consistent with the hypothesis. The better the fit, the smaller the χ^2 value.

Example 3.9. Apply the χ^2 test to the data given in Table 3.2 to determine the goodness of fit to the normal probability distribution.

SOLUTION. We tabulate the observed frequencies θ_i of the data and the expected (or theoretical) frequencies $\hat{\theta}_i$ of the normal density function in each category k. The values of $\hat{\theta}$ are calculated from values obtained in published tables of the normal density function or from normal probability graph paper. Given θ and $\hat{\theta}$, we compute the last column as shown.

k	Interval	θ	$\hat{\theta}$	$\frac{(\theta - \hat{\theta})^2}{\hat{\theta}}$
1	5–10	2	2	0
2	10–15	2	3	0.33
3	15–20	6	7	0.14
4	20–25	10	12	0.33
5	25–30	20	20	0
6	30–35	28	28	0
7	35–40	32	32	0
8	40–45	32	30	0 13
9	45–50	28	26	0.15
10	50–55	18	20	0.20
11	55–60	12	10	0.40
12	60–65	6	6	0
13	65–70	4	4	0

Summing the last column over all k intervals and using (3.97) we obtain

$$\chi^2 = \sum_{i=1}^{k} \frac{(\theta - \hat{\theta})^2}{\hat{\theta}} = 1.68.$$

Our example contains 12 degrees of freedom (df), where

$$\text{df} = k - 1 = 12.$$

Comparing χ^2 with the tabular value χ_0^2 from a published χ^2 table, we observe that

$$\chi^2 \leq \chi_0^2 (1.68 \leq 3.07)$$

for the 99.5 percentile and 12 degrees of freedom. In other words, there is a 0.995 probability that the observed χ^2 is less than or equal to the theoretical χ_0^2. Therefore the sample is consistent with the hypothesis at the 99.5% confidence level, and we consider the data from Table 3.2 as being normally distributed.

Note: Instead of the χ^2 test the Kolmogorov-Smirnov test for goodness of fit could have been applied. This test uses the *cumulative* instead of the *frequency* distribution used in the χ^2 test. For a discussion see [23, 65].

Log Normal Distribution [76, 84, 85, 91]. The log normal distribution is a distribution in which $f(\ln x)$ is normally distributed. We apply a log transformation of the data as an approximate normal probability distribution fit for skewed distributions. These are skewed distributions for phenomena that can be expressed in positive values only, such as some biological life and event-time interval (or event latencies) distributions, granulometry of coal, price-index making, actuarial study of equipment life, breakage of solids, and distributions of incomes. The Galton-McAllister distribution is log normal, and the Gibrat distribution is a form of the log normal.

The $\ln x$ normal probability frequency function $f(\ln x)$ is given by

$$f(\ln x) = (\sigma_{\ln x} \sqrt{2\pi})^{-1} \exp\left[\frac{-(\ln x - \overline{\ln x})^2}{2\sigma^2_{\ln v}}\right], \qquad (3.98)$$

where $\overline{\ln x}$ and $\sigma^2_{\ln x}$ are the mean and variance, respectively, of $\ln x$ and the probability distribution function $F(\ln X)$ is given by

$$F(\ln X) = (\sigma_{\ln x} \sqrt{2\pi})^{-1} \int_0^{\ln X} \exp\left[\frac{-(\ln x - \overline{\ln x})^2}{2\sigma^2_{\ln x}}\right] d(\ln x). \qquad (3.99)$$

Applications of the log normal probability distribution are explained in a later chapter. Figure 3.18 is an example of log normal probability paper. This graph paper can be used in the same way we use normal probability graph paper.

Exponential Distribution [81]. The exponential distribution is a continuous distribution in which the origin is at the start of the frequency function curve. We apply the exponential distribution to examples such as the following:

1. Lives of electron tubes.
2. Time intervals between successive breakdowns of electronic systems.
3. Life testing in many life distributions.
4. Purely random failure patterns.
5. Pure death process (fiber failure).
6. Failures of complex mechanisms.
7. Target noise and receiver noise after square law rectification.

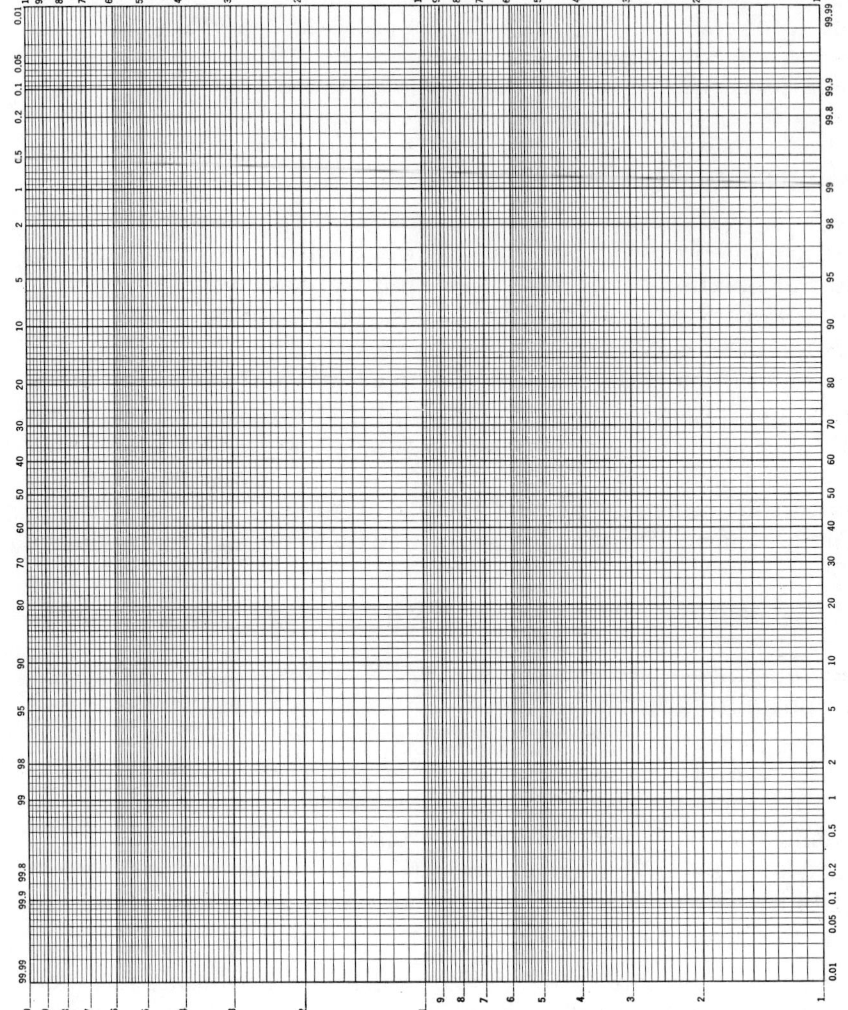

Fig. 3.18 Log normal probability graph.

The exponential distribution is also referred to as Pearson Type X distribution. The exponential frequency function $f(x)$ is given by

$$f(x) = \frac{1}{\sigma} e^{-\frac{x}{\sigma}} \tag{3.100}$$

where $0 \leq x < \infty$

and the probability distribution function $F(X)$ is given by

$$F(X) = \frac{1}{\sigma} \int_m^X e^{-\frac{x}{\sigma}} dx. \tag{3.101}$$

The mean and variance are given by

$$\mu = \sigma \tag{3.102}$$

$$\sigma^2 = \sigma^2, \tag{3.103}$$

respectively. The density function is illustrated in the graph in Fig. 3.19.

χ^2 *Distribution* [79]. The χ^2 distribution is a continuous distribution that arises from the univariate normal and has a unimodal, bell-shaped frequency function of positive values only of unlimited range. Tables of χ^2 functions are published in most handbooks and texts on probability and statistics and are applied in the χ^2 test for goodness of

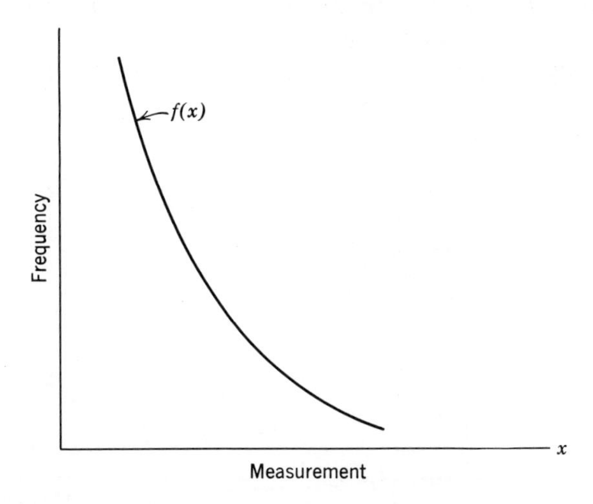

Fig. 3.19 Exponential probability frequency function.

fit of measurement data. The χ^2 frequency function $f(\chi^2)$ is given by

$$f(\chi^2) = \left(\Gamma\left(\frac{r}{2}\right) 2^{r/2}\right)^{-1} (\chi^2)^{(r/2)-1} e^{-(\chi^2)/2} \tag{3.104}$$

with r degrees of freedom, where $0 \leq (\chi^2) < \infty$ and $\Gamma(r/2) = [(r/2) - 1]!$. The probability distribution function $F(\chi^2)$ is given by

$$F(\chi^2) = \left(\Gamma\left(\frac{r}{2}\right) 2^{r/2}\right)^{-1} \int_0^\infty (\chi^2)^{(r/2)-1} e^{-\chi^2/2} d(\chi^2). \tag{3.105}$$

The mean equals the number of degrees of freedom and is given by $\mu = r$. The variance is given by $\sigma^2 = 2r$; χ^2 is not a second degree parameter, as the name might imply. The frequency function of the χ^2 distribution is illustrated in Fig. 3.20.

Example 3.10. Tables of the χ^2 probability distribution are given by H. Cramer, *Mathematical Methods of Statistics*, Princeton University Press, Princeton, N.J., 1963. A table to three decimal places is given on page 559, in which $\chi_p{}^2$ is a function of n and p, where $1 \leq n \leq 30$ and $0.1\% \leq p \leq 99\%$.

Other χ^2 probability distribution tables have also been published by H. D. Young, Chemical Rubber Co., Cleveland, Ohio, and R. S. Burington.

Student or t Distribution. The Student or t distribution is a continuous distribution which arises from the univariate normal and in which the frequency function $f(t)$ is unimodal and symmetrical, with the mean at the origin. Tables of the t distribution are published in most handbooks of probability and statistics. The t distribution is applied in the t-test to test the hypothesis that two independent samples have been

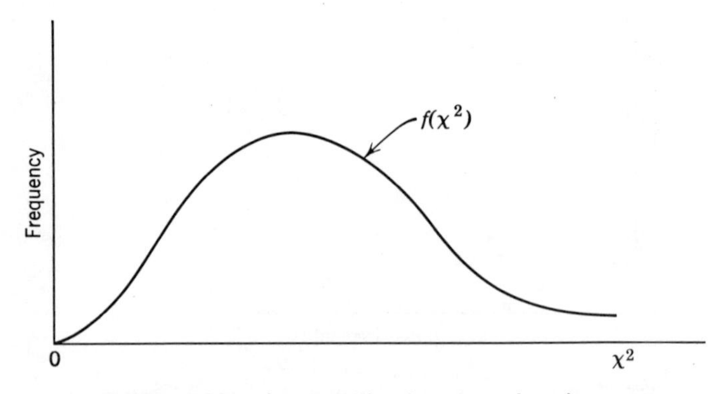

Fig. 3.20 χ^2 probability frequency function.

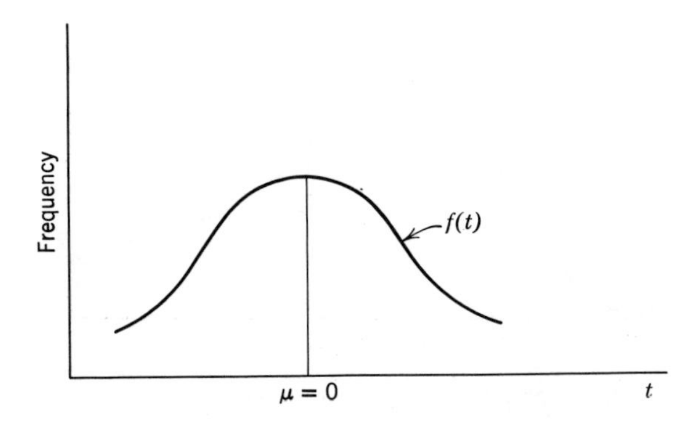

Fig. 3.21 Student or t probability frequency function.

drawn from populations with the same mean [59]. The t frequency function $f(t)$ is given by

$$f(t) = \frac{\Gamma[(r+1)/2]}{(\pi r)^{1/2}\Gamma(r/2)}\left(1+\frac{t^2}{r}\right)^{-(r+1)/2}, \tag{3.106}$$

where $-\infty < t < \infty$ with r degrees of freedom and the distribution function $F(t)$ is given by

$$F(T) = \frac{\Gamma[(r+1)/2]}{(\pi r)^{1/2}\Gamma(r/2)}\int_{-\infty}^{T}\left(1+\frac{t^2}{r}\right)^{-(r+1)/2} dt. \tag{3.107}$$

The mean and variance are given by

$$\mu = 0 \tag{3.108}$$

$$\sigma^2 = \frac{r}{(r-2)}, \qquad (r > 2) \tag{3.109}$$

respectively. The frequency function of the t distribution is shown in Fig. 3.21.

Example 3.11. A table of the t distribution is given in the reference by Abramowitz [143] in Table 26.10, page 990. The table contains three-place decimal values of t in terms of A and ν. Tables of the t distribution are also given in references by Burington and May [2] and by Cramer [38].

F Distribution. The F or variance ratio distribution is a continuous distribution which arises from the univariate normal and in which the frequency function $f(F)$ is of positive values only of unlimited range. Tables of the F distribution are published in most handbooks of

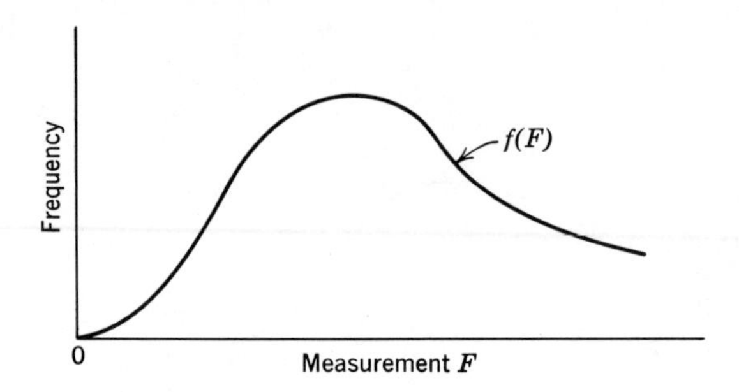

Fig. 3.22 *F* probability frequency function.

probability and statistics. The F distribution is applied to test the hypothesis that two samples have been drawn from populations with the same variance. The frequency function $f(F)$ is given by

$$f(F) = \frac{\Gamma[(m+r)/2]}{\Gamma(m/2)\Gamma(r/2)}\left(\frac{m}{r}\right)^{m/2} F^{(m/2)-1}\left(1+\frac{m}{r}F\right)^{-\frac{1}{2}(m+r)}, \quad (3.110)$$

where $0 \leq F < \infty$, and the distribution function $F(F')$ is given by

$$F(F') = \frac{\Gamma[(m+r)/2]}{\Gamma(m/2)\Gamma(r/2)}\left(\frac{m}{r}\right)^{m/2} \int_0^{F'} F^{(m/2)-1}\left(1+\frac{m}{r}F\right)^{-\frac{1}{2}(m+r)} dF. \quad (3.111)$$

The mean and variance of the F distribution are given by

$$\mu = \frac{m}{r-2} \quad (3.112)$$

$$\sigma^2 = \frac{r^2(m+2)}{m(r-2)(r-4)} \quad (3.113)$$

respectively, where m and r are degrees of freedom. A graph is shown in Fig. 3.22.

Example 3.12. A table of the F distribution is given in Abramowitz [143] in Table 26.9 on pages 986–989. A table is also given in Burington and May [2].

Beta Distribution. The β distribution is a continuous function in which the frequency function $f(x)$ is given by

$$f(x) = \frac{x^{\alpha-1}(1-x)^{\beta-1}}{[\Gamma(\alpha)\Gamma(\beta)]/\Gamma(\alpha+\beta)}, \quad (3.114)$$

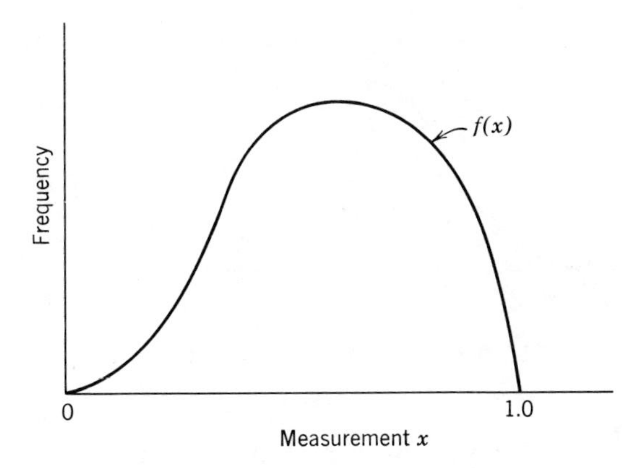

Fig. 3.23 Beta frequency function.

where $0 \leq x \leq 1$, $\alpha > 0$, and $\beta > 0$. The distribution function $F(X)$ is given by

$$F(X) = \left[\frac{\Gamma(\alpha)\Gamma(\beta)}{\Gamma(\alpha + \beta)}\right]^{-1} \int_0^X x^{\alpha-1}(1 - x)^{\beta-1}\, dx. \tag{3.115}$$

A graph is shown in Fig. 3.23.

Gamma Distribution [88, 92]. The Γ distribution is a continuous distribution. The frequency function $f(x)$ is unlimited in range and is unimodal. It is given by

$$f(x) = \frac{e^{-x}x^{\lambda-1}}{\Gamma(\lambda)}, \tag{3.116}$$

where $0 \leq x < \infty$ and $\lambda > 0$. The distribution function $F(X)$ is given by

$$F(X) = \frac{1}{\Gamma(\lambda)} \int_0^X e^{-x}x^{\lambda-1}\, dx. \tag{3.117}$$

A graph of the Γ frequency function in which $\lambda > 1$ is shown in Fig. 3.24.

Weibull Distribution [78, 86]. The Weibull distribution is a continuous distribution which describes data arising from life and fatigue tests. The frequency function $f(t)$ is given by

$$f(t) = \frac{\delta}{\theta}\, t^{\delta-1}e^{-t^{\delta}/\theta}, \tag{3.118}$$

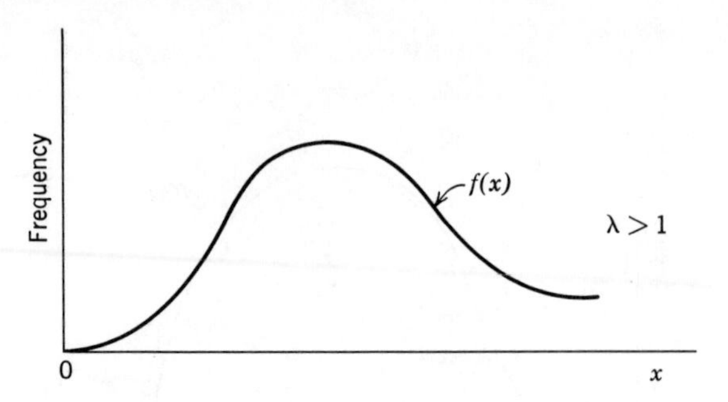

Fig. 3.24 Gamma frequency function.

where $t > 0$. The distribution function is given by

$$F(T) = \frac{\delta}{\theta} \int_0^T t^{\delta-1} e^{-t^\delta/\theta}\, dt = 1 - e^{-T^\delta/\theta}. \tag{3.119}$$

A graph of the Weibull frequency function $f(t)$ in which $\delta > 1$ is shown in Fig. 3.25. The Weibull distribution has a broad range of possible shapes, depending on the value of δ.

Hypergeometric Distribution. The hypergeometric distribution is a discrete distribution generally associated with sampling from a definite population without replacement. The density function $f(s)$ is given by

$$f(s) = \frac{\binom{Np}{s}\binom{Nq}{n-s}}{\binom{N}{n}} \tag{3.120}$$

where there are s successes from a sample n of a population N, p is the probability of success of any trial, $q = 1 - p$, and

$$\binom{n}{s} = \frac{n!}{s!(n-s)!}. \tag{3.121}$$

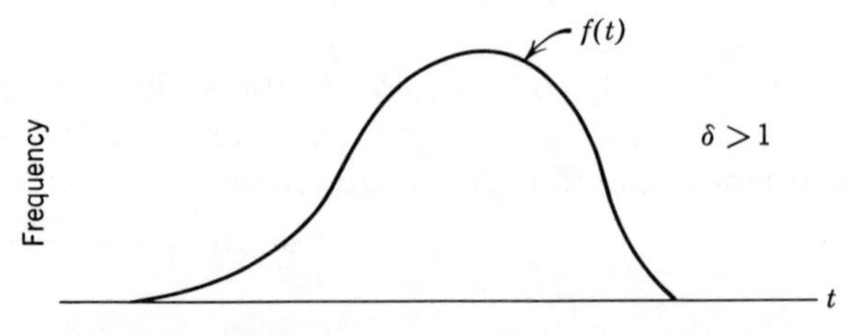

Fig. 3.25 Weibull probability frequency function.

The probability distribution function $F(s)$ is given by

$$F(m) = \sum_{s=0}^{m} \frac{\binom{Np}{s}\binom{Nq}{n-s}}{\binom{N}{n}} \tag{3.122}$$

where the mean and variance are given by

$$\mu = np \tag{3.123}$$

$$\sigma^2 = npq \frac{N-n}{N-1}, \tag{3.124}$$

respectively.

Pearson Distributions. The 12 Pearson distribution types are derived from the differential equation

$$\frac{dy}{dx} = \frac{y(x+a)}{b_0 + b_1 x + b_2 x^2}, \tag{3.125}$$

which is the limiting case of the hypergeometric series. Derivations are given in references by Elderton [41] and Kendall [14]. The Pearson distributions consist of three main types (I, IV, and VI); the remainder are transition types. The following are the frequency functions of the 12 types:

Pearson Type I is unimodal, skewed, of limited range, and with the origin at the mode. The frequency function $f(x)$ is given by

$$f(x) = k\left(1 + \frac{x}{a_1}\right)^{m_1}\left(1 - \frac{x}{a_2}\right)^{m_2}, \tag{3.126}$$

where

$$\frac{m_1}{a_1} = \frac{m_2}{a_2}. \tag{3.127}$$

Pearson Type II is symmetrical and usually bell-shaped. The origin is at the mean and the frequency function $f(x)$ is given by

$$f(x) = k\left(1 - \frac{x^2}{a^2}\right)^m. \tag{3.128}$$

Pearson Type III is a Γ distribution. Type III is unimodal, of unlimited range, and usually bell-shaped with the origin at the mode. The frequency function $f(x)$ is given by

$$f(x) = k\left(1 + \frac{x}{a}\right)^{\nu a} e^{-\nu x}, \qquad \begin{matrix} \nu > 0 \\ a > 0 \end{matrix}. \tag{3.129}$$

Pearson Type IV is unimodal and skewed. The frequency function $f(x)$ is given by

$$f(x) = k\left(1 + \frac{x^2}{a^2}\right)^{-m} e^{-\mu \tan^{-1}(x/a)}, \qquad \begin{matrix} a > 0 \\ \mu > 0 \end{matrix}. \tag{3.130}$$

Pearson Type V is unimodal with the origin at the start of the frequency curve. Type V is usually bell-shaped, and the frequency function $f(x)$ is given by

$$f(x) = kx^{-p}e^{-\nu/x}, \qquad \begin{matrix} \nu > 0 \\ p > 0 \end{matrix}. \tag{3.131}$$

Pearson Type VI is unimodal and may be skewed, bell-shaped, or J-shaped. The frequency function $f(x)$ is given by

$$f(x) = kx^{-q_1}(x - a)^{q_2}. \tag{3.132}$$

Pearson Type VII is unimodal, symmetrical, bell-shaped, and with the origin at the mean. The frequency function $f(x)$ is given by

$$f(x) = k\left(1 + \frac{x^2}{a^2}\right)^{m}. \tag{3.133}$$

Pearson Type VIII is unimodal and with the origin at the end of the curve. The frequency function $f(x)$ is given by

$$f(x) = k\left(1 + \frac{x}{a}\right)^{-m}, \qquad 0 \leq m \leq 1. \tag{3.134}$$

Pearson Type IX is unimodal and with the origin at the end of the curve. The frequency function $f(x)$ is given by

$$f(x) = k\left(1 + \frac{x}{a}\right)^{m}, \qquad m > 1. \tag{3.135}$$

Pearson Type X is the same as the exponential distribution.

Pearson Type XI is J-shaped and the frequency function $f(x)$ is given by

$$f(x) = kx^{-m}. \tag{3.136}$$

Pearson Type XII is a twisted, J-shaped curve with the origin at the mean. Type XII is a special case of Type I and the frequency function $f(x)$ is given by

$$f(x) = k\left(\frac{1 + x/a_1}{1 - x/a_2}\right)^{m}, \qquad |m| < 1. \tag{3.137}$$

GENERATION OF RANDOM STATISTICAL VARIATES

We now discuss the generation of random statistical variates, and in Part Four we discuss some applications of random statistical variates in computer modeling and simulation. First, we discuss uniform random number generation. Then we discuss nonuniform random number generation.

Uniform Random Numbers [123–125, 128]

Uniform random numbers may be selected from tables, such as one prepared by Rand Corporation [141], or uniform random numbers may be generated by a computer subroutine. The generative methods, which are usually multiplicative methods, are actually synthetic techniques of random number generation. Thus it is more accurate that we call the results "pseudouniform random numbers." In computer application we recommend a generative method rather than storing a lengthy table in computer memory.

The application of uniform random numbers is a basic process in Monte Carlo simulation. The two concepts (uniform random numbers and Monte Carlo) are practically synonymous. Whenever a stochastic variable has to be computed in a Monte Carlo simulation, an application of uniform random numbers is required.

A uniform random number ranges between zero and unity and has been randomly selected from the uniform probability distribution function

$$F(x) = \int_0^1 dx. \tag{3.138}$$

In this distribution there is an equal likelihood of any measurement occurring between the interval zero and one.

One of the simplest methods of pseudouniform random number generation, attributed to von Neumann, is known as the midsquares method. The middle digits of a random number are squared to generate the succeeding random number. Then this number is used for generation of the next random number and so on. This method is simple and fast. The obvious disadvantage of this method is that whenever a zero is generated all subsequent numbers will be zero unless we insert a nonzero whenever zero does occur.

In order to avoid this pitfall, other multiplicative methods are advised. Several uniform random number generators have been programmed for computers and are available in most computer library subroutines. We give three algorithms:

$$U_{i+1} = kU_i, \tag{3.139}$$

where $k = 8t \pm 3$, t is an integer, U_0 is odd, and U_i is the least significant part of U_{i-1}.

$$U_{i+1} = \tfrac{1}{2}|U_1U_0(\text{mod } 2^6)| \tag{3.140}$$

$$U_{i+1} = (2^a + 1)U_i + c(\text{mod } 2^{35}), \tag{3.141}$$

where $a \geq 2$ and c is odd.

Example 3.13. Compute a uniform random number by a multiplicative method.

SOLUTION. By application of (3.139) we compute a random number as follows, where

$$U_0 = 0.37843$$

$$t = 5$$

$$k = 8t - 3 = 37$$

$$U_{i+1} = kU_0 = 37(0.37843) = 14.00191.$$

Therefore we select the least significant portion of this calculation and the random number is 0.00191.

Several tests which can be used to test for randomness of a series of uniform random numbers include the frequency test, the serial correlation test, runs above and below the median, runs up and down, and mean square successive difference. Explanations of these tests are given in Ellis and Ryan [121], Mood [15], Wald [70], and Walsh [71]. As an example, in a frequency test we take N random numbers and count the number m that fall between 0.2113 and 0.7887, which is $\pm 1\sigma$. If $m/N \simeq 0.5774$, then the numbers are roughly uniformly random. Another rough check for randomness of N uniform random numbers U_i is to compute the mean and a partial variance. The numbers are uniformly random if

$$\frac{1}{N}\sum_{1}^{N} U_i \simeq \tfrac{1}{2} \tag{3.142}$$

and

$$\frac{1}{N}\sum_{1}^{N} U_i^2 \simeq \tfrac{1}{3}. \tag{3.143}$$

Example 3.14. Test the following series of 20 uniform random numbers for randomness:

0.48837	0.62543	0.44563	0.65778
0.21106	0.13529	0.78800	0.73486
0.68359	0.57873	0.02039	0.17846
0.99027	0.89064	0.93461	0.38083
0.30057	0.29381	0.82115	0.54592

We observe that in this series 12 numbers, or 60%, fall in the range of values between 0.21130 and 0.78870. Sixty percent is the closest possible value to 57.74% for a series of 20 numbers. For that test we consider the numbers a good sample.

We can also apply (3.142, 3.143) and obtain

$$\sum U_i = 10.70539$$

$$\frac{1}{N}\sum U_i = \tfrac{1}{20}(10.70539) = 0.53 \simeq 0.5$$

$$\sum U_i^2 = 7.13$$

$$\frac{1}{N}\sum U_i^2 = \tfrac{1}{20}(7.13) = 0.356 \simeq 0.33.$$

We observe that 0.53 and 0.356 are approximately 0.5 and 0.33, respectively. Therefore from the above tests we consider the series a good sample of uniform random numbers.

Nonuniform Random Numbers [127, 129, 130, 133]

Nonuniform random numbers may be selected from tables or may be generated on a high-speed computer. A nonuniform random number is a number that has been randomly selected from any discrete or continuous probability distribution. Nonuniform random numbers can be generated for any nonuniform distribution. However, we will discuss only three distributions: normal, binomial, and Poisson random numbers.

In every case of random-number generation we must always start by generating one or more uniform random numbers. We then apply a transformation of variables technique, such as the Jacobian of the transformation, to generate the nonuniform random number. We may use exact methods or approximation methods for nonuniform random number generation. Or we may execute a table lookup. We discuss several methods below.

Normal Random Numbers [130, 134–138, 141]. A normal random number may be generated by selecting a uniform random number, which is then used as the ordinate of the probability distribution function curve. The corresponding abscissa value is the normal random number. We can store these values in the computer and execute a table lookup. This same table lookup method can be applied to generate a circular normal random number or a spherical normal random number. We recommend this method generally in preference to the others listed below. We describe the implementation of this method for the computer in Chapter 9.

We can apply the central limit theorem for the generation of normal random numbers that are reliable for values within the 3σ limits. The central limit theorem is a very elegant theorem in probability theory, and a special case shows that the normal is the limiting distribution reached in a number of different ways as the number of observations is increased. The approach of the uniform distribution to normalcy is very rapid; thus we can generate a normal random number R by

$$R = \frac{\sum_{1}^{N} U_i - (n/2)}{(n/12)^{1/2}}, \tag{3.144}$$

using n uniform random numbers U_i, where n is an integer. The range $6 \leq n \leq 12$ is sufficient condition.

We can generate normal random numbers by the rejection method. Using two random numbers U_1 and U_2 we designate a point X, Y from a rectangle which encloses the normal probability density curve. If the point falls below the curve, we accept the abscissa value of the point as the normal random number. Otherwise, we reject the point and select another pair U_3, U_4 or continue until we have a point that falls under the curve.

We can generate a normal random number by another rejection method attributed to von Neumann. We generate two uniform random numbers U_1 and U_2. If the inequality

$$\ln U_2 \leq -2b^2(U_1 - \tfrac{1}{2})^2 \tag{3.145}$$

is satisfied we compute the normal random number by

$$R = b(2U_1 - 1), \tag{3.146}$$

where b is a constant.

By another rejection method we generate two uniform random numbers U_1 and U_2. If the inequality

$$- \ln U_2 \leq (- \ln U_1 - 1)^2/2 \tag{3.147}$$

is satisfied, we accept

$$R = - \ln U_1 \tag{3.148}$$

as the normal random number.

We can generate a pair of normal random numbers R_1, R_2 from the same standard normal distribution of mean zero and variance one by a method suggested by Muller [139]. We generate two uniform random numbers U_1 and U_2 and compute R_1 and R_2 from

$$R_1 = (-2 \ln U_1)^{1/2} \cos (2\pi U_2) \tag{3.149}$$

$$R_2 = (-2 \ln U_1)^{1/2} \sin (2\pi U_2). \tag{3.150}$$

Example 3.15. Generate a normal random number by a method other than table lookup.

SOLUTION. If we apply the central limit theorem by using (3.144), we generate six uniform random numbers such as 0.63112, 0.17716, 0.34499, 0.87574, 0.27905, and 0.22282. Substituting in (3.144), we obtain

$$\sum U_i = 2.53088$$

$$\frac{n}{2} = 3$$

$$\left(\frac{n}{12}\right)^{1/2} = 0.7071$$

$$R = \frac{\sum U_i - \frac{n}{2}}{(n/12)^{1/2}} = \frac{2.53088 - 3}{0.7071} = -0.66$$

Therefore the desired normal random variate is -0.66.

We can test for randomness of a series of N normal random numbers R_i by a frequency test. Also the numbers are random normal if

$$\frac{1}{N} \sum_{1}^{N} R_i \simeq 0 \tag{3.151}$$

$$\frac{1}{N} \sum_{1}^{N} R_i^2 \simeq 1. \tag{3.152}$$

Example 3.16. Test the following series of 20 normal random numbers for randomness:

−0.41	−1.80	0.60	1.30
−0.53	0.08	−2.12	0.10
−0.05	0.02	0.36	0.91
0.77	1.10	−1.44	1.99
0.22	−0.18	−0.20	−0.88

SOLUTION. If we apply (3.151) and (3.152), we obtain

$$\frac{1}{n}\sum R_i = \tfrac{1}{20}(-0.16) = -0.008 \simeq 0$$

$$\frac{1}{n}\sum R_i^2 = \tfrac{1}{20}(19.95) = 0.99 \simeq 1.0,$$

respectively.

We observe that −0.008 and 0.99 are approximately 0 and 1, respectively. Therefore from the above rough test we consider the series a good sample of normal random numbers.

Random Binomial Variates. For small value of n we generate n uniform random numbers U_i. The binomial random variate s is the count of uniform random numbers that are less than or equal to p.

Example 3.17. Generate a binomial random variate using the above method. Generate it from a binomial distribution in which $n = 7$ and $p = 0.3$. We select seven uniform random numbers, such as 0.02011, 0.85393, 0.97265, 0.61680, 0.16656, 0.42751, and 0.69994. We observe that two of these numbers are less than or equal to 0.3. Therefore the binomial random variate is 2.

For large values of n and small values of p we generate a random number U and make iterative computations until the inequality

$$U \leq \sum_{0}^{N} r_i \tag{3.153}$$

is satisfied, where

$$r_0 = (1 - p)^n \tag{3.154}$$

and

$$r_{i+1} = r_i\left(\frac{n-i}{i+1}\right)\left(\frac{p}{1-p}\right). \tag{3.155}$$

The binomial random variate s is the value of N iterations necessary to satisfy the inequality.

We can test for randomness of a series of M binomial random variates s_i for given n and p. The numbers are random if

$$\frac{1}{M}\sum_{1}^{M} s_i \simeq np \tag{3.156}$$

$$\frac{1}{M}\sum_{1}^{M} s_i^2 \simeq np(np + q).* \tag{3.157}$$

Example 3.18. Test for randomness the following series of 10 binomial random variates:

$$0, 0, 1, 0, 1, 0, 2, 0, 1, 0,$$

that have been generated from a binomial distribution for $n = 5$ and $p = 0.1$.

SOLUTION. We apply (3.156) and (3.157) and obtain

$$np = 0.5$$

$$np(np + q) = 0.7$$

$$\frac{1}{M}\sum s = \tfrac{1}{10}(5) = 0.5 \simeq 0.5$$

$$\frac{1}{M}\sum s^2 = \tfrac{1}{10}(7) = 0.7 \simeq 0.7.$$

We observe that the series is a good selection of binomial random variates.

Poisson Random Variates. In a method suggested by Kahn we multiply N uniform random numbers U_i successively until the inequality

$$\prod_{1}^{N} U_i < e^{-np} \tag{3.158}$$

is satisfied. $N - 1$ is the Poisson random variate s with mean np. If the inequality is satisfied with the first uniform random number, then $s = 0$.

* Note that $q = 1 - p$.

Example 3.19. Suppose we desire to generate a Poisson random variate from a Poisson distribution of mean 2.5. We multiply uniform random numbers successively until (3.158) is satisfied as follows:

$$(0.91646)(0.89198)(0.64809)(0.16376)(0.91782) < e^{-2.5}$$

From the calculations we obtain $0.07963 < 0.08208$.

Therefore the Poisson random variate is 4, as it is 1 less than the number of uniform random numbers necessary to satisfy the inequality.

We can test for randomness of a series of M Poisson random variates s_i for given n and p. The numbers are random if

$$\frac{1}{M}\sum_{1}^{M} s_i \simeq np \tag{3.159}$$

$$\frac{1}{M}\sum_{1}^{M} s_i^2 \simeq np(np+1). \tag{3.160}$$

Example 3.20. Test for randomness the following series of 10 Poisson random variates generated from a distribution for $n = 20$ and $p = 0.1$:

2, 1, 1, 3, 2, 1, 4, 2, 3, 3.

SOLUTION. We apply (3.159) and (3.160) and obtain

$$np = 2.0$$

$$np(np+1) = 6.0$$

$$\frac{1}{M}\sum s_i = \tfrac{1}{10}(22) = 2.2 \simeq 2.0$$

$$\frac{1}{M}\sum s_i^2 = \tfrac{1}{10}(58) = 5.8 \simeq 6.0.$$

We observe that the series is a good selection of Poisson random variates.

PROBLEMS

3.1 Evaluate the definite integral

$$y = 2\int_0^1 x^2\,dx$$

analytically and by Monte Carlo method using at least 20 random numbers from the random number table in Appendix D. Compare the results of the two methods.

3.2 Distinguish between frequency function and distribution function.

3.3 Which of the following measurements represent frequency functions and which represent distribution functions?

3, 4, 8, 7, 6, 5, 2.
3, 7, 15, 22, 28, 33, 35.
−2.0, −1.7, −1.5, −1.0, 0, 0.5, 1.3, 1.8, 2.0.

3.4 Distinguish between discrete and continuous distributions.

3.5 From the following list select which ones are represented by discrete and which ones by continuous distributions.

Defective transistors.
Asphalt thickness.
Weights of animals.
Decay of sound waves.
Routes over a network.
Heights of buildings.
Docking delays.
Cloud density.
Businccss successes.
Power failures.
Summer temperature variations.
Tide changes.

3.6 Must the uniform distribution be always symmetrical and continuous? Why?

3.7 What is the probability of tossing 10 heads out of 20 tosses of a coin? Describe two methods of determining the probability.

3.8 Draw smooth graphs of (3.62) for values of n along the abscissa (horizontal) where $0 \leq n \leq 100$, and for $p = 0.1, 0.4, 0.5$, respectively.

3.9 Compute the mean and standard deviation for the following data points assumed to be normally distributed:

35, 38, 43, 23, 30, 33, 41, 37, 50, 36, 39, 42, 48, 44, 59, 51, 55, 46, 45, 49.

3.10 Apply the χ^2 test to 3.9 to determine the goodness of fit.

3.11 Select a series of 20 uniform random numbers from a published table and apply a test for randomness.

3.12 Select a series of 10 normal random numbers from a published table and apply a test for randomness.

3.13 Given six uniform random numbers: 0.2365, 0.8356, 0.6539, 0.8965, 0.5638, 0.4756. Generate a normal random number by application of the central limit theorem.

3.14 Given two uniform random numbers: 0.7346, 0.4685. Generate a normal random number using the formula in (3.146).

3.15 Given normal random numbers: −1.2, 0.9, 1.5. Calculate three random measurements x_i normally distributed with mean 10 and standard deviation 2.

3.16 Given normal random numbers: 0.3, −0.5, −1.6. Calculate three random time intervals T distributed according to the log normal probability distribution with mean $\ln T = 5$ and standard deviation $\ln T = 0.9$.

3.17 What is the probability of obtaining at least one success of a Poisson event for $np = 15$? $np = 7$? $np = 10$?

3.18 What is the probability of obtaining at least two successes in 3.17?

3.19 Generate a Poisson random number for $np = 5$ using random numbers from the table in Appendix D.

3.20 Generate a binomial random number for $n = 5$ and $p = 0.2$. Use the uniform random number table in Appendix D.

4

DATA HANDLING

With any computer modeling and simulation problem we immediately associate with it data handling tasks, as in data collection, data generation, data reduction, and data analysis. This association is due to the fact that computer modeling and simulation is a quantitative problem, even though it may contain nonquantitative features. Depending on the specific problem being solved, data handling may range from simple tasks to those in which a tremendous volume of data is required and is manipulated in the problem solution.

In this chapter we discuss four major data handling tasks: data collection, data generation, data reduction, and data analysis.

DATA COLLECTION

First we define and describe various kinds of data that are applied in computer modeling and simulation.

Kinematic data deal with the motion of bodies in space and time and have a coordinate reference, such as Cartesian, and a time reference. Data measurements of XYZ coordinates versus t of trajectories of projectiles or missiles, orbits of satellites or planets, and movement of vehicles, ships or aircraft are all examples of kinematic data.

Dynamic data change over time but do not necessarily involve movement in space; for example, dynamic data include market values of stocks, change in land values, daily temperature, and consumption of fuel.

Static data do not change; they include such examples as the height of a building, width of a street, weight of an object, and length of a vehicle.

Statistical data deal with a distribution or arrangement of measurements. Examples include measurement error, response error, reliability of a system, data on a population, such as heights of children or yields of a crop.

The kinds of data required for a particular problem affect the data collection method as well as the means and devices for data gathering; for example, kinematic data have to be gathered on-line and usually very quickly, as in gathering orbital data on a satellite. Dynamic data are gathered periodically, depending on their growth phenomena, and can usually be treated in a more leisurely manner than kinematic data. Static data generally have to be gathered only once; for instance, when we have measured the height of a building, it is not necessary to repeat the measurement. Statistical data may require many repetitions of data gathering to establish a distribution. Therefore, if we are interested in heights of children, we must gather their height measurements in sufficient number to determine statistical parameters.

The task of data gathering for data banks or data files necessary for certain problems may be so huge that it must be treated as a separate project, such as some current space probes which produce large quantities of data. Very often special data gathering instrumentation, such as electronic satellite tracking equipment, is necessary to gather kinematic data on orbiting satellites.

Many agencies are devoting their efforts to gathering data that are applicable in models of various types. With increased use of automated devices, such as computers, data gathering and the development of a wide variety of data bank types will be further increased; for example, certain models in urban renewal or transportation planning may require large data banks, consisting of land-value information, tax rates, commodity movements.

Oftentimes the data we need may have already been collected and published. Depending on the subject field of the data, whether the data deal with humans, systems, or the environment, there are many public and private sources in various fields.

The following is only a partial list of examples of data sources:

1. U.S. Federal Government Executive Branch departments, such as Departments of Defense, Commerce, Agriculture, Labor, Health, Education and Welfare, Housing and Urban Development, Transportation, and Federal Government agencies and bureaus, such as FAA, FBI, CAB, NASA, Weather Bureau, Geologic Survey. One of the principal sources of data collected by the U.S. Government is the Bureau of the Census whose task was designated by the U.S. Constitution to collect census data. The Census Bureau publishes several catalogs which list all their published and unpublished data dealing with a variety of subjects, such as population, labor, manufacturing, transportation, economics, and business. Much of the Bureau of Census data are available on magnetic tapes which can be obtained for a fee.
2. Foundations, institutions and nonprofit corporations, such as the National Science Foundation, National Academy of Sciences, National Research Council, National Academy of Engineering, Highway Research Board, National Safety Council, Brookings Institution.
3. Other sources are R. L. Polk and Co. (urban statistics), Standard and Poor's Corporation (corporations, executives, directors), Thomas Publishing Company (American manufacturers), Dun and Bradstreet, Institute of Physics, American Medical Association, labor unions, insurance companies, colleges and universities, local and state governments, legal associations, manufacturers, industries, newspapers, magazines, journals.

Some data are proprietary or classified and therefore are not available to the general public. Proprietary or classified data are only available to the user who has appropriate clearances and arrangements with the data sources.

Whenever the data we need are not available in published or unpublished form, however, we must determine means of procuring them. We can plan and conduct laboratory or field experiments. We can perform tests to generate the data. We can conduct interviews or make surveys or distribute questionnaires to a sample population.

What are some data-gathering devices? Data gathering can range anywhere from manual data collection through the most sophisticated and automated models. Often laborious means are necessary to gather sufficient data to design, develop, and exercise a mathematical model. Often data must be gathered so quickly that the task must be fully automatic. Data can be gathered on recorders, photographs, electronic counters, closed television circuits, punch tapes or cards, magnetic tapes, telephonic devices, soundings, and with pencil and paper. The choice of device depends on the kind of data to be gathered.

Whenever it is impractical or impossible to obtain real data in sufficient quantity to fill our requirements, we can generate synthetic data by using a mathematical model programmed for a digital computer. There are many occasions on which it is desirable and necessary to use synthetic data.

DATA GENERATION

We can generate synthetic data by computer mechanization of a synthetic data generator. Synthetic data are artificial because they have been generated on a computer, rather than being obtained from a real-world situation. However, synthetic data can be representative of real-world data associated with a process or operation. Synthetic data are often useful as input data for a real-world or simulated system.

Large-scale simulations may be implemented entirely for the computer, or large-scale simulations may integrate the computer complex with system hardware or humans. System hardware consists of actual systems and subsystems as employed in a real-world situation, or it may consist of simulated systems and subsystems in a laboratory environment. These simulated systems may be analog devices or simplified versions of the actual system.

In large-scale simulations synthetic input data can be generated in a separate computer program to be used subsequently as inputs for the computer model. Or synthetic input data can be used as inputs for an integrated computer complex system simulation. These data are fed into the real-world system or laboratory mockup in order to exercise the system. For example, (a) the input data can be generated and stored on magnetic tapes to be used at a later time, or (b) the input data can be generated on line to be put into the system in real time, in which there is a direct electronic tie-in between the computer and the system. This latter procedure is more complicated and difficult to implement than the former because of the demands for synchronization between computer and system.

Synthetic input data can be generated from deterministic functions, or synthetic data can be generated from nondeterministic functions in which the data are perturbed according to probability distribution functions. Or synthetic input data can contain features of both deterministic and nondeterministic elements.

Frequently synthetic input data are kinematic data, in which dynamic time-space XYZ versus T data are generated. Kinematic (or motion) data include, for example, time-space data for flight paths, missile trajectories, space vehicle trajectories, and ship, rail, or automobile movements. Kinematic data may be deterministically generated, or the actual values of XYZ and velocity and acceleration components may be perturbed according to a probability distribution, usually normal.

Another example of synthetic input data is simulated input signals for a system. For instance, this may be data for data link messages in a communications system. Or it may be positional data from radar blip returns in a radar system. The synthetic input data can flow intrasystem or intersystem; i.e., the data circulate within the system or come from outside the system, respectively.

Synthetic data that are probabilistically perturbed include measurement errors, time delays, and queues. Each type of probabilistic data is perturbed by the appropriate probability distribution function. For example, one-dimensional measurement error is given by

$$X_{\text{measured}} = X_{\text{actual}} + \epsilon_X \tag{4.1}$$

where ϵ_X is sampled from a probability distribution.

Mechanization of a data generator for the computer mainly involves writing a computer program to generate the data. A data generation

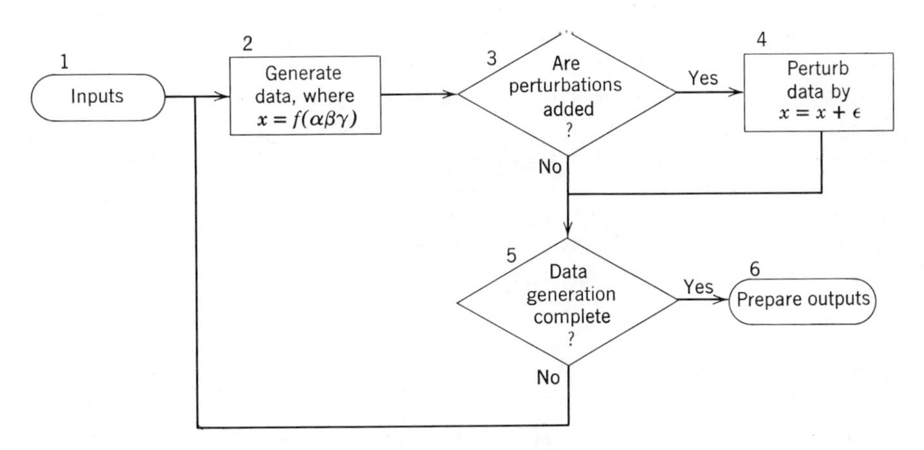

Fig. 4.1 Gross flow of data generation program.

program is usually fairly straightforward and simple. Such a program accepts input parameters, computes the data, adds perturbations if desired, and transforms the data to the appropriate format for compatibility with system inputs.

Data generation would normally be applied in the steps shown in Figure 4.1.

Example 4.1. We describe an example of a data generation program:

A large-scale computer program was used to integrate with the evaluation process of a flight control system designed to track and monitor air traffic at any large metropolitan airport. The flight generation program accepts flight input parameters and performs the computations on the path of motion equations. The program outputs synthetic kinematic data for a laboratory model of a flight control system.

The program is in three parts. Part 1 generates a true flight path in a conventional three-dimensional Cartesian coordinate system. Part 2 converts the flight path into a format compatible with the flight generator format and data requirements. Part 3 converts the flight path into a format compatible with the data link generator format and data requirements. The flight generator simulates radar returns of airborne planes in the local area, and the data link generator simulates message transmissions on aircraft being monitored in remote and adjacent areas.

The flight generation program generates flight coordinates for N flights. Coordinate information is computed for each flight trajectory for any desired time interval. The flight course paths are constructed from leg inputs. Several types of legs are possible. The legs may be straight line, straight line with linear acceleration or deceleration, right or left turns of constant g, dive or climb at a constant rate, dive or climb combined with a right or left turn. Additional types of legs can be added, if desired.

The program outputs three magnetic tapes. First, the true flight tape contains all flight position coordinates and velocity components in yards and yards per second, respectively. Second, the flight generator tape is used as synthetic data inputs for simulated radar returns at the tracking radar at the control site. The synthetic data contain quantized flight polar coordinates $R\theta\phi$ in a three-dimensional space and their first derivatives $\dot{R}\dot{\theta}\dot{\phi}$, as well as auxiliary information. Third, the data link generator tape is used to input synthetic data transmitted in real time on the automatic data link with external sources to the system. Messages contain quantized flight rectangular coordinates XYZ and velocity components $\dot{X}\dot{Y}\dot{Z}$, as well as auxiliary information.

An additional routine is used in the generation of the flight generator and data link generator tapes. This routine is used to introduce perturbations in the flight data at random according to a probability distribution. Perturbations are added to positional and velocity components in the flight path.

DATA REDUCTION

In data reduction we process a mass of ungrouped, unorganized output data into a body of regrouped, reorganized data. The purpose of data reduction is to make order out of chaos. The output data from a system or computer model are not necessarily in a format readily amenable to analysis, so that we must apply a data reduction manipulation to the data before we can analyze the data.

For example, a communications link may contain messages from multiple addressors to multiple addressees at random. If the link is monitored the messages, including both source and destination, are recorded and appear at random. One method of data reduction would be to regroup all of the messages so that all messages between a unique transmitter and receiver combination are grouped together.

Data reduction is a sorting problem whose difficulty increases with the volume of data and the amount of information to be extracted. If there is a small amount of data, the data reduction process can easily be performed manually. If the amount is voluminous, however, the data reduction process usually requires a high-speed computer.

For a mass of ungrouped data it is first necessary to decide upon the required manipulation of the data. We must know what we expect to extract from the data. Then we must decide what grouping and sorting is required. Next it is necessary to mechanize the process for the computer.

Data reduction is an intermediate process between the output data generated by the model or system and the analysis of the data. The output data should be organized in a format that facilitates data analysis and from which data analysis can follow directly.

Example 4.2. We describe an example of a data reduction program:

The data reduction program was used in conjunction with the flight control system mentioned in Example 4.1. The data reduction program reconstructs all the flights flown in the local area of the flight control system and all the flights reported in the adjacent and remote areas. The program prints the results in various formats. A typical run on the flight control system produces hundreds of thousands of data information items to be processed by the program. The data reduction program sorts through all the data and tries to determine the times of occurrence of certain significant system events and to determine which flights were involved.

The program is in three major parts. Part 1 checks message information and rejects illegitimate message frames according to certain rejection criteria. Part 2 compresses message frames that are repeated into one message frame. Part 3 is a plotting routine that produces X-T, Y-T, and XY plots for a specified ΔT plotting interval. A variety of plotting symbols are used in order to distinguish the various flight tracks.

The program printout includes all the plots of all flights tracked by the control system radars, the times of certain events, such as flight identity established, and any changes in message transmissions. The user can evaluate the flight control system performance by analyzing the data reduction program outputs.

DATA ANALYSIS [38, 47, 54, 63, 73, 75]

Data analysis is the process of extracting meaningful results from a mass of data. Normally we apply data analysis only after we have performed data reduction. Data reduction is a manipulative process to regroup the data, whereas by data analysis we operate on the data. By mathematical operation on the data it is possible to condense the data to relevant mathematical functions that are meaningful, easy to manipulate, and reproducible. Analytical techniques applicable to data analysis include regression analysis, curve fitting, goodness of fit, hypothesis testing, and other probability and statistical procedures.

If the data are deterministic we can fit them to an appropriate deterministic function, such as a polynomial of order n, exponential or logarithmic function, or a linear function.

If the data are probabilistic and represent random or chance elements we can fit the frequency data to an appropriate probability frequency function. The distribution function can be continuous or discrete, depending on the nature of the data and whether the data represent continuous or discrete phenomena. If it appears that the data follow a standard, classical probability distribution, such as normal, then we should apply statistical tests to determine the closeness of fit. These are tests such as χ^2, Student t, or F test.

For probabilistic data the statistical parameters, usually the mean and variance, are determined either by graphing techniques or by computational method. In general a small amount of data is required to determine the mean. A large amount is required to determine the variance, and a still larger amount is required to determine the probability distribution function.

For empirical data measurements for which we will derive the statistical probability distributions, we should calculate the following:

1. Cumulations of the measurements in each dimension, e.g., ΣX, ΣY, ΣZ, . . . , where X, Y, Z, . . . are the individual measurements.
2. Cumulations of the squares of the measurements in each dimension, e.g., ΣX^2, ΣY^2, ΣZ^2, ...
3. Cumulations of the cross-products of the measurements, e.g., ΣXY, ΣXZ, ΣYZ, ...

With these calculations of N measurements it is possible to compute the means, variances, correlation coefficients, correlation ratios, and other statistics.

Example 4.3. Suppose the following are cumulations of n empirical data measurements in X and Y.

$$\Sigma X = 100$$
$$\Sigma X^2 = 600$$
$$\Sigma Y = 110$$
$$\Sigma Y^2 = 530$$
$$\Sigma XY = 470$$
$$n = 25.$$

Compute the means $\bar{X}$ and $\bar{Y}$, the variances $S_X{}^2$ and $S_Y{}^2$, and the correlation coefficient r. These statistics are calculated as follows:

$$\bar{X} = \frac{1}{n} \sum X = \tfrac{1}{25}(100) = 4$$

$$\bar{Y} = \frac{1}{n} \sum Y = \tfrac{1}{25}(110) = 4.4$$

$$S_X{}^2 = \frac{1}{n} \sum X^2 - \bar{X}^2 = \tfrac{1}{25}(600) - (4)^2 = 8$$

$$S_X{}^2 = \frac{1}{n} \sum Y^2 - \bar{Y}^2 = \tfrac{1}{25}(530) - (4.4)^2 = 1.84$$

$$r = \frac{\Sigma XY - n\bar{X}\bar{Y}}{\sqrt{(\Sigma X^2 - n\bar{X}^2)(\Sigma Y^2 - n\bar{Y}^2)}} = \frac{470 - 25(4)(4.4)}{\sqrt{(600 - 25(4)^2)(530 - 25(4.4)^2)}} = 0.31.$$

If it appears that the data do not follow a classical probability distribution, yet we know they are probabilistic data, then the distribution is expressed by

$$P = f(\alpha, \beta, \gamma, \ldots), \tag{4.2}$$

where $\alpha, \beta, \gamma, \ldots$ are parameters and variables. These do not depend on the functional form of distribution functions.

Presentation of the results of data analysis is shown graphically or by mathematical functions. It may be desirable to show the results in both formats, especially if the readers include both mathematical and nonmathematical persons. For the mathematician equations are often sufficient, but for nonmathematicians graphs usually convey considerably more meaning than equations alone.

The method of presentation of the results of data analysis is important. The meaning of the data as interpreted by the reader is affected by the presentation. Ambiguous or esoteric presentations of the data tend to confuse the reader. The presentation of the results must be in terms that the reader can understand and use to interpret the significance of the data. In Chapter 10 we give some illustrations of the presentation of model results, as well as examples of computer programs to perform statistical analysis.

Example 4.4. Suppose we have run three replications of an experiment and obtained the following output data:

Run 1		Run 2		Run 3	
X	Y	X	Y	X	Y
1.00	6.30	1.00	6.31	1.61	7.63
1.49	7.39	1.50	7.40	2.10	8.72
1.60	7.62	2.00	8.50	2.40	9.38
2.09	8.71	2.41	9.38	2.90	10.47
2.89	10.47	2.90	10.48	3.20	11.14

We examine the data and determine that they are linear. Then we fit the data points to a straight line and obtain the form

$$Y = 2.20X + 4.10.$$

Our next step is to relate the coefficients (2.20 and 4.10) to phenomena about the system, if possible, in order to make the equation completely general.

PROBLEMS

4.1 The following encoded messages were monitored on a multichannel data link, where the first letter designates addressee, the digit represents addressor, and the second letter is a coded message. Regroup the messages in various logical schemes. Tabulate the number of messages in each group in the different schemes.

A2B	A1Z	D3K	G4P
A3Z	A1Y	A3F	A4P
B1C	B2Y	C1H	C5W
C1C	B3M	A2K	G5V
B1F	D3M	B2K	C4R
A2F	C2L	A3J	D5Q
B2F	A4K	D3J	G2Q
C2G	B3F	D2Y	B2R
C3H	C4C	D1Y	E3V
C4H	D2F	B2F	A4R

4.2 Distinguish between data reduction and data analysis.

4.3 Suppose you have been placed in charge of a large data reduction task involving data gathering, telemetry, and data reduction. Suggest procedures for implementation of the task.

4.4 Suppose you were handed a mass of ungrouped data containing XYZ-T satellite tracking information gathered at a ground control station. What procedures would you suggest to reduce and analyze the data?

4.5 Compute ΣX and ΣX^2 for the following data points: 2, 3, 5, 2, 3, 4, 3, 4, 2, 3.

4.6 Compute the means, variances, and standard deviations for the following cumulations:

(a)	(b)
$\Sigma X = 110$	$\Sigma X = 102$
$\Sigma X^2 = 635$	$\Sigma X^2 = 543$
$\Sigma Y = 106$	$\Sigma Y = 96$
$\Sigma Y^2 = 590$	$\Sigma Y^2 = 602$
$n = 32$	$\Sigma Z = 115$
	$\Sigma Z^2 = 524$
	$n = 45$

4.7 Write a brief essay on your assessment of problems in (a) data reduction, (b) data analysis.

4.8 Compile a list of various data-gathering techniques ranging from manual to highly automated methods.

4.9 Look through some current electronics magazines or manufacturers' catalogs. List a few data-recording devices available in the market today.

4.10 Select two data-recording devices and compare their features. What are suggested applications of each? Are the outputs compatible with input requirements for any current computers? Which ones?

5

STATISTICAL TECHNIQUES

EXPERIMENTAL DESIGN

The experimental design is the logical structure of the experiment. In this case it is the logical structure of the synthetic experiment. The experimental design is the layout for the application of the treatment of the experimental unit and the program for the conduct of the experiment. First, we formulate the problem. Next, we determine the method of experiment.

Experimental design involves the following:

1. The selection of parameter values and parameter levels to use in the computer runs.
2. The sampling techniques to apply to the experiment.
3. The determination of the amount of replication.

In most experiments we are interested in many factors (or parameters and input variables). Thus, two approaches are possible: (a) we can vary one factor at a time and hold everything else constant until we have manipulated every possible combination, or (b) we can design a factorial arrangement.

In the first approach if we have n parameters and wish to exercise each parameter at L levels and replicate each combination r times, then rL^n computer runs are necessary. We can easily see that for large n and $L > 1$ an inordinately large number of computer runs is necessary. Normally the first approach is impractical, and so we use the second approach and apply modern small-sampled statistical techniques. Various methods of sampling are available to obtain observations in an experiment.

We list some methods of sampling without including any discussion. These methods include straightforward sampling, importance sampling, random sampling, stratified random sampling, two-stage sampling, randomized block, ratio estimate, systematic sampling, quota sampling, expected value, correlation, Russian roulette, split plot, fractional replications, nested hypercubes, compacted hypercubes, orthogonal designs, random balance, multiple balance, sequential bifurcation, Latin squares, Greco-Latin squares, and Youden squares. These methods are discussed in references by Cochran and Cox [33, 34], Deming [40], Fisher [43, 45], Jacoby and Harrison [51], Kahn and Marshall [104], and Wald [70].

According to Professor Jebe* at the University of Michigan there are seven functions or purposes of an experimental design:

1. To obtain unbiased estimates of the effects for the factor levels under investigation.
2. To avoid confounding factors with each other or with the variability of the experimental material.
3. To remove or isolate as much as possible the variation of the experimental units so as to obtain a low basic variability or experimental error for the experiment.
4. To provide an adequate estimate of the experimental error for the experiment.
5. To give the desired precision for the estimated mean value of the response to a factor level or for the differences in response between levels.
6. To attain a pattern of correlation among the residuals that is minimal in absolute value.
7. To provide a feasible program in terms of resources, materials, and time available.

Example 5.1. We illustrate an example of a random balance design, which is used primarily with 10 or more variables each represented at two or more levels. This example contains 10 variables at two or more levels each and using 12 computer runs.

* Delivered in a lecture at the University of Michigan, Ann Arbor, Michigan, Summer, 1960.

Run No.	Factors (Variables)									
	A	B	C	D	E	F	G	H	I	J
1	2	2	1	3	2	4	4	3	1	1
2	1	2	1	2	3	1	2	4	3	3
3	3	2	2	3	1	2	1	1	4	2
4	3	1	1	1	1	3	2	2	1	3
5	1	2	1	2	3	1	1	4	3	1
6	1	1	2	3	2	2	3	3	2	2
7	1	1	2	2	4	4	3	1	3	1
8	2	1	1	2	1	4	4	2	4	2
9	3	2	2	1	2	2	2	2	1	3
10	2	2	2	1	4	3	4	1	2	2
11	2	1	2	3	3	1	1	4	4	1
12	3	1	1	1	4	3	3	3	2	3

For example, Level 2 of Variable A is used in Run 1, Level 1 of Variable A is used in Run 2, etc.

The following general routine for designing and running an experiment is quoted from E. L. Crow et al. [4]:

1. *State the objectives of the experiment.*
   a. Use information from previous experiments.
   b. Choose experimental conditions to represent the conditions under which the results will be applied. This may be done by either systematic choice or randomization.
   c. State the precise hypotheses that are to be tested.
2. *Draw up a preliminary design.*
   a. Take into account the experimental error, and the number of degrees of freedom for estimating it, provided by each proposed design.
   b. Consider the cost of experimentation versus the cost of wrong decisions.
3. *Review the design with all collaborators.*
   a. Reach an understanding as to what decisions hinge on each outcome. Keep notes.
   b. Encourage collaborators to anticipate all factors that might affect the results.
   c. Discuss the experimental techniques in sufficient detail to discover any procedures that might lead to bias.

4. *Draw up the final design.*
   a. Present the design in clear terms to assure that its provisions can be followed without confusion.
   b. Include the methods of analysis as part of the design, ascertaining that conditions necessary for the validity of these methods will be met.
5. *Carry out the experiment.*
   a. During the course of the experiment, maintain communication among all collaborators, so that questions arising from unforeseen experimental conditions or results may be answered in keeping with the design agreed upon.
6. *Analyze the data.*
   a. Follow the methods outlined in the final design (Step 4).
7. *Write a report.*
   a. Present the data and results in clear tables and graphs.
   b. Compare the results with the stated objectives of the experiment (Step 1).
   c. If the results suggest further experimentation, outline the course that such experimentation should take.

In stochastic models it is necessary to replicate each run r times in order to produce statistically valid results. The number of replications r is determined either of two ways: (a) beforehand and independent of the observational results; (b) during each run of the model by applying a sequential test as we go along.

In the first method the sample size (or number of replications r) is determined before the model is run on the basis of the desired level of significance; usually the 5% level is chosen. This method is the classical way of determining sample size, but is less efficient than the second method.

In the second method we apply a sequential test after each replication (or observation) and decide whether to end the process or make one further observation. Generally this is done by comparing the cumulative outcomes during the model run with accepted regions, i.e., those regions in which the results are within the desired level of significance. At that point when the outcome is within the accepted region we end the process. The accepted region can be determined by the Wald probability ratio test; for a discussion see [10, 15, 70].

By using sequential tests the process requires fewer replications over all than the first method, and thus the same results can be obtained at a reduced cost. However, we never know in advance the number of replications that will occur for a given set of input parameters.

RESPONSE SURFACE

The response surface is the geometric representation of the relation between the numerical results of a measurement made for a particular set of levels of all the factors used in a given trial and two or more factors. Response surface equations are the functional relations of the factors (or parameters and variables).

In the over-all performance of a large-scale system or operation it may be desirable to relate functionally the many system parameters and input variables to some criterion or criteria, such as system effectiveness, or some measure of over-all system or operation performance. The system response equations may be in the form

$$C = f(x_1, x_2, x_3, \ldots, x_n), \tag{5.1}$$

where C is the criterion of system performance and $x_1, x_2, x_3, \ldots, x_n$ are system parameters and input variables.

The response surface can be shown by a system of equations, or the response surface can be illustrated with suitable charts or graphs showing the relationships among variables. However, we still find difficulty in showing graphically the relationships among many variables, such as eight or more. We illustrate an example of a response surface in Fig. 5.1.

In the next section we discuss methods of curve fitting in order to derive the response surface equations.

CURVE FITTING [4, 27–29, 42, 61, 67]

Curve fitting is a mathematical method of determining the equation of a line or curve of best fit for a set of empirical points. We can apply a method of least squares to fit the best curve to the data points. The unknown coefficients of the regression equations are determined by least squares, in which the process is based on calculus.

Empirical data may be fitted to various types of equations, such as linear, multiple linear, curvilinear (parabola, cubic parabola), logarithmic, or exponential.

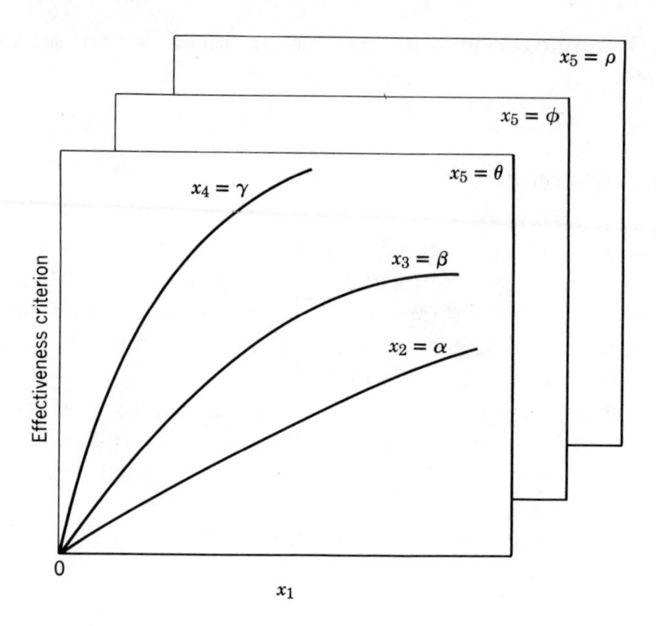

Fig. 5.1 Illustration of graphs of the response surface.

Linear. For N data points x_i, y_i which follow a linear relationship we establish the form

$$y = \beta_0 + \beta_1 x, \tag{5.2}$$

where β_0 is the Y intercept and β_1 is the slope of the line. We solve for the linear coefficients $\beta_0 \beta_1$ from the simultaneous equations

$$\beta_1 = \frac{\sum^N x \sum^N y - N \sum^N xy}{\left(\sum^N x\right)^2 - N \sum^N x^2} \tag{5.3}$$

$$\beta_0 = \frac{1}{N}\left(\sum^N y - \beta_1 \sum^N x\right). \tag{5.4}$$

Example 5.2. Find the equation of the straight line that fits the following data:

X	2.0	4.0	6.0	8.0	10.0
Y	5.5	6.3	7.2	8.0	8.6

SOLUTION. Let the equation of the line be $y = \beta_0 + \beta_1 x$. We compute the coefficients for (5.3), (5.4) and obtain the following results:

$$n = 5$$

$$\Sigma Y = 30$$

$$\Sigma X^2 = 220$$

$$\Sigma Y = 35.6$$

$$\Sigma XY = 229.4.$$

Substituting in (5.3), (5.4) we have

$$\beta_1 = \frac{30(35.6 - 5(229.4)}{(30)^2 - 5(220)} = 0.395$$

$$\beta_0 = \tfrac{1}{5}[35.6 - 0.395(30)] = 4.75.$$

Therefore the required equation is

$$y = 4.75 + 0.395x$$

and is illustrated in the graph (Fig. 5.2).

Multiple Linear

We use a multiple linear form to establish a relationship between a variable y and several other variables $x_1, x_2, \ldots, x_n$. We use the form

$$y = \beta_0 + \beta_1 x_1 + \beta_2 x_2 + \cdots + \beta_n x_n. \tag{5.5}$$

We solve the regression coefficients $\beta_0, \beta_1, \beta_2, \ldots, \beta_n$ from a set of equations that involve the deviations of each value from the mean of that variable as follows:

$$\beta_1 \sum_1^N M_1^2 + \beta_2 \sum_1^N M_1 M_2 + \cdots + \beta_n \sum^N M_1 M_n - \sum M_1 M_y = 0 \tag{5.6}$$

$$\beta_1 \sum^N M_1 M_2 + \beta_2 \sum_1^N M_2^2 + \cdots + \beta_n \sum^N M_2 M_n - \sum M_2 M_y = 0 \tag{5.7}$$

$$\vdots$$

$$\beta_1 \sum^N M_1 M_n + \beta_2 \sum^N M_n^2 + \cdots + \beta_n \sum^N M_n^2 - \sum^N M_n M_y = 0 \tag{5.8}$$

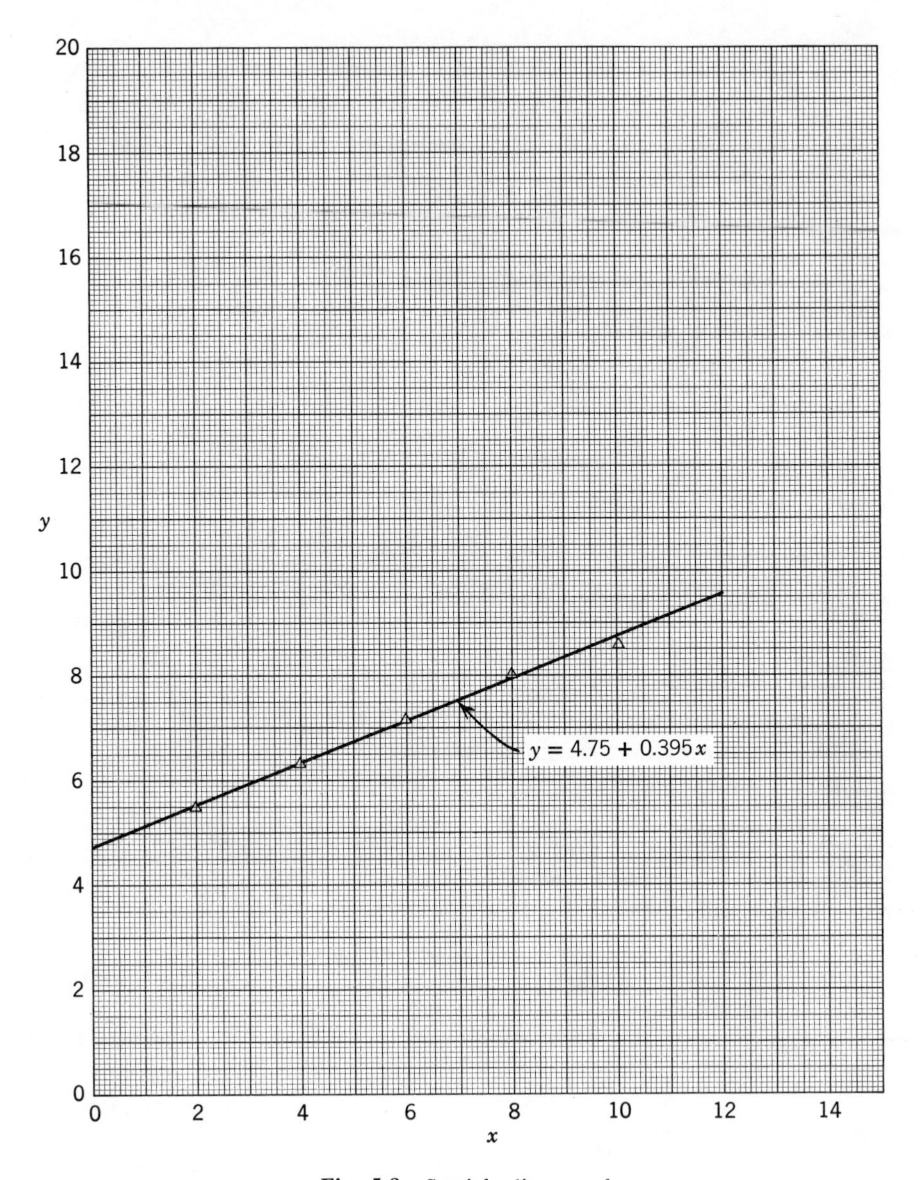

Fig. 5.2 Straight line graph.

where

$$M_1 = x_1 - \bar{x}_1 \quad (5.9)$$

$$M_2 = x_2 - \bar{x}_2 \quad (5.10)$$

$$\vdots$$

$$M_n = x_n - \bar{x}_n \quad (5.11)$$

$$M_y = y - \bar{y} \quad (5.12)$$

$$\beta_0 = \bar{y} - \beta_1\bar{x}_1 - \beta_2\bar{x}_2 - \cdots - \beta_n x_n. \quad (5.13)$$

Curvilinear

We can establish a simple relationship in two variables in the form

$$y = \beta_0 + \beta_1 x + \beta_2 x^2. \quad (5.14)$$

We solve for the linear coefficients $\beta_0\beta_1\beta_2$ in the simultaneous equations

$$N\beta_0 + \beta_1 \sum^N x + \beta_2 \sum^N x^2 - \sum^N y = 0 \quad (5.15)$$

$$\beta_0 \sum^N x + \beta_1 \sum^N x^2 + \beta_2 \sum^N x^3 - \sum^N xy = 0 \quad (5.16)$$

$$\beta_0 \sum^N x^2 + \beta_1 \sum^N x^3 + \beta_2 \sum^N x^4 - \sum^N x^2y = 0. \quad (5.17)$$

Example 5.3. Find the equation of the form $y = \beta_0 + \beta_1 x + \beta_2 x^2$ that fits the following data:

X	2.00	4.00	6.00	8.00	10.00	12.00	14.00
Y	3.76	4.44	5.04	5.56	6.00	6.36	6.64

SOLUTION. We compute the coefficients for (5.15–5.17) and obtain the following results:

$$n = 7$$

$$\Sigma X = 56$$

$$\Sigma X^2 = 560$$

$$\Sigma X^3 = 6272$$

$$\Sigma X^4 = 74816$$

$$\Sigma Y = 37.80$$

$$\Sigma XY = 330.28$$

$$\Sigma X^2Y = 3454.64.$$

Substituting in (5.15–5.17), we have the simultaneous equations

$$7\beta_0 > + 56\beta_1 + 560\beta_2 - 37.80 = 0$$

$$56\beta_0 + 560\beta_1 + 6272\beta_2 - 330.28 = 0$$

$$560\beta_0 + 6272\beta_1 + 74816\beta_2 - 3454.64 = 0.$$

Solving for β_0, β_1, and β_2, we obtain

$$\beta_0 = 3.0$$

$$\beta_1 = 0.4$$

$$\beta_2 = -0.01.$$

The required equation is therefore

$$y = 3 + 0.4x - 0.01x^2.$$

Logarithmic

We can establish the relationship between two variables x, y in the form

$$y = \beta_0 x^{\beta_1}, \tag{5.18}$$

where β_0 is the y intercept and β_1 is the slope. We solve for the linear coefficients β_0, β_1 from the equations

$$\beta_1 = \frac{\sum^N \log x \sum^N \log y - N \sum^N \log x \log y}{\left(\sum^N \log x\right)^2 - N \sum^N (\log x)^2} \tag{5.19}$$

$$\log \beta_0 = \frac{1}{N}\left(\sum^N \log y - \beta_1 \sum^N \log x\right). \tag{5.20}$$

Example 5.4. Fit the following data points to a logarithmic curve of the form of (5.18).

X	1	2	3	4	5	6
Y	3	12	27	48	75	108

SOLUTION. Apply (5.19), (5.20), in which we calculate

$$\Sigma \log X = 2.85733$$

$$\Sigma \log Y = 8.57738$$

$$\Sigma (\log X)^2 = 1.77441$$

$$\Sigma \log X \log Y = 4.90164.$$

for $N = 6$. Substituting in the equations, we obtain

$$\beta_1 = \frac{2.85733(8.57738) - 6(4.90164)}{(2.85733)^2 - 6(1.77441)} = 2$$

$$\log \beta_0 = \tfrac{1}{6}\,[8.57738 - 2(2.85733)] = 0.477.$$

Therefore the equation for the above data points is

$$y = 3x^2,$$

where

$$\text{antilog } 0.477 = 3.$$

Exponential

We can establish a simple exponential relationship between two variables in the form

$$y = \beta_0 e^{\beta_1 x}, \tag{5.21}$$

where β_0 is the y intercept and β_1 is the slope. We solve for the linear coefficients in the equations

$$\beta_1 = \frac{\sum^N x \sum^N \log y - N \sum^N x \log y}{\log e\left[\left(\sum^N x\right)^2 - N \sum^N x^2\right]} \tag{5.22}$$

$$\log \beta_0 = \frac{1}{N}\left(\sum^N \log y - \beta_1 \log e \sum^N x\right), \tag{5.23}$$

where $\log e = 0.4343$.

Example 5.5. Find the equation of the form $Y = \beta_0 e^{\beta_1 X}$, by plotting the following data points on semilog graph paper:

X	2.0	3.0	4.0	5.0	6.0	7.0	8.0	9.0	10.0
Y	3.5	5.0	6.2	9.0	13.0	16.0	23.0	30.0	40.0

SOLUTION. We plot the data points as shown in Fig. 5.3 and draw the best fit line that passes through the points. The Y intercept gives us the value of β_0, which equals 2. Substituting $\beta_0 = 2$ in the equation gives us $Y = 2e^{\beta_1 X}$, with β_1 unknown. Next we select a point on the line, say $X = 5$ and $y = 9$, and substitute in the above equation, which gives

$$9 = 2e^{5\beta_1}.$$

Solving for β_1 in the above equation gives

$$\beta_1 = \frac{\log 9 - \log 2}{5 \log e} = \frac{0.95424 - 0.30103}{5(0.4343)} = 0.3.$$

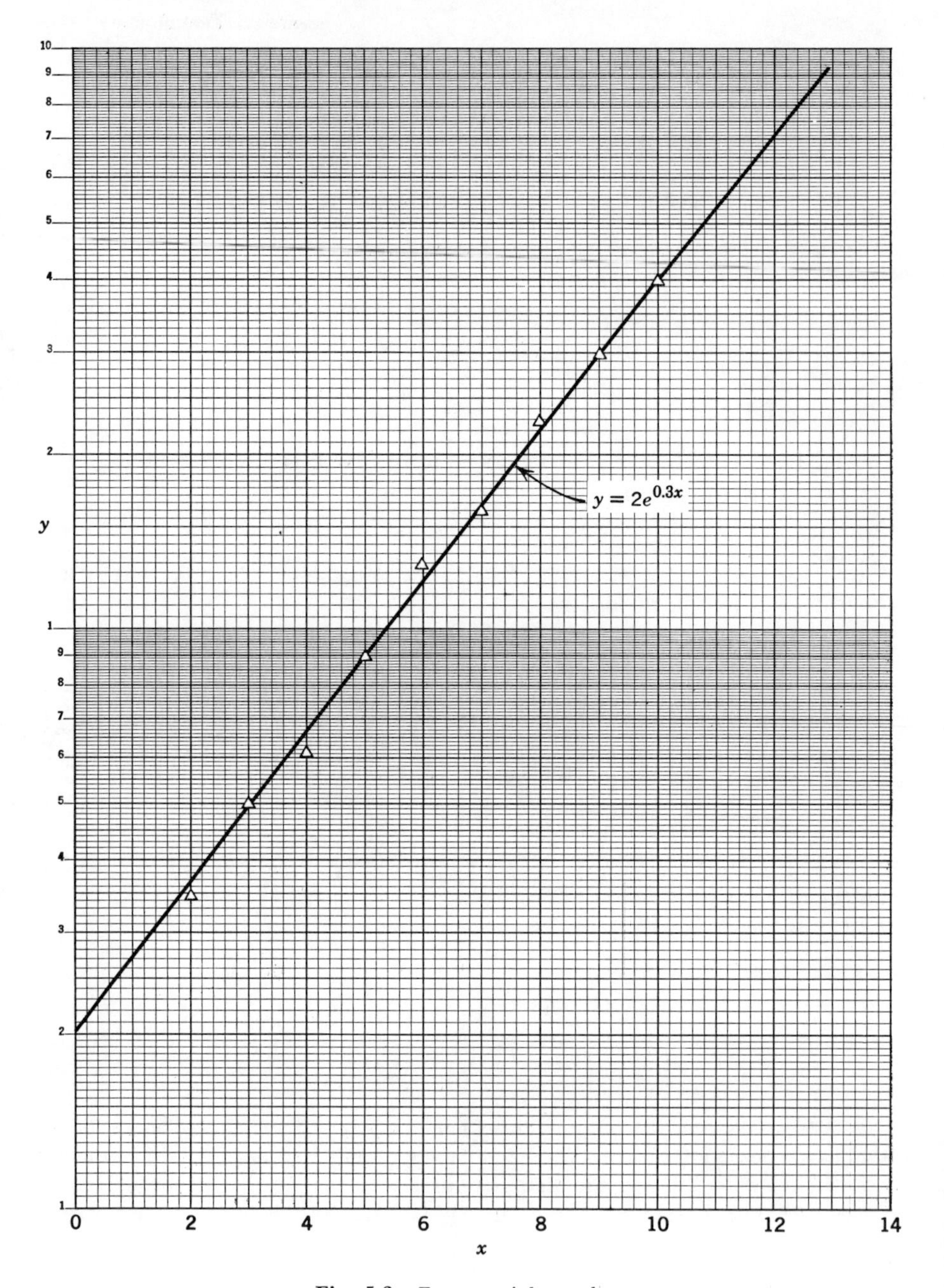

Fig. 5.3 Exponential graph.

The required equation is therefore

$$y = 2e^{0.3x}.$$

We can establish a simple exponential relationship between two variables in the form

$$y = \beta_0(\beta_1{}^x) \qquad (5.24)$$

where β_0 is the y intercept and β_1 is the slope. We solve for the linear coefficients in the equations

$$\log \beta_1 = \frac{\sum^N x \sum^N \log y - N \sum^N x \log y}{\left(\sum^N x\right)^2 - N \sum^N x^2} \qquad (5.25)$$

$$\log \beta_0 = \frac{1}{N}\left(\sum^N \log y - \log \beta_1 \sum^N x\right). \qquad (5.26)$$

In general we can use the polynomial formula

$$y = \beta_0 + \beta_1 x + \beta_2 x^2 + \cdots + \beta_n x^n \qquad (5.27)$$

to fit any set of data by taking a sufficient number of terms.

We can graph a set of data points to establish the type of equations to fit the data and determine the coefficients. We can graph data on straight ordinate-abscissa scale, on semilog scale, or log-log scale graph paper. A straight-line graph on any of these scales is indicative of a certain type of equation. Various scales and types of equation are summarized as follows:

Scale	Type of Equation	
Straight graph	$y = \beta_0 + \beta_1 x$	(5.28)
Semilog graph	$y = \beta_0 e^{\beta_1 x}$	(5.29)
	$y = \beta_0(\beta_1{}^x)$	(5.30)
Log-log graph	$y = \beta_0 x^{\beta_1}$	(5.31)

An example of a straight-line graph is shown in Fig. 5.4. Examples of 1-cycle, 2-cycle, and 3-cycle semilog graphs are shown in Figs. 5.5, 5.6, and 5.7, respectively. Examples of 1 × 1 cycle, 2 × 2 cycle, and 2 × 3 cycle log-log graphs are shown in Figs. 5.8, 5.9, and 5.10 respectively.

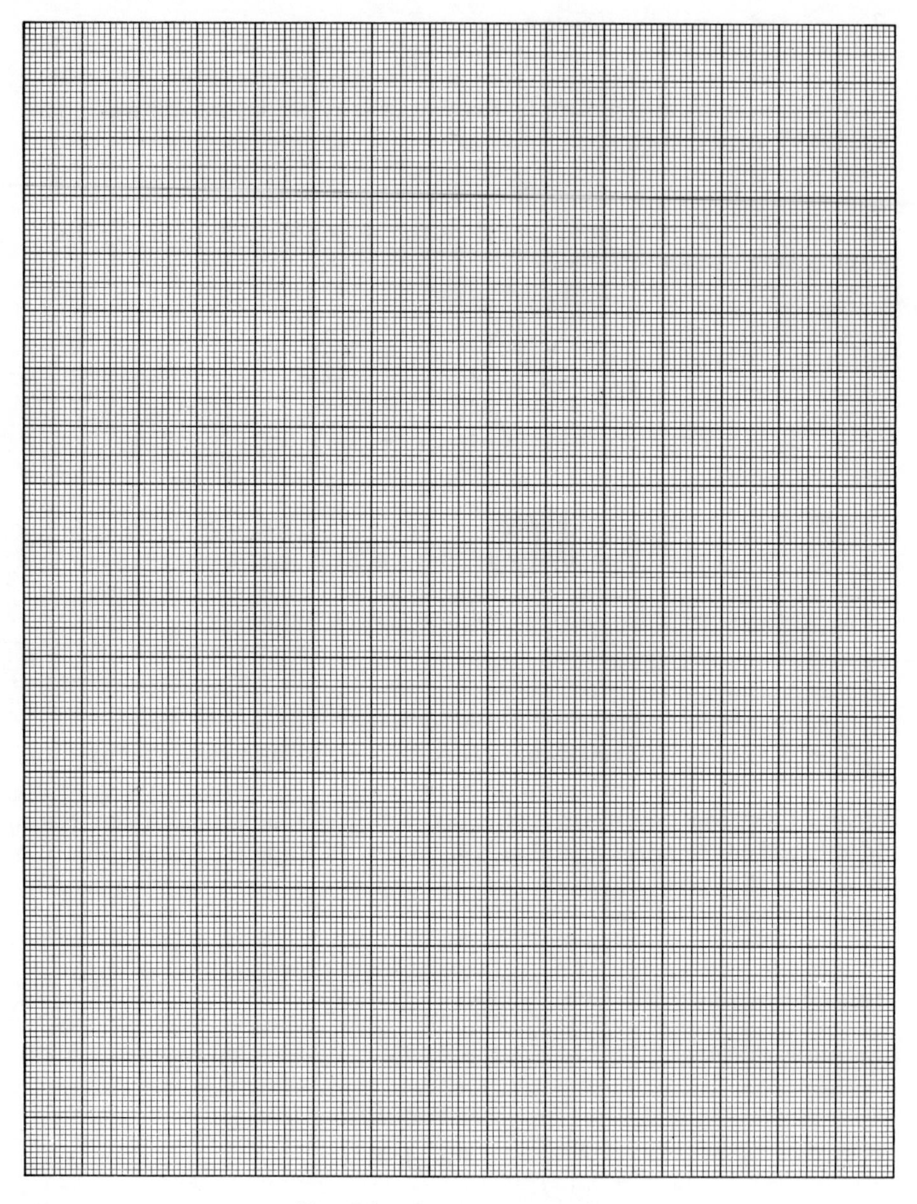

Fig. 5.4 Straight scale graph.

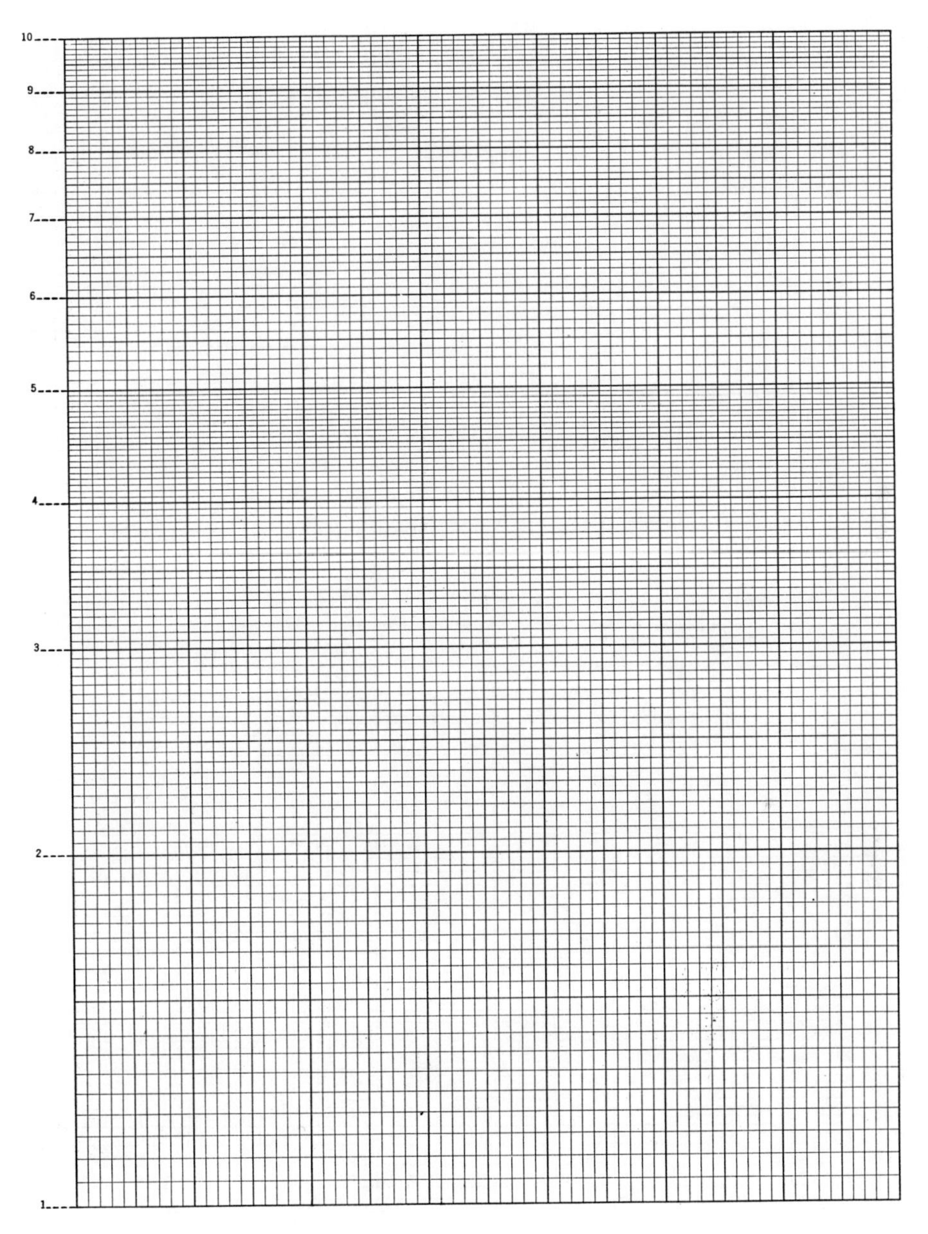

Fig. 5.5 Semilog graph (1 cycle).

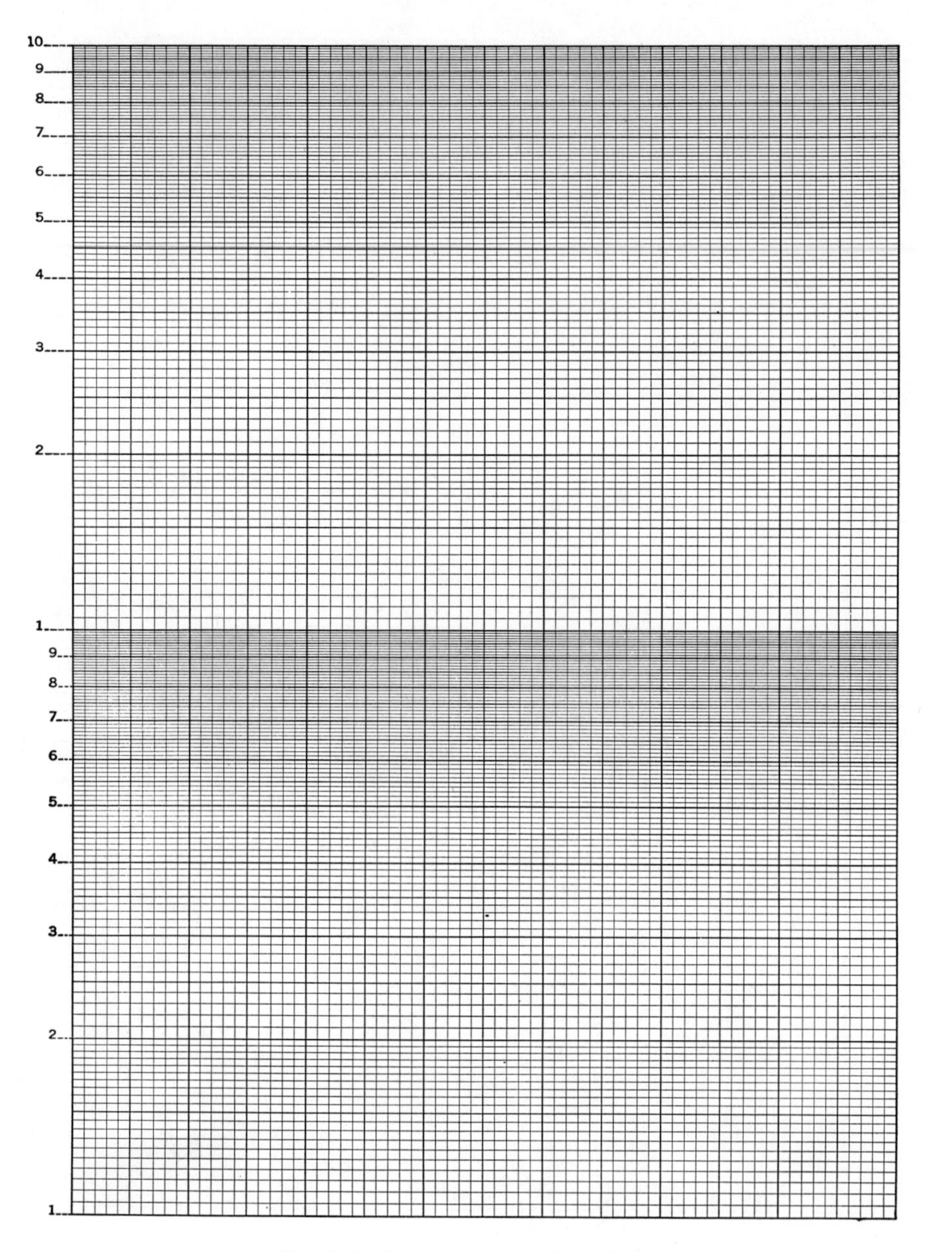

Fig. 5.6 Semilog graph (2 cycles).

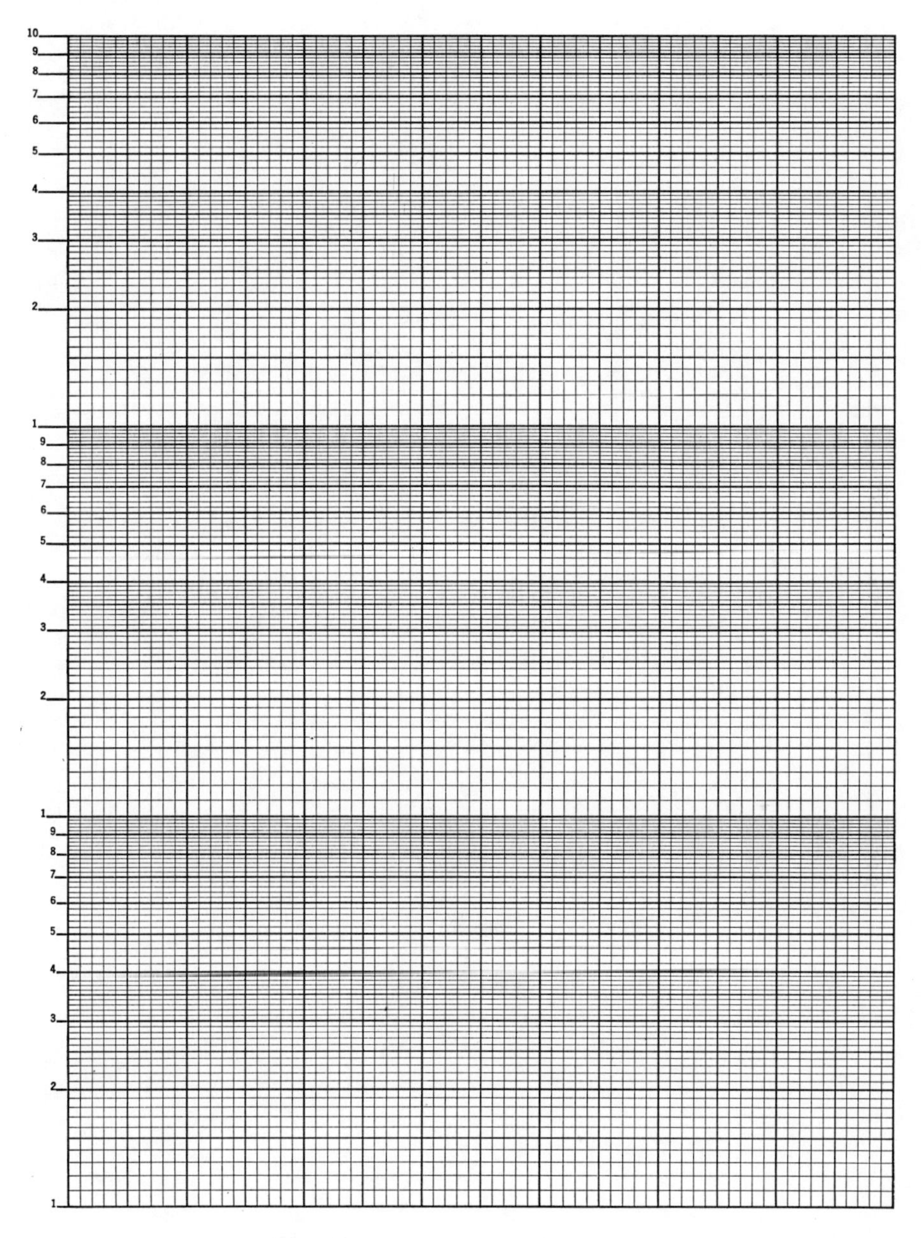

Fig. 5.7 Semilog graph (3 cycles).

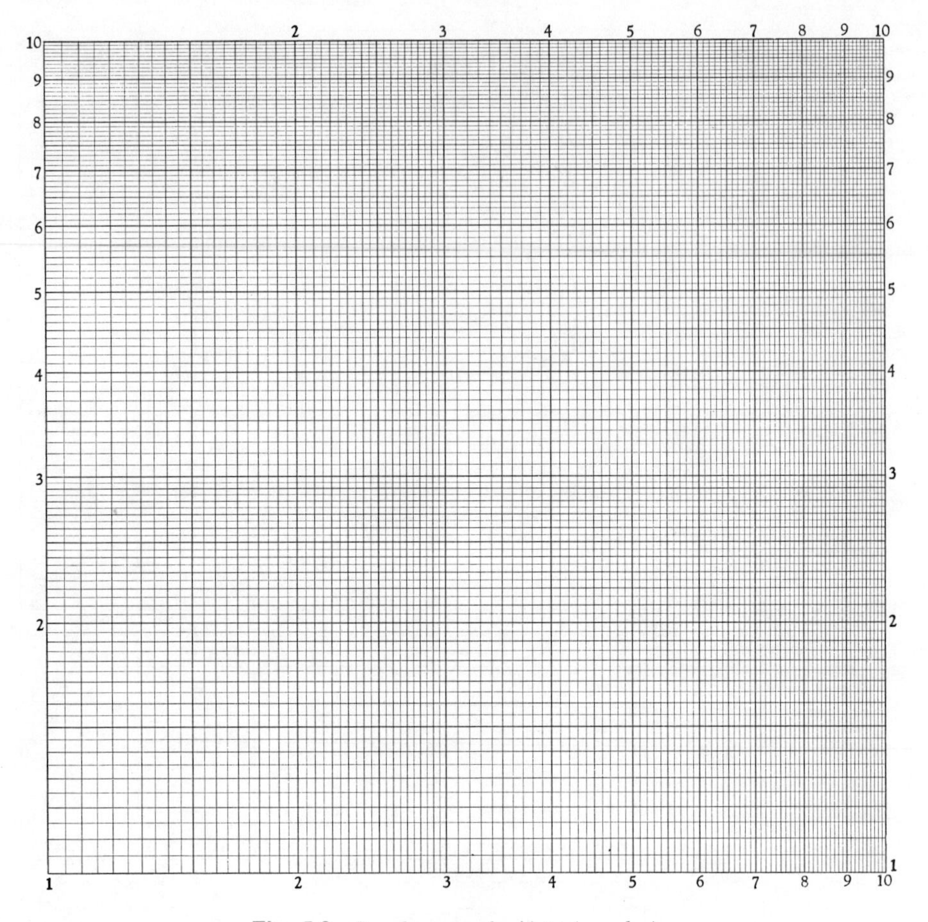

Fig. 5.8 Log-log graph (1 $\times$ 1 cycles).

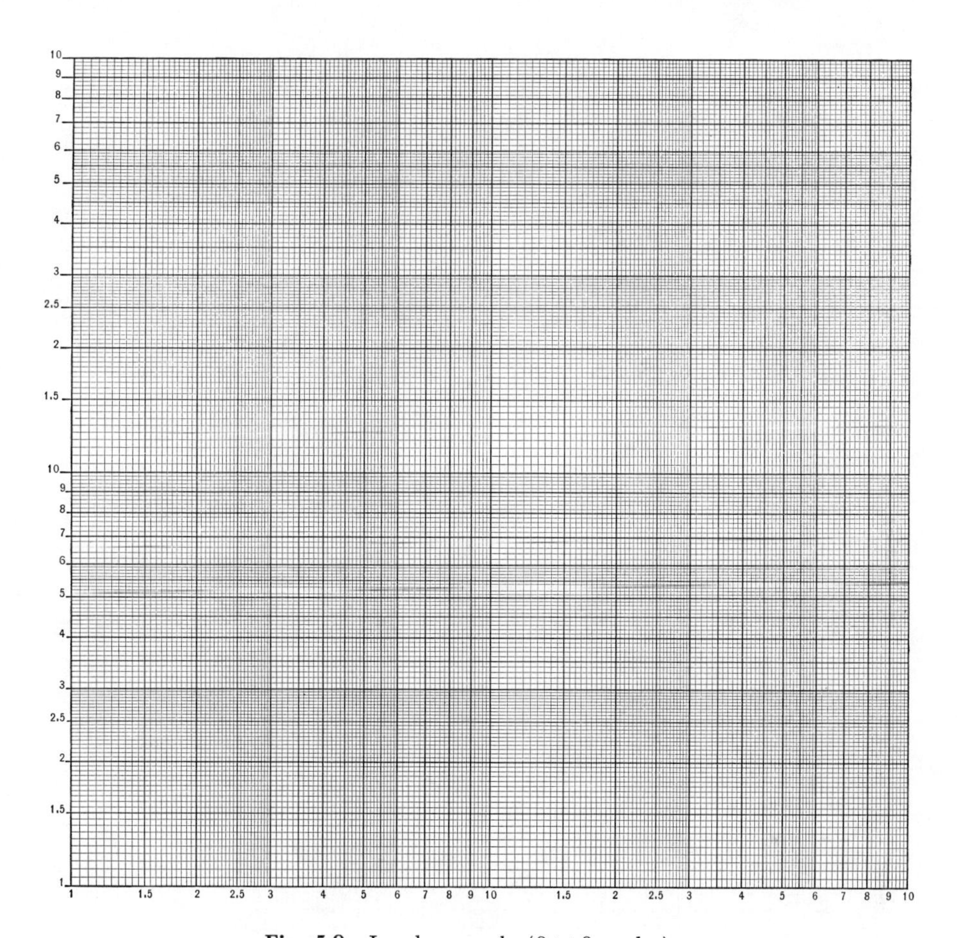

Fig. 5.9 Log-log graph (2 × 2 cycles).

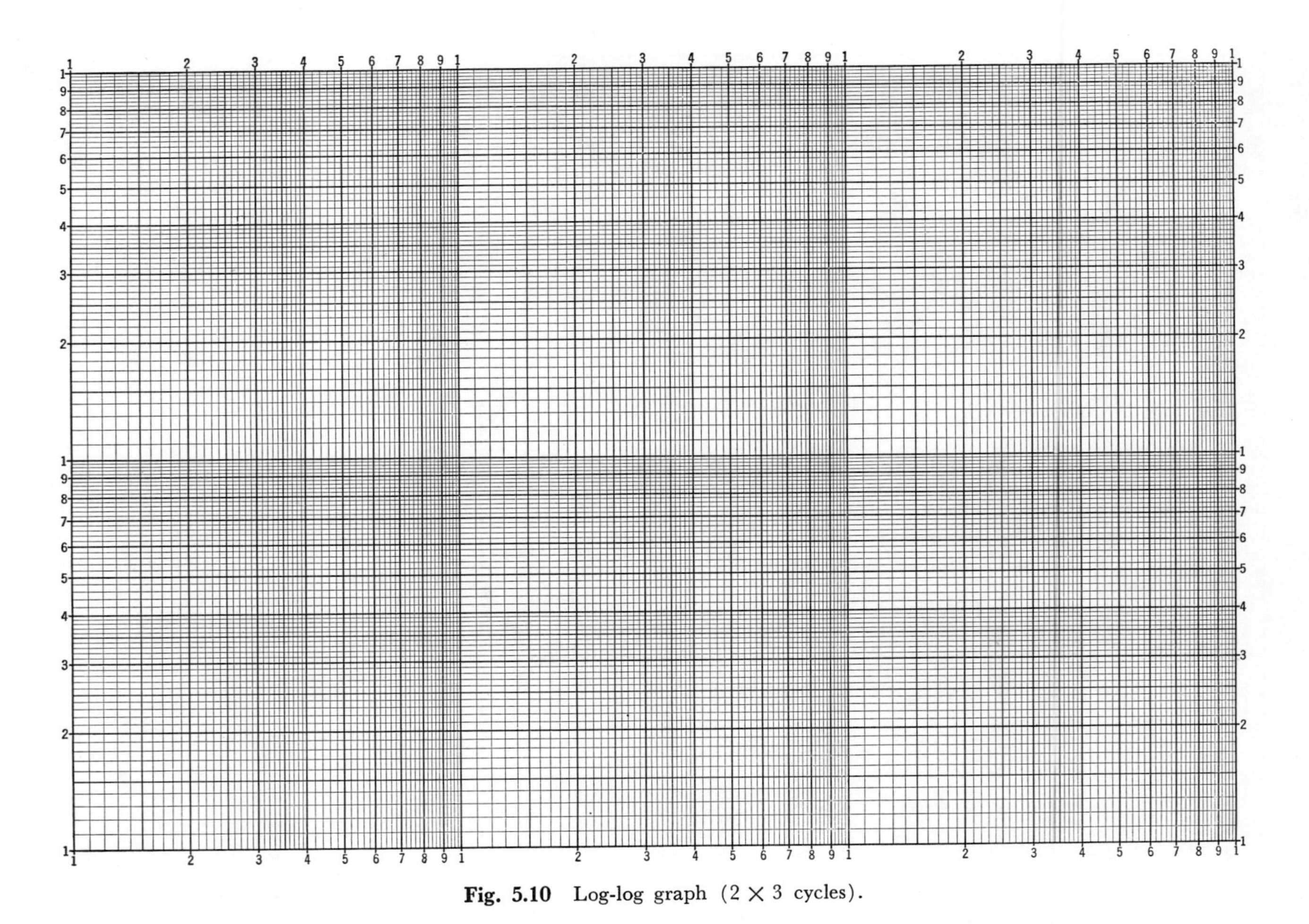

Fig. 5.10 Log-log graph (2 × 3 cycles).

PROBLEMS

5.1 Draw an experimental design matrix for an experiment with parameters A, B, C, D, and E with three levels of each parameter.

5.2 Draw graphs of the "best fit" curves for the following data points:

(a)	(b)	(c)
0, −2	0, 3	0, 0
1, 1	1, 2	1, 2
2, 4	2, 3	2, 6
3, 7	3, 6	3, 12
4, 10	4, 11	4, 20
	5, 18	5, 30

(d)	(e)	(f)
0, 1	0, 0	1.5, 5.2
2, 4	2, 1	2.0, 6.0
4, 6	4, 4	2.5, 7.0
6, 8	6, 11	3.0, 7.2
8, 10	8, 15	3.5, 8.0
10, 12	10, 17.5	4.0, 8.4
12, 13	12, 19	5.0, 9.4
14, 14	14, 19.7	6.0, 10.0
	16, 20	7.0, 10.2

5.3 Select the best equations for 5.2 and compute the regression coefficients.

5.4 Compute regression coefficients for the following data points in three-dimensional space.

(a)	(b)
0, 0, 0	0, 0, 0
0, 1, −1	1, 1, $-\frac{1}{4}$
1, −2, 0	2, 2, $-\frac{1}{2}$
2, −5, 1	3, 5, $-\frac{1}{4}$
4, 0, −8	5, $9\frac{1}{2}$, 1
5, −3, −7	

5.5 Select the data points that appear unreasonable.

1, 1	5, 3
2, $\frac{1}{2}$	6, $3\frac{1}{4}$
3, 2	$6\frac{1}{2}$, 2
4, $2\frac{1}{2}$	7, $3\frac{1}{2}$
$4\frac{1}{2}$, $4\frac{1}{2}$	

5.6 Draw the "best fit" curve for the data points in 5.5.

6

MODELING TOOLS AND TECHNIQUES

FLOW CHARTING

Flow charting is a tool that is applicable in problem analysis and in the programming task. Flow charting is a "software" technique which when properly applied is an indispensable aid in the logical development of a model. We define a *flow chart* as an orderly representation of a process, i.e., a graphic illustration in which activities are defined and their interrelationships are illustrated. The generic term "flow chart" represents a broad technique concept. Attaching adjectival descriptors, such as gross, detail, logical, or program, distinguishes among various types of flow charts.

Therefore a gross flow chart is one in which activities are broadly or grossly identified and shown, but without any detail. The gross level of flow charting gives a picture of the broad, over-all flow. The gross flow is that level of flow charting in which the general structure is shown without all the detailed substructures. It is like a national map that shows major road networks and points for the cities, but not the city streets.

The gross level of flow charting indicates "what to do," but does not go into any further detail. For example, a gross flow may indicate any of the following: "Go to Events Generator," "Go to Sine Subroutine," or "Compute $f(X)$."

A detail flow chart represents refinement that is not shown in the gross flow chart. The detail flow chart indicates "how to do it." This level of flow charting goes into sufficient depth and detail that there is no ambiguity as to how a given function, process, or procedure is performed. The detail flow chart shows the substructures and sub-substructures of the gross flow chart. Various levels of detail may be used in stepping from the grossest level to the most detailed level of flow charting.

A logical flow chart illustrates the logical flow of a system or operation. The logical flow is the orderly process of activity of the system or operation. The process is illustrated by variously shaped figures connected by arrows showing the direction of flow. Within each figure is a statement of what activity, such as a computation or testing, takes place.

A program flow chart illustrates the program flow of the model. The (computer) program flow chart is the programmer's version of the logical flow chart. For each activity specified in the logical flow chart there is an implementation of this activity flow in the computer program flow chart. In appearance this version does not look the same as the logical flow chart, but the difference stops there. Actually in going from the logical flow to the program flow the substance of the model remains the same. The logical flow chart is system-oriented, and the program flow chart is computer program-oriented.

Both the logical flow chart and the program flow chart can be represented in gross level or in detail level. We can have a gross logical flow chart, a detail logical flow chart, a gross program flow chart, or a detail program flow chart. Of course, in practical application it may not always be necessary to make all these distinctions.

Flow charting should be applied with a certain amount of judgment and flexibility, rather than rigidly. Because flow charting is an aid in the construction of a computer model, it would be pedantic to produce or require more flow charts than are necessary for the analysis and programming tasks. A flow chart is a shorthand device that contains written instructions, symbology, and geometric figures. The flow chart should contain only enough information to show the activity at the given level of detail represented. The flow chart should contain no irrelevancies, redundancies, or florid representations.

Some efforts have been made to standardize flow chart symbology. However, no standard conventions are universally accepted. Some of the efforts at standardization have been characterized by arbitrariness. There seems to be no advantage in adopting one convention over another, although there is nothing wrong in accepting some conventions, such as we describe below.

Arrows are usually used to show the direction of flow. Left-to-right flow seems to be easy to implement and easy to follow, probably because of our convention of reading from left to right in Western cultures. Most flow chart activities can be represented by selecting from five formats: input/output, computation, decision point, modification, and connector (or transfer).

Input/output functions accept inputs from external sources or produce outputs for external use. Input/output functions are usually given inside an ellipse. Computational activities are usually designated inside a rectangular box. A decision point in which a "yes or no" decision is made is usually shown in a diamond-shaped figure in which the "yes" flow continues to the right and the "no" flow proceeds downward. A modification of an existing value or values, such as a parameter, index, or computer register, can be shown by a hexagonal figure. A connector or transfer forms a connection in the flow, such as from one line to the next, and is shown by a circle. These symbols are illustrated in Fig. 6.1 and a simple flow chart using these symbols is illustrated in Fig. 6.2.

Automated methods have been devised to generate flow charts automatically, given the necessary information about the logical flow. A computerized method is explained in the reference by Sherman [218].

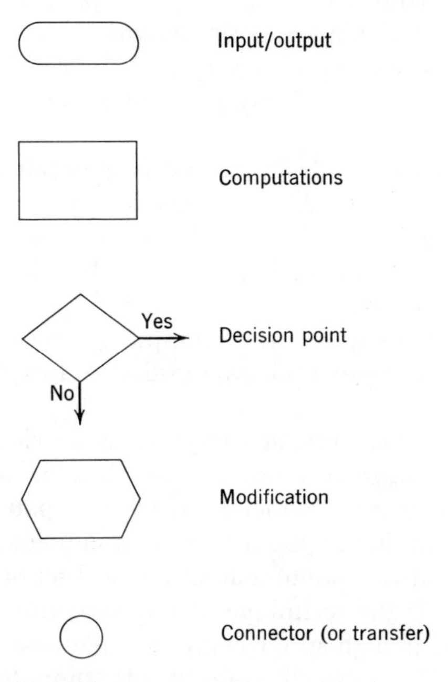

Fig. 6.1 Flow chart symbols.

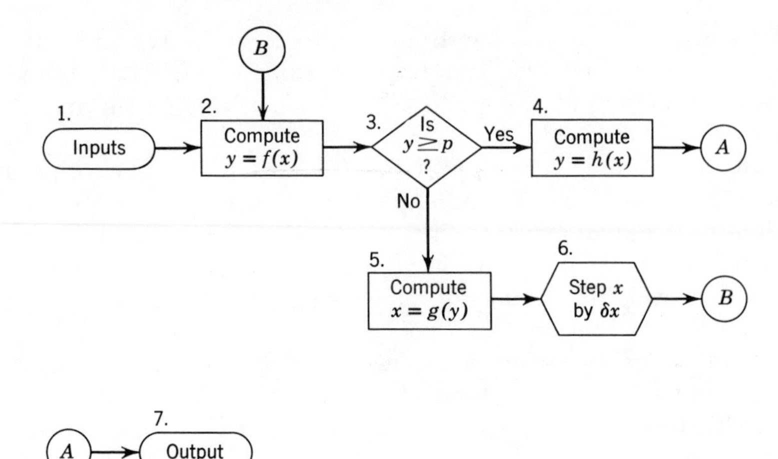

Fig. 6.2 Example of a simple chart with flow chart symbols.

COMPUTER PROGRAMMING

We consider the computer and computer programming a most significant tool in the modeling and simulation technique. The computer is an extremely powerful and necessary tool. Its role is vital and important throughout the solution of any problem solved by computer modeling and simulation.

We feel that anyone involved in modeling problems needs to be intimately familiar with digital computers and computer programming techniques. This familiarity with both hardware and software is essential even though the model builder is not involved in writing the computer program. Nevertheless, he needs an understanding of the tool. In this section we give a brief exposition of computers and computer programming. We describe computer characteristics and explain techniques of application.

We define a *high-speed digital computer* as an electronic system that can be programmed to solve numerical problems in which the solutions are discrete. A computer is characterized by its capability for high-speed computation, for retaining digital information in memory, and for following a preprogrammed computational and logical set of procedures. Computer programming is the technique of implementing a numerical problem for solution on a high-speed computer. Automatic data processing (ADP) refers to the over-all concept of computers and computer programming.

The terms "software" and "hardware" are frequently used to designate two major features of automatic data processing. Software includes the computer programs, programming systems, compilers, and assemblers. Hardware includes all electronic and electromechanical devices, such as computers and their peripheral equipment. Thus software refers to all nonhardware items, and vice versa.

Hardware in computer modeling and simulation is important as a device to obtain model results quickly and accurately. Without hardware, results. With an inferior model the results will be inferior and meaning-simulations we could never hope to obtain results without computers.

Before proceeding we want to make an important point. As vital as hardware is, the significance lies in the mathematical model itself. The success or failure of any computer simulation depends on the excellence of the mathematical model and only incidentally on the computer. With a good model the simulation can be expected to produce successful results. With an inferior model the results will be inferior and meaningless regardless of the excellence of the computer.

Early in the stages of model development we should give consideration to computer selection. As the model is developed, as its magnitude is realized, and as the requirements upon model outputs become clear, we can then intelligently select the appropriate computer to use. There are several criteria we can apply in the selection of the computer.

Ease of Programming. The method and system of programming should be easiest and most appropriate for the specific model.

Least Expense. The total cost of the model includes all *manpower costs* plus *computer costs.* A comparative cost analysis shows which computer system is least expensive per computer run for the problem solution. Manpower costs include all charges for analysis, programming, manual input preparations, and manual output analysis. Computer costs include all charges made for running the model on the computer. For example, Fig. 6.3 is a graph of the comparison of two hypothetical computing systems, A and B, in which we can see that computer system B is less expensive than A for less than n_1 model runs and more expensive than A for more than n_1 runs. In this graph we assume linearity in costs.

Computer Accessibility. The computer selected for the model must be accessible. Starting with the nearest, usually an in-house computer is the most accessible. If, however, the in-house computer is not appropriate for the model in terms of computing requirements, we should explore the feasibility of using a computer at an outside facility.

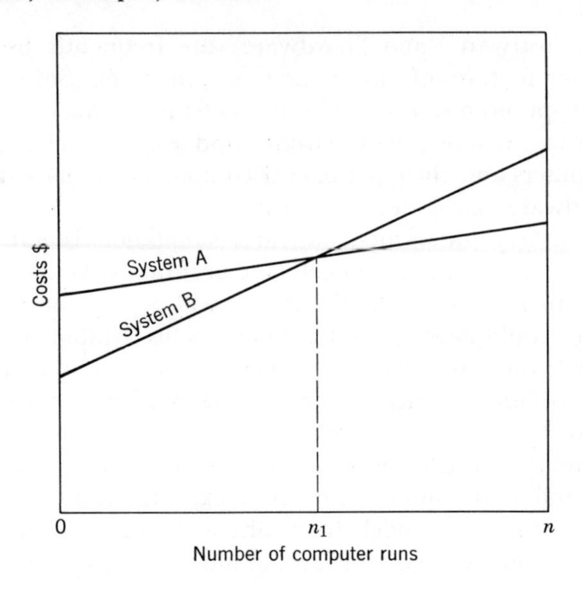

Fig. 6.3 Comparative costs for computer systems A and B (hypothetical, linear costs assumed).

Fastest Results. The timeliness of results is a critical factor in problems solved by computer modeling and simulation. The time required to obtain results includes time required for analysis, programming, debugging, input preparations, production runs, and follow-up analysis, plus any delays due to inaccessibility of the computer. All programming tasks must be performed within the problem time frame.

Computing Requirements. Consideration must be given to the requirements for computer memory, input/output devices, computer run preparations, computing time, and processing of outputs.

The five criteria listed above will have different significance as computer technologies change. Other criteria may have a different role in computer selection. For example, with the advent of third-generation computers, computer accessibility becomes a less significant factor in computer selection, since third-generation computers offer the user the capability of real time sharing at remote installations. With this kind of computer complex many users remotely located from the central processing unit can tie in to the unit for use on a time sharing basis.

With sufficient consideration given to the above criteria, we have now a rational basis for deciding on computer selection. We must bear in mind that frequently the choice can be made equally well among several alternative computers, and the ultimate selection is often made on the basis of expediency.

On Hardware

The digital computer and all its peripheral equipment constitute the major hardware items applied in modeling and simulation. Photographs of several currently manufactured computers are shown in Figs. 6.4 to 6.8. High-speed electronic computers are manufactured in all sizes, shapes, and speeds of operation. We have computers ranging in size from very small compact packages to computers weighing several hundreds of pounds and requiring large areas of floor space. Each computer has its unique features and capabilities. Each computer has its own language of instructions and logic of operation.

Regardless of operation speed, size, or shape, all digital computers consist basically of similar functional units. The outward appearance of the hardware may vary tremendously from one computer to another. Even the implementation and speed of execution may vary tremendously, but these are differences in degree. Basically the functions are still similar.

Memory. This is the device used to retain information. Some permanent devices, such as magnetic tapes, can retain information indefinitely.

Fig. 6.4 CDC 3600 computer (Courtesy of Control Data Corporation).

Fig. 6.5 CDC 3600 computer, large-scale system, shown alongside CDC 160A computer, medium-sized system (Courtesy of Control Data Corporation).

Fig. 6.6 IBM 360 system (Courtesy of International Business Machines).

Fig. 6.7 Sigma 7 computer (Courtesy of Scientific Data Systems).

Fig. 6.8 μ-comp DDP-516 computer (Courtesy of Honeywell, Inc.).

Other, more volatile devices, such as core memory, lose their information when the electric current is turned off. Memory devices include core, drum, magnetic tapes, disks, and nonelectronic devices, such as punched cards or paper tapes.

Address System. All memory locations are assigned an address according to some address system, usually in the octal number system. Addressing makes possible access to any memory location for the purpose of reading or writing information. Access time varies according to the memory device. For example, access to core memory requires only a few microseconds,* whereas access to magnetic tapes is limited to mechanical speeds of winding or rewinding the tape before achieving access to the desired information.

Number System. All computers use an internal number system for purposes of addressing, information storage, arithmetic operations, and logic. The internal number systems in electronic computers are binary-

Example 6.1. The following brief table illustrates the equivalents in three number systems:

Decimal	Octal	Binary
0	0	0
1	1	1
2	2	10
3	3	11
4	4	100
5	5	101
6	6	110
7	7	111
8	10	1000
9	11	1001
10	12	1010
11	13	1011
12	14	1100
13	15	1101
14	16	1110
15	17	1111
16	20	10000
17	21	10001
18	22	10010
19	23	10011
20	24	10100

* One microsecond = 10^{-6} second.

Fig. 6.9 IBM 1402 card reader punch (Courtesy of International Business Machines).

octal. Octal-decimal or binary-decimal conversions are made for communication between the computer and outside world.

Format of Information Flow. Each computer is designed and manufactured with a unique information flow. The flow design indicates how the information flows from one functional unit to all others.

Input/Output Devices. These devices are the two-way communication links between the computer and the outside world. They may include card readers, typewriters, Flexowriters, printers, tape drives, and console displays. Input/output may be either "on-line" (tied in to the computer operation) or "off-line" (apart from computer operation). Photographs of some currently manufactured input/output devices are shown in Figs. 6.9 and 6.10.

Program Control. This functional unit is the master control, which directs the computer processes in the orderly execution of the computer program. The unit controls the necessary computer logic to execute each unique program instruction. The computer operation is always under control of program control.

Fig. 6.10 IBM 1403 printer (Courtesy of International Business Machines).

Command Structure. Each computer contains a command structure, which includes all program instructions to the computer. The command structure consists of arithmetic, logical, control, shifting, indexing, and input/output operations. These are explained later.

Arithmetic Unit. This unit executes all arithmetic operations in the program execution. The arithmetic unit is an electronic device that performs basically one operation: *binary addition.* Binary addition rule has three basic equations:

$$\begin{aligned} 0 + 0 &= 0 \\ 0 + 1 &= 1 \\ 1 + 1 &= 10_2 \end{aligned} \tag{6.1}$$

From this rule the computer performs all arithmetic operations: addition, multiplication, subtraction, and division. Multiplication is performed by a series of additions. Subtraction is performed by a procedure complementary to addition. Division is performed by a series of subtractions.

Example 6.2. The following examples illustrate the use of the binary addition rule. In each case we show the equivalent computations in binary, octal, and decimal number systems.

	Binary	Octal	Decimal	
(a)	010	2	2	
	+101	+5	+5	
	111	7	7	Results
(b)	100	4	4	
	+110	+6	+6	
	1010	12	10	Results
(c)	011011	33	27	
	+101010	+52	+42	
	1			
	+100			
	101			
	+10000			
	10101			
	+10000			
	100101			
	+100000			
	1000101	105	69	Results

A simplified block diagram of a digital computer is shown in Fig. 6.11, in which input/output, program control, memory, and arithmetic units are shown. The information flow is illustrated by arrows. The other functional units, such as the number system, are implicit in the blocks.

Peripheral equipment includes all hardware items that are tied in with the computer to perform some specified function either on line

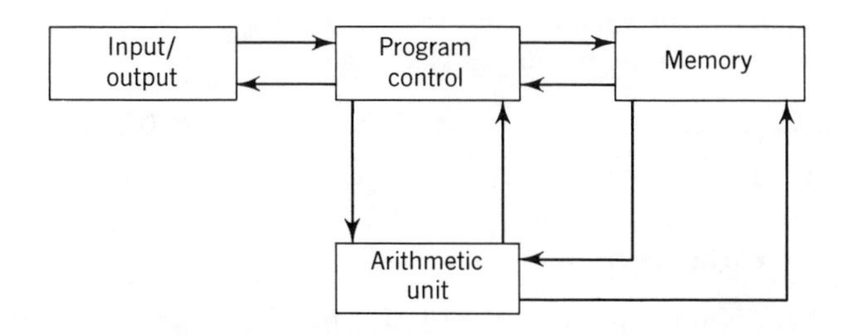

Fig. 6.11 Simplified block diagram of a digital computer.

or off line. Peripheral equipment includes input/output devices, floating point hardware, tape drives, and card punches.

Example 6.3. We briefly describe the functional units of three current large-scale digital computers: CDC 3600, Honeywell 1800II, and IBM 7094.

Function	CDC 3600	Honeywell 1800II	IBM 7094
Memory	260,000 core, 48 bits/word, tapes	65,000 core, 48 bits/word, tapes, disk	32,000 core, 36 bits/word, tapes, disk
Cycle time	1.5 μsec	2 μsec	2 μsec
Address system	Octal	Octal	Octal
Number system	Binary	Binary-coded decimal	Binary
Arithmetic system	Fixed and floating point	Fixed and floating point	Fixed and floating point
Input/output	Tapes, disk, card reader, card punch, printer, paper tapes	Paper tapes, card punch, printer, magnetic ink	Tapes, card reader, card punch, printer
Program control	Internal, solid state	Internal, solid state	Internal, solid state
Command structure		63 instructions	264 instructions
Arithmetic unit	Solid state	Solid state	Solid state
Addition timing	2.07 μsec	8 μsec	2 μsec
Multiplication timing	2.07–6.55 μsec	54 μsec	4–10 μsec
Peripheral equipment	Asynchronous input/output devices	Input/output devices	Input/output devices

The most advanced computers being manufactured are the third-generation computers. These computers have two characteristics that were not present in earlier computers:

1. Multiprocessing on a real-time sharing basis, in which more than one program can be run on the computer at the same time. Interrupt

capabilities allow the computer to sequence through various programs continuously in such a manner that several users can be accommodated simultaneously. The operation can be so fast that the users are unaware of the interruptions.

2. Input/output devices at remote locations in which the central processing unit can be physically located many miles away from the input/output devices.

These features of third-generation computers provide for greater flexibility and accessibility to the central processing unit than earlier computers.

On Software

We have discussed flow-charting techniques in the previous section, and we discuss the application in subsequent chapters. Flow charting is a most useful and necessary technique in computer programming. We begin with a logical flow chart of the model and from it we draw the program flow chart at an appropriate level of detail. Then we can proceed to the coding task.

Coding is the task of translating the model from the program flow chart to computer coding for a given computer. Coding follows prescribed rules and procedures. Coding can be done in *basic computer language* or in some *higher order synthetic language,* such as FORTRAN. In basic computer language the coding directly addresses and instructs the computer. This kind of coding is more difficult and usually takes longer to program for some computers, but basic language is faster to execute on the computer. A higher order language addresses the computer through a synthetic interpreter. This method is usually shorter to program but takes longer to execute on the computer. This method of programming requires more memory spaces and is not always applicable to all modeling problems.

Basic computer language instructions fall into various categories [208, 209, 210, 214].

Arithmetic Operations. These are the four basic arithmetic operations (addition, subtraction, multiplication, and division) in fixed decimal point or floating point. In fixed point the location of the decimal is fixed in the program. In floating point the location of the decimal point is designated by a characteristic number that accompanies the mantissa, similar to logarithms. The results of the arithmetic operations usually appear in a register, such as the accumulator.

Example 6.4. In floating point the characteristic 50 is used to designate a decimal number equal to or greater than 0.1 and less than 1. The characteristic 51 is used to designate a number equal to or greater than 1 and less than 10. The characteristic 49 is used to designate a decimal number equal to or greater than 0.01 and less than 0.1. Other floating point numbers are designated by extensions of the above.

The following are examples of real numbers and their floating point designation:

Number	**Floating point**
0.0010356	48.10356
0.010356	49.10356
0.10356	50.10356
1.0356	51.10356
10.356	52.10356

Logical Testing. These are tests that execute simple decisions, such as testing the magnitude of a number to determine a "yes-no" answer.

Shifting. These are instructions to execute left or right shifts of a given number, usually in the accumulator.

Addressing and Indexing. These are instructions associated with memory addressing, tallies, and dynamic addressing.

Input/Output. These are all the instructions associated with computer inputs and outputs. These instructions direct the two-way communications link between the computer and the outside world.

Example 6.5. The following are instructions taken from approximately 264 machine instructions given in the computer manual for the IBM 7094 (1962). For each instruction we give the alphabetic code, octal operation code, and instruction timing in microseconds.

Instruction	Operation Code Alphabetic	Octal	Timing
Clear and add	CLA	0500	4
Multiply and round	MPR	—0200	4–10
Floating subtract	FSB	0302	4–24
Floating divide and halt	FDH	0240	6–18
Long left shift	LLS	0763	2–24
Accumulator left shift	ALS	0767	2–8
Store decrement	STD	0622	4
Store address	STA	0621	4
Transfer on overflow	TOV	0140	2
Transfer on plus	TPL	0120	2
Store index in address	SXA	0634	4
Load indicators	LDI	0441	4
Write end of file	WEF	0770	4

When the coded program is completed it is transcribed to computer input format, such as punched cards or tapes. Simple test cases should be run on the computer to test program integrity. This is a checkout that checks on the logical flow and the computational procedures in the program. Program checkout answers the question: Does the program do what it is supposed to do? Obtaining an answer is not necessarily easy. In Chapter 9 we suggest techniques of program checkout.

We now mention several features of computer programming in basic machine language. These are techniques, skills, and processes or subprocesses that are extremely useful in computer modeling and simulation when appropriately applied. We discuss these features in order to provide the model builder with a knowledge of programming concepts in machine language, but not with the objective of teaching computer programming. With an understanding of these concepts, the model builder can develop an appreciation for computer capabilities and for problems in computer programming.

First, we define *computer word* as an integral arrangement of a series of bits (binary digits). A computer word can be of fixed or variable length. For a given computer of fixed word length format the computer word consists of a specified (fixed) number of bits, such as 36 bits. In computers of variable word length the format can be varied to suit the programming needs.

The internal number system of the computer is binary, in which the digits are zeros or ones. The complete word or portions of it can be interpreted numerically or logically according to the program context.

For example, the 12 bits 001110010010 can be interpreted in several ways. Numerically it is 1622_8 (in octal) or 914 in decimal. This number can be used in an arithmetic operation, such as addition. Logically, we can use this number to compare with another number to make a simple decision, or we can use the number to address a memory location 1622_8. The interpretation given this number, either numerically or logically, depends on the program context in which the number appears.

In hardware a computer word may appear in core, in a band or sector of drum memory, in a segment of magnetic tape, or in a portion of memory disk file. Because each computer word has a unique address in computer memory it can be specifically referred to by its appropriate address.

The execution of basic *arithmetic computations* is one of the underlying features of the high-speed electronic computer. Computations on high-speed computers can be executed in the order of a few microseconds; for example, typical high-speed computers can easily perform one-quarter million simple additions per second. Therefore it can be extremely practical to use a computer to perform voluminous computations.

Computations on computers can be executed with extreme *precision.* In fixed point operation the necessary precision can be achieved by applying the appropriate scale factor. Floating point operations have precision commensurate with the mantissa of the floating point number. On some computers double precision arithmetic is possible, in which the precision of a multiplication product can be twice the size of the computer word. For example, in double precision, assuming a three-digit word for simplicity, the product of XXX and YYY is ZZZZZZ, which appears in two computer words. In single precision the product is ZZZ000; that is, we can get precision only to three significant digits.

Boolean logic, that is, zero or one representation, can be applied in computer modeling and simulation whenever parameters or variables can be represented by coded Boolean values. This makes it possible to include all possible combinations of a set of coded parameters. For example, suppose we use 3 bits for climate location parameters as follows:

First bit:	0—hot	1—cold
Second bit:	0—wet	1—dry
Third bit:	0—north	1—south

We would then interpret the following combinations as

001—hot, wet climate in the southern hemisphere.
011—hot, dry climate in the southern hemisphere.
110—cold, dry climate in the northern hemisphere.

Binary techniques can be applied whenever appropriate to achieve faster computation and logic speed; for example, the value of a binary number is doubled by executing one shift in the direction of most significance, or we can divide by 2 by shifting in the direction of least significance. This is similar to the principle of moving the decimal point when we multiply or divide by 10 in the decimal system. Another example is table lookup, in which we gain faster access to the table in computer memory if we address the table arguments in octal and map the tabular values in a range equal to powers of 2, such as 32, 64, or 128. We will explain more about table lookup later.

We can *transfer data blocks* from one storage area to another with relative ease. Thus data blocks can be transferred between core and magnetic tapes with great ease and efficiency. This feature can be applied whenever it is not possible to store all the data and the program in the central memory, such as core.

Computers can effectively perform *iterative processes.* This feature is especially applicable to subroutines that require iteration or looping, such as Newton's square root approximation, trigonometric function generators, linear programming, convergence series, and replication.

Computations of series or higher order polynomials can be efficiently calculated by using the *nesting technique.* Nesting technique is a rearrangement scheme of a factored polynomial. We illustrate the technique with three polynomials.

n-order polynomial:

$$y = \sum_0^n A_i x^i = A_0 + A_1 x + A_2 x^2 + \cdots + A_n x^n. \qquad (6.2)$$

Nesting:

$$y = ((\cdots((A_n)x + A_{n-1})x + A_{n-2})x + \cdots + A_1)x + A_0. \qquad (6.3)$$

n-order polynomial with even powers only:

$$y = \sum_0^n A_{2i} x^{2i} = A_0 + A_2 x^2 + A_4 x^4 + \cdots + A_{2n} x^{2n}. \qquad (6.4)$$

Nesting:

$$y = ((\cdots((A_{2n})x^2 + A_{2n-2})x^2 + A_{2n-4})x^2 + \cdots + A_2)x^2 + A_0. \qquad (6.5)$$

n-order polynomial with odd powers only:

$$y = A_0 + \sum_0^n A_{2i+1} x^{2i+1} = A_0 + A_1 x + A_3 x^3 + \cdots + A_{2n+1} x^{2n+1}. \qquad (6.6)$$

Nesting:

$$y = ((\cdots((A_{2n+1})x^2 + A_{2n-1})x^2 + A_{2n-3})x^2 + \cdots + A_1)x + A_0. \qquad (6.7)$$

In using the nesting technique we start with the innermost parenthesis and operate inside the parenthesis. We expand to the next outer parenthesis and repeat the operation until we have solved the polynomial.

Masking is a technique in which only select bits are read from a memory word or are written in memory. For example, suppose we have a 15-bit word, 101101101111011, in which we mask bits 6–10. We then have 000001011000000, in which all the bits other than 6–10 are replaced by zeros. By masking technique we are able to use only the part of the word that we want.

Tallying or counting in a computer can be done with great ease. We keep a tally merely by adding or subtracting some unit amount to or from a computer word or by using a register. By tallying we can keep inventory or keep score in a computer model up to the limits of the computer word size or register size.

We can use *index registers* to increment or decrement a counter which we set to range between n and k. When k is reached the program executes the next designated leg of the program. Index registers are applied in the systematic, sequential operations of matrices, to execute address changes, count, tally, count replications, etc.

All memory locations are conveniently *addressed* for accessibility in the computer program. The internal address system in the binary computer is in the octal number system. Binary and octal are closely related, and conversion from binary to octal and vice versa is very simple to perform and amenable to implementation in computer design. Computers are implemented with binary counters for internal counting operations, octal addressing of memory locations, octal readout for displays or output, and binary coding of computer instructions because of the convenient interchange of binary and octal.

Example 6.6. We illustrate the binary-octal relation by the following table.

Binary	**Octal**
000	0
001	1
010	2
011	3
100	4
101	5
110	6
111	7
1000	10

Consider the relationship $2 \times 4 = 8$. We can observe that the octal cycle corresponds to four binary cycles, which we have shown with braces. Consider the relationship $2^3 = 8$. If we look down each column separately from right to left in the binary number system, we can observe the repetitive patterns 01010101, 00110011, and 00001111, respectively. The three patterns correspond to one octal cycle and are repeated in the next cycle, which begins with 10^8.

Sorting is a procedure of regrouping any desired set of information from a large body of data in which the regrouping is executed according to a preplanned organizational format. Sorting can be executed internally in the computer or externally by the use of peripheral equipment. Internal sorting was difficult or impossible in earlier computers. However, present-day computers with large internal memories and external memory devices, such as magnetic tapes, are especially suited for sorting processes.

Computer words in registers can be shifted left or right any desired number of shifts. *Shifting* toward the most significant bit multiplies the number by 2 for each shift provided that there is no significance lost in overflow. Every time a shift operation is executed the extreme bit in the direction of the shift is dropped, and at the other extreme a zero is added. For example, if we shift 101100010111 one bit to the left we obtain 011000101110. If we shift it four bits to the right we obtain 000010110001.

A shift toward the least significant bit divides the number by 2 for each shift. Shifting can eliminate irrelevant information from a word very quickly. Shifting is useful whenever operating with powers of 2 or for Boolean logical operations.

Simple *logical decisions* can be easily made according to some preplanned logical design. We can examine the sign of a number at a logic branch to determine which logical route to proceed to. We can examine a number for zero or nonzero magnitude in order to branch logically. We can compare two numbers for relative magnitude in order to branch logically. For example, we can program the computer to make a simple logical decision at a test node, such as, if $X_1 \leq X_2$, branch left; otherwise, branch right.

Function generators can be conveniently programmed for computations. These generators can be programmed as entities, usually called subroutines, which are contained in memory and are called in for active operation in the program as needed. Examples of frequently used generators include those to generate random statistical variates or those to generate trigonometric functions.

One of the basic features of a high speed computer is its *storage* or memory. Any computer word can be stored indefinitely in permanent memory for subsequent use. That word remains in memory until another computer word is written in its place. Writing a word in memory location automatically erases the previous word. The process of reading a word from memory does not destroy the word in memory. In nonpermanent memory a computer word can be stored until another word is written in its place or until the memory device is inactivated, such as by turning the electricity off. Memory devices most frequently used include core, magnetic drum, magnetic tape, and magnetic disk. All are permanent memories, except core.

Filing information, such as resource data or data banks, can be structured and stored in computer memory so that the information can be readily available during the program run. The file structure can be organized by a technique comparable to any efficient external filing system, such as library catalogs or book of tables. Files are organized by sets and subsets. For example, we can have a vehicle file that can be subdivided into vehicle specifications data, fuel consumption data, auxiliary devices, etc.

A high-speed computer can be effectively used for *matrix operations,* such as matrix inversion, matrix multiplication, and so on. An $n \times m$ matrix can be stored in an array of memory corresponding to the element arrangements of the matrix. By the use of registers we can index any element in memory as required for the matrix operations.

Tables can be stored in computer memory for use of *table lookup* in the program. We can store all kinds of tables, such as probability tables or trigonometric functions. We can store one-dimensional tables easily. However, we can also store and use n-dimensional tables. We can arrange table arguments so that there is correspondence between the argument and the memory address. For example, suppose we store a sine table from 0 to 89 degrees in locations K through $K + 110_8$, in which $110_8 = 89$ in decimal. In order to find the sine for θ, we convert θ to octal θ_8. The value of the sine is then located in memory location $K + \theta_8$, where K is also in octal.

Another technique is to transform the table from the decimal arguments to a table in some integral power of 2, such as 32, 64, 128, etc. We show this method of storing tables in Chapter 9. We illustrate with tables of nonuniform probability distribution functions. This method is probably the most efficient way of applying table lookup in a computer program.

Whenever possible in computer programming the programmer should organize the program into *routines and subroutines.* Using routines and subroutines is an efficient method of programming. Routines and subroutines are intergral subdivisions of the program that perform a specific function or activity, such as generating a sine function. Routines and subroutines are stored in a specified section in memory and can be called into program operation as needed.

The distinction between routines and subroutines is that the latter are subsets of the former. Routines and subroutines are usually given identifiers, such as ASORT, COMSORT, UPDATE, or DYNUP, for purposes of easy management in the computer program and computer storage. The use of the identifier in the program will immediately call that unique routine or subroutine into active program operation.

There is extreme flexibility in the format of the computer *printout.* Most computer programs contain separate output routines or output processors which prepare the outputs for any desired printout format. Printouts can be in the form of tables with appropriate heading and dimensional units, graphs with appropriate identification of the axes, pictorials, narratives, and so on. The output printer can print α-numerics in addition to a wide selection of symbols, such as asterisks, punctuation marks, parentheses, dashes, and dollar signs.

The preceding discussion has been primarily machine language–oriented, and has given a brief overview of the capabilities and flexibilities of digital computers and their applications in modeling and simulation. For greater depth and detail on machine language programming, the reader is referred to the computer manuals for any given computer and the references listed in Bibliography Sections J and K. With knowledge of basic machine language, the programmer has a greater understanding and appreciation of the intricacies and subtleties of computers.

However, many languages have been developed to facilitate the programming task without requiring knowledge of the basic machine language of the computer. Machine languages are often complex and complicated, whereas programming languages are especially designed to eliminate these complexities from the programming task. For large computer systems, such as IBM 7094 or CDC 3600, a considerable amount of time is necessary for the programmer to learn coding in basic machine language. On the other hand, programming languages can be learned much faster than machine language.

One of the most widely known and used programming languages is FORTRAN [213, 215]. FORTRAN is an automatic coding system for most large data-processing systems. FORTRAN accepts a program written in FORTRAN language, called a source program, and produces a program in machine language, called an object program, ready to be run on the computer. The original FORTRAN language, developed in the mid-1950s, was designed to be carried out by the IBM 704 computer. Since then FORTRAN has been applied in several other computers. The present-day FORTRAN IV is considerably more flexible and useful than its predecessors.

FORTRAN language closely resembles the language of mathematics. The language is capable of expressing any problem of numerical computation. It deals with problems containing a large number of formulas and many variables. FORTRAN operations are designated as follows:

Exponentiation (**).
Multiplication (*).
Division (/).
Addition (+).
Subtraction (—).

Example 6.7. The following are examples of FORTRAN designations:

Mathematical expression	**FORTRAN**
X^2	$(X**2)$
XY	$(X*Y)$
$3X^2$	$(3*X**2)$
$a \div b$	(a/b)
$a + b$	$(a + b)$
$a - b$	$(a - b)$
$4(a + b)^2$	$(4*(a + b)**3)$

Several functions are available in FORTRAN, and the following is only a partial list of typical functions:

SINF—sine function.
COSF—cosine function.
TANF—tangent function.
LOGF—log function.
SQRTF—square root function.

Note that the final character is always an F, thus precluding the use of F as a final character in other applications.

For fixed point parameters and variables the first character must be I through N. If four or more characters are used for any variable, the last character cannot be an F. For floating point variables the first character must be a letter, but cannot be I through N. Thus this distinguishes between fixed point and floating point.

The following are examples of FORTRAN statements:
GO TO n—an unconditional jump.
IF(e)n_1 n_2—a conditional jump.
DOnI = n_1 n_2—next sequence of statements.
STOP—terminate program.

The following are examples of input/output statements in FORTRAN:

READ.
PUNCH n.
PRINT n.
WRITE.
WRITE OUTPUT TAPE t.

Example 6.8. We now illustrate examples of the mathematical formulation and the corresponding FORTRAN statement. Notice the resemblance between the mathematics and FORTRAN.

Mathematics	**FORTRAN Statement**
$\sum_{i=1}^{10} (a_i c_i)^2$	SUM1 = SUM1 + (A(I)*C(I))**2
$z_i = \sqrt{A_i x_i^2 - B_i y_i}$	Z(I) = SQRTF(A(I)*X(I)**2 − B(I)*Y(I))

Consider the quadratic equation

$$4x^2 + 2.3x - 11.6 = 0.$$

The algebraic representation for one of the roots of the equation is calculated by

$$\text{root} = \frac{-B + (B^2 - 4AC)^{1/2}}{2A},$$

where $A = 4$, $B = 2.3$, $C = -11.6$.

The complete FORTRAN program that describes this calculation is given below:

```
  A = 4
  B = 2.3
  C = −11.6
  ROOT = (−B + SQRTF(B**2. − 4.*A*C))/(2.*A)
PRINT 1, ROOT
STOP
```

The above source program is translated to the object program on the FORTRAN compiler; then the program is ready to be run on the computer.

Basically, a high-speed digital computer does the following:

1. Performs simple arithmetic operations.
2. Performs simple "yes-no" logical decisions.
3. Retains information.
4. Follows a sequenced program of operation.

Any model or simulation whose simplest elements can be expressed in terms of the above four basic items can be programmed for solution on a high-speed digital computer. These basic items or characteristics of operation make the computer one of the most versatile and useful devices available for solution of the most complicated and complex problems. For example, the following is a partial list of applications of high-speed digital computers:

Perform simple arithmetic operations.
Generate trigonometric functions.
Generate logarithms and exponentials.

Generate hyperbolic functions.
Perform algebraic operations.
Perform matrix operations.
Perform numerical integrations and differentiations.
Execute numerical solutions of differential equations.
Solve linear programming and dynamic programming problems.
Execute numerical transformations.
Operate on fixed or floating point numbers.
Compute maximum or minimum values of a function.
Perform vector operations.
Compute prime numbers.
Execute conversions from one number system to another.
Perform complementary arithmetic.
Execute conversions of measurement units.
Fit data to a regression equation.
Compute eigenvalues.
Generate uniform random numbers.
Generate nonuniform random numbers.
Compute statistics, such as mean, variance, and correlation coefficients.
Perform regression analysis and statistical tests, such as χ^2 test.
Trace through logic processes.
Generate a logic structure.
Make logical decisions.
Operate on sets.
Operate on logic statements.
Generate truth tables.
Compile and assemble information.
Operate on higher order computer languages.
Operate on metasystems.
Execute tallies, increment or decrement tallies.
Sort out hierarchical structures.
Dynamically allocate memory storage spaces.
Transfer information from one memory area to another.
Perform document information retrieval.
Loop iteratively, such as in series computations.
Execute table lookup.
Generate *n*-dimensional tables.
Store and retrieve information.
Search and sort files of information.
Manipulate lists of items.
Dynamically update information.

Print α-numeric outputs.
Print outputs in a variety of preselected formats.
Print outputs in graphic or pictorial arrangements.
Output information on line.
Control real time processes, such as chemical mixtures.
Answer programmed interrogations.
Execute multiprocessing on a time sharing basis.
Execute man-machine mode of operation.
Generate synthetic data.
Tie in with analog devices.

We close this section with a brief discussion of problems in computer programming. These are problems that must be faced often enough in computer modeling and simulation to warrant a brief discussion of each. These problems are not insurmountable, and they can be resolved with the proper approach and attitude.

The model builder is often faced with the decision of computer selection. As he looks about he will discover that there are many computers, and sometimes there are too many computers from which to select. For example, Burroughs, CDC, GE, Honeywell, IBM, RCA, and UNIVAC all produce large-scale computers that are somewhat comparable in size. In trying to weigh the advantages and disadvantages of each computer, the problem usually reduces to one of economics. Which computer system will provide the most for the lowest cost? We have given criteria for computer selection earlier. We hope that the model builder can apply these criteria to help with the selection of the computer.

There are many programming systems, and in addition, new ones are being added rather frequently. Various manufacturers and software industries have developed a large number of programming systems. Each system is usually professed to be the best, and often a given system has been an improvement over its predecessors. The computer programming discipline seems to be continually in a process of self-improvement by introducing new programming systems. Even though self-improvement is commendable, too frequent changes in systems can cause problems for programmers.

Coding can also be a problem. In programming, the same thing may often be done in many different ways, so that there is variation between one programmer and another in the style of programming. There is also the decision whether to code the program in basic machine language, which generally takes longer to program, or to use a higher order synthetic language, such as FORTRAN. The decision must be made in light of the purposes of the particular computer program being written.

Program checkout or "debugging" can often be the greatest single source of frustrations in computer programming. This is due to the unpredictability of the nature of the problem. At the root of this problem are two factors: (a) computers explicitly do what they are told, and (b) humans make mistakes, and they will continue to make mistakes. This situation is further complicated because computers are not self-corrective and display no judgment of the correctness or incorrectness of the program, unless preprogrammed diagnostics are used. There are programming checkout techniques that can be applied in debugging. Some are suggested in later chapters.

Computer programming can consume an inordinate amount of time. This problem is aggravated by the unpredictability of the length of time needed to program a given problem. Studies have been made of the number of instructions a programmer can code per day. The findings generally show that there is wide variability, and the variations are due to many factors arising from the given problem and within the programmer himself.

When computer programming consumes excessive time, then it is costly. The costs accrue as the programming task extends beyond the budgeted amount. In turn this may cause delays, which can be costly in themselves. In addition to programming costs, the charges of the computer often place real constraints on what can be done with computer modeling and simulation.

There is a need for time/cost budgeting of program tasks. Computer programming is an integral task in itself, and it should be a budgeted task just like any other task, with clear understanding among all principals concerned. How much time? How much cost? What are the consequences of failure to meet the time/cost budget? What penalties are attached? These should be very clearly understood beforehand.

Finally, there is a need for more simplification and standardization in computer programming. The industries and the programming discipline have been characterized by diversity rather than by any attempt at standardization and simplification. It will be a challenge to the industries and the discipline to achieve more standardization and simplification, and it will be a sign of maturity on their part when they move toward these goals.

SIMULATION LANGUAGES

As digital computers have increased in complexity, a wide spectrum of interpretive and synthetic programming languages, such as FORTRAN, COBOL, and ALGOL, have been developed to simplify the programming task. Likewise, as computer modeling and simulation has developed and received more widespread attention and application, simulation languages, such as GPSS, SIMSCRIPT, and SIMPAC, have been developed to provide the user with tools of simulation. These tools are designed for the purpose of eliminating much of the tedium involved and to simplify the procedures in preparing simulations for computer implementation. Any simulation language that does achieve that objective is well worth consideration in a simulation project.

Various simulation languages are operational at the present time. Each language has certain characteristics and applications, and each language can be extremely useful when applied properly. We briefly describe a few simulation languages below in order to introduce some languages available to the user. The reader is referred to the bibliography (Section M) to obtain references giving more comprehensive coverage on specific languages.

GPSS [244, 247]

GPSS (General Purpose System Simulator) was developed by Gordon at IBM for use on the IBM 7090 computer. GPSS is a program that employs a language designed for describing simulation models of a system. The user constructs a logical model of the system using a block diagram consisting of specific block types, in which each block type represents some basic system action.

The program allows the user to do the following:

1. Study the logical structure of the system.
2. Follow the flow of traffic through the system.
3. Measure the effects of blocking caused by the need to time-share parts of the system or by limitations on capacity of parts of the system.

GPSS elements are *blocks, transactions,* and *equipment*. Specific block types have a name, a characteristic symbol, and a block number ranging from 1 to 2047. Each block has a designated block time that indicates the number of time units required for action represented by the block. The block time may vary over a range of values in a random or nonrandom manner. Transactions are basic units that move through the system. *Facilities* are items of equipment that can handle one transaction at a time. *Stores* are items of equipment that can handle many transactions simultaneously.

The following are examples of specific block types in GPSS:

Originate block creates transactions and enters them into the simulation.

Advance block represents any action requiring time but not involving equipment.

Hold block allows a transaction that enters the block to engage the facility for as long as the transaction remains in the block.

Store block allows a transaction to occupy space in the store associated with the block for as long as the transaction is in the block.

Terminate block removes transactions from the system the instant they enter the block.

Branch block is similar to the advance block, but allows up to 127 exits from the block.

Seize block allows a transaction to engage the facility upon entering the block.

Release block removes the transaction from the facility.

Enter block allows a transaction to take up space in the store.

Leave block gives back space in the store.

Queue block maintains any statistics about queues.

Mark block makes a note of the current clock time on each transaction that enters the block.

Tabulate block calculates clock time upon arrival at this block less mark time.

Split block allows one transaction to be created by another.

Match block synchronizes pairs of transactions created at the split block.

Gate block tests the status of a piece of equipment.

The following GPSS routines are available through IBM branch offices:

"General Purpose Systems Simulator," File No. 7090-CS-05X.
"General Purpose Systems Simulator II," File No. 7090-CS-13X.

SIMSCRIPT [242, 249, 254, 255, 256]

SIMSCRIPT was developed by Markowitz at Rand Corporation for use originally on the IBM 7090 computer. It has also been applied on other computers, such as CDC and UNIVAC computers. SIMSCRIPT is a useful and versatile tool for solving complex problems with simulation models.

SIMSCRIPT is based upon the notion that every model system is composed of elements with numerical values that are subject to periodic change. The state of a system can be described in terms of *entities, attributes,* and *sets,* in which events modify the status of the simulated system at various points in simulated time. *Entities* are objects of which the system is composed. Entities may be classified as temporary or permanent during the simulation. *Attributes* are properties associated with entities or items that describe entities. *Sets* are groups of entities. *Status* is the numerical description of the simulated system. *Events* are series of statements grouped together which modify the status of the simulated system at various points in simulated time.

Example 6.9. Any unit identified independently in a simulation is an *entity,* for example, an aircraft, a ship, a depositor, a warehouse. *Attributes* of an aircraft may include cargo handling, passenger types, fixed wing, or rotary wing. Attributes of a ship may include the tonnage, operating cost per nautical mile, fuel used, etc. Attributes of a depositor may include income bracket, age group, and marital status. Attributes of a warehouse may include commodity types, ownership, and size.

Aircraft and ships may be members of a *set* of transportation modes. Depositors and borrowers may be members of a set of bank customers. Warehouses, stores, and office buildings may be members of a set of origin and destination locations.

Events may be exogenous (from outside the simulation system) or endogenous (from within the simulation system). The different kinds of events are enumerated in an events list. A separate event subroutine is written for each different kind of event.

Example 6.10. The following are examples of *exogenous events* in a simulation of ship movements:

Low tide begins.
High tide ends.
Current shifts.
Visibility drops to zero.

The following are examples of *endogenous events:*

Ship *A* leaves port.
Ship *A* at sea.
Ship *A* enters port.
Ship *A* docks.

Normally a SIMSCRIPT simulation is accomplished as follows:

1. Elements of the simulated system are described and entered by definition cards.
2. Initial conditions assigning values to permanent entities and attributes are entered.
3. Input data providing sets of values for temporary entities and attributes are entered.

4. Subroutines are written for each event.

5. Each kind of event is entered in the event list, in which the time an endogenous event is to occur is contained in the event notice. The time an exogenous event is to occur is contained on an event card.

SIMSCRIPT instructions are grouped as follows:

1. Entity operations, such as CREATE, DESTROY, FILE, and REMOVE, which operate upon temporary entities, event notices, or variables.
2. Arithmetic and control commands, such as LET, STORE, and FOR, which perform arithmetic and control operations on variables, permanent entities, or sets.
3. Decision commands, such as IF, GO TO, and FIND.
4. Input/output commands, such as SAVE, READ, WRITE, and FORMAT.
5. Special commands, such as POST, ADD, STOP, and COMPUTE. For example, COMPUTE allows the computation of sums, means, standard deviation, and other statistical quantities.

The following SIMSCRIPT routines are available through IBM branch offices and CDC sales offices, respectively:

"SIMSCRIPT—A Simulation Programming Language," File No. 7090-3031RSSIMS.

"3600 Computer System SIMSCRIPT—General Information Manual," CDC Publication No. 60133000.

SIMPAC [253]

SIMPAC was developed by Lackner at System Development Corporation for use on the IBM 7090 computer. SIMPAC contains four basic type elements: transactions, queues, resources, and reference files. *Transactions* are temporary objects that are created, moved, modified, and destroyed by performance of activities. Transactions possess attributes called variables. *Queues* are ordered sets of transactions. *Resources* are associated with the performance of individual activities. *Reference files* provide a system-wide medium to store and exchange variables information.

Other Languages

CSL (Control and Simulation Language) was developed by Buxton and Laski in the United Kingdom. CSL is a machine-based language based on FORTRAN notation and is in use on both IBM and Honeywell computers. In CSL the model system is described in terms of classes of entities, sets of entities, and arrays of numbers (data).

ESP (Elliott Simulator Package) was developed by Williams, and SIMON was developed by Hill. Both ESP and SIMON are based on ALGOL language and were developed for the Elliott computers. Other simulation languages include GSP, developed by Tocher; MONTECODE, developed by Buxton and Head; SIMULA, developed by Dahl and Nygard; DYNAMO, developed by Pugh; and OPS, developed by Greenberger, the last two at Massachusetts Institute of Technology. ESP, GSP, SIMON, MONTECODE, and SIMULA were all developed in Europe.

MODEL VALIDATION

Model validation is the most critical problem in computer modeling and simulation. Without a valid model we have nothing, and it is pointless to engage in any other tasks in computer modeling and simulation or even to discuss model outputs. Model validation is a problem that cannot be overlooked. Testing and demonstrating model validity itself can be a formidable task. In this section we will discuss some features and general techniques of model validation, and in the remaining chapters we will apply these techniques.

What is a valid model? A valid model measures what it is supposed to measure. A valid model mathematically and logically approximates the functional system, operation, concept, or phenomenon that we are modeling. Decision points in the model simulate real-world decision points, and the mathematics approximates real-world functions. Probability features in the model simulate chance elements in real-world functions. Given proper inputs, a valid model produces results that are meaningful when properly interpreted.

Model validation is in *two* parts: validation of model concept and validation of model implementation. We discuss each part below.

The *conceptual model* is the framework or structure from which we later implement the model. The conceptual model consists of the rationale and an implicit or abstract version of the model. Chronologically, we determine the model concept before we actually design and implement an explicit model that can be exercised on a computer to produce results.

We look at the real world and we describe a conceptual model of the real-world situation. Thus our first validity check is in this process of transformation from real-world phenomena to a conceptual model. In this validity check we ask the question: Are we using the appropriate transformation? When we have answered affirmatively and we have determined the conceptual model, we ask another question: Is the conceptual model a valid representation of the real world?

The above questions must be examined with objectivity. However, the task of conceptual model validation is often at best a subjective, opinionated task. These questions are often answered on the basis of human judgment. We discuss some techniques of validating the conceptual model in Part Four.

Given a valid conceptual model, one in which we can answer the above questions in the affirmative, we then design and implement an explicit model. We validate this process of transformation from conceptual model to a tangible, operational model in several steps. First, we validate the logical flow chart. Second, we validate the program flow chart. Third, we validate the computer program.

Validation of model implementation consists primarily of validating the model at specific milestones of model development by comparison with the model of a previous phase. We validate the logical flow chart by comparing it with the conceptual model. We validate the program flow chart by comparison with the logical flow chart. We validate the computer program by comparison with the program flow chart.

After validating the computer program against the program flow chart, we find that the use of sample problems to validate the computer simulation model is important and useful. We can prepare sample calculations independently of the model implementation and then use these calculations to exercise the model. Use of sample problems is one of the best procedures to demonstrate model validity. Whenever model outputs compare with sample problem outputs for the same inputs, we can conclude that the model is valid for problems of the same type as the sample problem.

Sample problems can be generated by using simple, artificial inputs which are not necessarily representative of real-world data. These inputs are fairly easy to design, as the actual values are selected arbitrarily. This method is useful and is reasonable to determine model validation in most cases. However, sometimes we may feel that this method does not adequately exercise our specific model.

Another method is to generate sample problems by using *real-world* data inputs to exercise the model. This method is especially suitable if we have the real-world outcomes associated with the real-world inputs, and it is unquestionably the best method of all. Although more difficult than the former, using real-world data can bring into focus all the problems associated with obtaining real-world inputs. This method brings the model builder into close contact with the real world and brings to light real-world problems.

PROBLEMS

6.1 Draw a logical flow chart to solve the equation.

$$y = 2x^2 + 3x - 5$$

for values of X ranging from 0 through 10 in increments of $\Delta X = 2$.

6.2 Select and discuss one of the criteria for computer selection.

6.3 A given model can be programmed for either the SLIK or CRAM computers, in which the modeling requirements are summarized below:

	SLIK	CRAM	
Preanalysis	300	300	man-hours
Programming	700	250	man-hours
Computer time per run	5	25	minutes
Postanalysis per run	5	8	man-hours

One hour of computation on the SLIK is equivalent in cost to 40 man-hours, and one hour on the CRAM is equivalent in cost to 18 man-hours. Illustrate by graph the comparative costs between the SLIK and the CRAM computers. Show man-hours versus computer runs. Assume linearity of costs.

6.4 In 6.3, when is it more economical to use the SLIK computer? When is it more economical to use the CRAM computer?

6.5 Select any currently manufactured computer and describe its characteristics, such as control unit, memory, input/output, arithmetic unit, instructions, timing, and size.

6.6 Obtain a FORTRAN manual and write a FORTRAN program to solve the equation in 6.1.

6.7 Write a brief memo addressed to a client, recommending the selection of the AUTOTRON 500 (a hypothetical computer) to use for a given model. Substantiate your recommendation with reasons for the selection.

6.8 Add 1011 and 0110 binary by application of the binary addition rule. Check by binary subtraction.

6.9 Select a model described in Chapter 2 and suggest some possible validation procedures.

6.10 Write a short essay on your assessment of the problem of validation. How important is it? What are some alternative solutions? How would you determine model validity?

6.11 Obtain a manual for a simulation language, such as SIMSCRIPT or GPSS. Study the manual carefully. Learn the content and decide upon application of the language. Prepare a critique of the simulation language.

6.12 Prepare a detail flow chart to generate sin X, where

$$\sin X = X - \frac{X^3}{3!} + \frac{X^5}{5!} - \frac{X^7}{7!} + \cdots + \qquad |X| < \infty$$

and X is given in radians. Be sure to determine the appropriate sign for the quadrant that contains X.

6.13 Prepare a detail flow chart to sort incoming messages to a communications central. Sort by addressor and addressee when there is a specified maximum number of each.

6.14 Prepare a flow chart to calculate

$$y = \int_0^1 x\,dx$$

by Monte Carlo (See Chapter 3).

6.15 Prepare a flow chart to calculate

$$y = 3 \sin x, \qquad 0 \le x \le \frac{\pi}{2},$$

$$y = 0, \qquad x > \frac{\pi}{2}.$$

(Do not show any detail for the computation of sin X.)

6.16 Search through current literature on programming languages and identify some present-day languages.

6.17 Select a current programming language. Describe it briefly and give applications.

6.18 Compare two current programming languages. Give advantages and disadvantages of each.

6.19 Select a model explained in Chapter 2. Determine whether a current simulation language could have been applied.

6.20 Search through current technical literature for an article or document on a simulation language. Review the salient points made about the simulation language.

6.21 What present-day computers have "time-sharing" capability?

6.22 What are the advantages of "time-sharing" computers?

6.23 Select two currently manufactured computers. Compare the operational specifications of each.

6.24 Search through computer magazines or manufacturer's catalogs for currently manufactured data plotters. Select an example and review its features. What are the on-line and off-line capabilities? What is the plotting resolution? What symbols are available? What are the input/output requirements?

6.25 Prepare a chart that lists functional features for several present-day computers. (Suggestion: make the chart similar to Example 6.3.)

PART FOUR

Model Construction

7

MODEL CONSTRUCTION, INTRODUCTORY

Whether we are simulating a system, a subsystem, or an operation, the following remarks and comments are applicable. We are generally referring to systems, but bear in mind that we are making reference to subsystems or operations as well.

Computer modeling and simulation is a useful technique for the analysis and evaluation of complex systems characterized by complicated probabilities. These probabilities may be associated with the following:

1. *System reliability,* such as the probability that a system can operate without failure for a specified period of time.
2. *System effectiveness,* such as the probability that a system performs at a certain level of effectiveness.
3. *Event occurrence,* such as the probability that a given system event will occur.
4. *Functional operation time,* such as the probability that the operation time of a given system function will not exceed a certain time duration.
5. *Measurement error,* such as the probability that a given error will not exceed a certain value.

Whenever the probabilistic context of the system demands a solution not easily obtainable by standard analytic or numerical methods, we can bypass the functional equations completely and apply the Monte Carlo technique to solve the complex system. Monte Carlo refers to a type of calculation of a straightforward substitution in problems involving stochastic processes. A process is stochastic if it includes random variables whose values depend on a parameter, such as time.

Monte Carlo technique is frequently applied in computer modeling and simulation. However, most models generally are a combination of deterministic computations and Monte Carlo technique. Monte Carlo is useful to (a) evaluate definite integrals, (b) solve integrodifferential equations, (c) solve systems of linear equations, (d) analyze certain very complex systems, such as business or military systems.

The Monte Carlo approach in simulation consists of playing a game of chance in such a way that the random features of the process are exactly imitated step by step. In a large simulation it is more efficient to program the process for digital computer calculation than to attempt a solution by another method.

In modeling a system the deterministic and nondeterministic (stochastic) features of the system are determined from system information. Whenever system data, such as reliability or effectiveness data, are available, empirical functions describing these system processes are derived by employing standard mathematical curve-fitting techniques. Whenever system data are not available, hypotheses about the system are made, reasonable assumptions are adopted, and theoretical, a priori functions are derived. As concrete information and data become available, the mathematical functions can be readapted to assimilate the new knowledge.

Derivation of the mathematical functions is a formidable and significant task in modeling procedures, and the validity of the model representation is dependent on the validity of the mathematical functions derived.

A computer simulation model can be constructed and applied during any phase of system design or predesign conceptualization. When to construct a model depends upon the desired answers about the system.

1. The model can be constructed *before* the system is designed in order to determine parameter sensitivity and to optimize or evaluate the system design.

2. The model can be constructed *during* the system design phase in order to test and experiment with system design concepts.

3. The model can be constructed *after* a system has been designed and built in order to supplement system test results and to evaluate over-all system effectiveness.

A properly constructed model is an extremely flexible and useful device. Model inputs can be systematically and easily changed to test any desired combinations of system parameters and input variables. Model outputs are useful for answering specific questions about the system. Outputs are useful for system design optimization and system evaluation and to provide a comprehensive picture of the system and system performance.

Poor design of a system is uneconomical, as it is time-consuming and costly to diagnose system weaknesses. Corrective action on an existing system is expensive and often impractical and infeasible. Trial-and-error method of system design, although frequently applied, is inefficient for the solution of system problems. Field testing of a large system is expensive and inconclusive. Certain field testing results are never feasible to attain. Therefore computer modeling and simulation is often the only practical approach possible to a systems or operations analysis problem.

What level of system resolution must be represented in the model? How detailed must the model be to give a valid representation of the system? The answers depend on the resolution necessary to achieve the expected results of the simulation. The extent of resolution and amount of detail selected depend on the manpower and financial resources available to solve the problem, the accessibility of information and the data on the system and environment, and the time frame within which the problem solution is required. The level of system resolution and detail chosen must be rationalized.

For certain modeling and simulation problems it is often advantageous to approach the ultimate solution iteratively by constructing more than one generation of computer models. In the iterative approach, an initial model (or first-generation model), which is usually simple and straightforward, is designed and implemented and then applied to the problem. With the knowledge and experience gained from the first-generation model, a second-generation model is designed and implemented. This second-generation model is usually more sophisticated and more complete in coverage than the first-generation model. The second model can be a revision of the first, or it may be an entirely new model with a different approach to the problem.

We apply the second-generation model to the problem and, if necessary, we decide whether to follow up with a third-generation model. We continue this iterative process until we have a model that we consider the most adequate for the solution of the problem. Normally the model generation is designated by Roman numerals, such as FAR I and FAR II for the first- and second-generation FAR models, respectively. This convention is applied frequently.

The iterative approach has many applications and advantages. This approach can be applied whenever resources are limited, and approximate or gross results are acceptable in the problem context. The same approach can be applied as a training device in order to develop a background of knowledge and better understanding of the problem before building the second- or third-generation models. The iterative approach can be applied whenever we lack sufficient information to design and implement a sophisticated model or a complete model at first. Very often in research problems we lack the necessary information to construct a sophisticated model during the initial phases of research. Yet a simple first-generation model can be useful in the research. Frequently, once a model has been completed, it may turn out to be unsatisfactory and followup with second- or third-generation models will be imperative.

In model building we should always consider whether the situation calls for an iterative approach. Whenever such an approach is appropriate and necessary, we should state the objective explicitly and plan and organize the research effort accordingly.

There is a general approach to all systems and operations problems that are amenable to solution by computer modeling and simulation. Even though simulations differ and alternative approaches in problem solution are possible, there are common features among the procedures and tasks in problem solution by computer simulation. These common features form the basis for our discussion in the chapters that follow.

In Chapter 2 we discussed some applications of computer modeling and simulation. In Part Three we reviewed some methods, techniques, and tools applicable to modeling and simulation. In Chapters 8–10 we will apply some of the materials from Part Three and will describe the procedures and tasks in model construction. We have grouped the tasks into three major phases: (a) conceptualization, (b) implementation, and (c) results. We describe the tasks and procedures in each phase in Chapters 8, 9, and 10, respectively. The tasks usually follow in the sequence given. However, we have avoided numbering them in sequence because variations in the given order are possible.

8

MODEL CONCEPTUALIZATION

During the first phase of model construction—conceptualization—we define the conceptual model. Phase 1 is the "thinking and planning" phase, or, more exactly, we *reflect, react,* and *decide*. That is, we reflect on the problem and all of its aspects and implications. Then from our thinking we discuss procedures for problem solution. Discussion may lead us to reflect some more on the problem and stimulate more discussion. Finally, we decide on the conceptual model, which we will implement in Phase 2.

Phase 1 tasks represent about 20% of the total effort in model construction. In this phase we define and analyze the problem. We gather and evaluate information and data. We make assumptions and hypotheses. We establish a model rationale. We determine and define parameters, variables, and effectiveness measures. We define implicitly the approximation procedures to simulate the real world. We develop and describe the conceptual model in abstract terms and concepts.

Before proceeding to the next phase we should check the concept validity and at the conclusion of Phase 1 write a concept paper or document that describes the conceptual model. We now describe the procedures and tasks of model conceptualization.

DEFINE THE PROBLEM

Our first task in model construction is to define the problem. We define and state the problem in a comprehensive statement in two parts, which (a) formulate the problem definitively and (b) indicate a suggested methodology and scheduling for problem solution.

Initially, a problem or problem area must be recognized to exist, and we must acknowledge a need for the problem solution. Initial problem formulation is usually broad and vague, and we may have to study the problem carefully to clarify it. But as we understand and define the problem better, a more definitive statement, which defines the problem precisely, can be expressed.

Once a problem is recognized it raises various questions for us to answer. These are questions dealing with methodology, resources, problem breakdown into subelements, priorities, and the solution itself. We expect that the answers will ultimately lead to a solution of the problem. However, sometimes the answers in one problem only raise other questions, indicating follow-on problems. Attacking one problem often creates a host of new problems to solve. This development of new problems is not unusual in research activities.

The problem statement must provide some insight into the scope of the problem. The scope indicates the magnitude and delimitations, which give us an idea of the size of the problem we seek to solve, and its boundaries.

If there are logical subdivisions of the problem, such as functional subdivisions, we can further refine the problem statement by subproblem breakdown. In turn, these subdivisions can be subdivided into "lower level" breakdown; e.g. subproblem *A* consists of sub-subproblems *x,y,z*. The number of levels of breakdown depends on the complexity of the problem and the requirements of a comprehensive problem statement.

A definitive problem statement should indicate the following features about the problem:

1. Recognition of problem existence.
2. Questions to be answered.
3. Scope of the problem.
4. Subproblem breakdown.

We expect that the ultimate statement will accurately represent the problem. A proper solution of the problem is difficult or impossible unless it is properly understood and stated. It is our responsibility to be sure we understand the problem before attempting its solution.

The second part of the comprehensive problem statement indicates the expected methodology and scheduling for problem solution. Methodology deals with principles of procedure, or the manner in which we will solve the problem. A statement on methodology and scheduling should include the following:

1. Priorities of subproblem solution.
2. Suggested or alternative methods of solution.
3. Estimated manpower requirements, computer requirements, and work schedule.

The definitive statement and methodology provide a comprehensive statement that indicates what the problem is and how we intend to solve it. Only at this point in understanding the problem can we intelligently proceed toward a solution. However, we must always be willing to re-examine our statement during the process of problem solution in order to determine whether we are still moving in the right direction.

Example 8.1. The following excerpt is an example taken from a problem statement on intersection delay by Kell [305].

"One task frequently faced by traffic engineers is the evaluation of intersection performance. Is a particular intersection operating as efficiently as possible? Is the form of control adequate, or should a more restrictive form of control be installed? What benefits could be derived by changing the type of control? In the contemplation of these and similar questions, intersection delay comes to mind as the 'figure of merit' used to evaluate performance.

"Total delay experienced by all vehicles at the intersection would be the most desirable datum, but this is almost impossible to obtain through field studies. Usually a photographic study or some similar technique is required whereby individual vehicles can be traced through the intersection from a point in the approach before being influenced by the intersection to a point beyond the exit where the influence has dissipated. Collection of such data is usually quite difficult and the analysis of the limited information obtained is extremely tedious and time consuming.

". . . The development of high speed computers has opened a new technique for evaluating intersection performance. This technique is traffic simulation. Almost any traffic situation is capable of simulation and, as techniques improve, can be rapidly programmed. Individual variables and/or controls can be changed and their effects analyzed. Peak traffic flows can be simulated for hundreds of hours under precise conditions to provide data concerning a specific problem instead of the field study method where only one or two hours of data per day can be collected under controlled conditions.

"Progress in simulation has been slow to date due primarily to the lack of knowledge concerning driver behavior. Basic mathematical distributions of commonplace driver behavior, such as gap acceptance (and rejection) and amber signal response, are not available in a sufficiently detailed form to be included directly in the simulation model. These obstacles are being overcome as they arise by field studies covering each specific item. As the store of driver behavior data increases, programming becomes simpler and future simulation 'models' can be developed more rapidly."

ANALYZE THE PROBLEM

Throughout the conceptualization phase of model construction we analyze the problem rigorously. The importance of thorough analysis in this phase cannot be overemphasized because an adequate analysis performed now does much to eliminate difficulties later. It is better to "overanalyze" than to analyze the problem insufficiently.

During the conceptualization phase most modeling tasks are analysis-oriented. Besides Phase 1 analysis, we can do preliminary analysis for the implementation and results phases. Actually some kind of analysis must be performed in all phases of model construction. The analysis task is one continuous task from start to finish of the modeling project.

Normally we perform the following analysis tasks during Phase 1:

1. Select and define system parameters and variables.
2. Determine and define measures of effectiveness.
3. Select the type of approximations to apply in the model.
4. Perform preanalysis of the implementation phase by determining the following: (a) mathematical equations to derive, (b) model checkout methods, (c) selection of computer system and programming system, (d) program specifications, and (e) program checkout methods.
5. Perform preanalysis of the results phase by giving attention to the following: (a) experimental design, (b) data reduction and analysis techniques to apply to the computer results, (c) methods of illustration of expected model outcomes, and (d) response surface equations to derive, or the response surface to illustrate.

We will discuss each of the above analysis tasks more thoroughly throughout the remaining chapters.

DETERMINE INFORMATION AND DATA REQUIREMENTS

Once we understand the problem, we determine the information and data requirements for problem solution. Information and data provide us with the necessary qualitative and quantitative materials for problem solution. From the information and data we can derive some insights for problem solution, and we may learn of new techniques to apply to the problem. In determining the information and data requirements we ask ourselves the following questions:

1. What information and data will be necessary?
2. Where will the information and data be obtained?
3. How will the information and data be handled?

With the appropriate answers we proceed to collect the information and data. However, when we find that no information or data are available, we must examine and determine methods of information and data substitutes, and we must examine alternative approaches. This may require laboratory or field experimentation or the generation of artificial data on a mathematical model.

COLLECT INFORMATION AND DATA

Collection of information and data involves the task of physical acquisition and evaluation of the information and data. The acquisition of information and data may include any of the following subtasks:

Initiating literature searches.
Compiling bibliographies.
Gathering source materials.
Gathering documents and reports.
Generating artificial data.
Collecting data by experimentation.
Consulting with specialists and experts.

Example 8.2. In each discipline there is a body of information, literature, and data, as well as experts and specialists in that particular field. Initial explorations into any area of specialization consist of obtaining information, literature, and data on the subject and finding out who the specialists and experts are and their areas of expertise. Many government agencies, from the local through the national level, can provide useful information and data. Each agency has publications that can usually be obtained, free or at a nominal fee. Federal government publications can be obtained through the U.S. Government Printing Office, Washington, D.C. Many nonprofit institutions, colleges, and universities, foundations, private consulting firms, private industries, and societies can also provide useful information and data for a particular field.

When large quantities of information and data are acquired, a systematic filing system should be used. This calls for information and data repositories, such as filing cabinets and loose-leaf notebooks. Proper filing permits easy access whenever the data or information are needed.

The information should be evaluated for its relevance to the problem solution. Usually only a fraction of the information gathered is relevant, and so we should extract the relevant information and eliminate unnecessary information and data. This is a selective process which we continually apply to new information.

The raw data are not necessarily in the required format to apply to the problem solution. Often intermediate manipulation or analysis of the data will be required, because the raw data may be ungrouped and require grouping. Where it is feasible, we should use the computer to perform these intermediate data reduction and analysis tasks. The feasibility of using the computer depends on the time schedule, volume of data, and resources available.

As soon as we recognize and understand the basic problem, we should start to collect information and data. We make several suggestion below regarding information and data collection.

1. We should *immediately* initiate bibliographic and literature searches. The best sources are your own library or nearest technical library as your "home base," from which you may expand. However, one of the single best sources for published information and data is the Defense Documentation Center (formerly known as ASTIA) with headquarters at Alexandria, Va., and field offices throughout the United States. Defense Documentation Center is part of the U.S. Department of Defense. Their facilities are primarily for military use. However, there is limited accessibility for nonmilitary purposes also. Defense Documentation Center acquires Department of Defense classified and unclassified technical documents from the originators and organizes and stores them for retrieval. The documents are announced regularly in the "Technical Abstract Bulletin." Defense Documentation Center retrieves them on request and supplies them free to its contractors and grantees. Members of the general public requiring unclassified documents from Defense Documentation Center listings may contact the Office of Technical Services, U.S. Department of Commerce, Washington, D.C. Unclassified documents with unrestricted distribution can be obtained on a charge per document basis. Whenever we request a literature search, we should be as specific in our request as possible. A specific request eliminates extraneous information. For example, a request for a bibliography on "jet aircraft reliability since 1960" gives us a more select bibliography than a request for "aircraft reliability." We should not use the latter request if we need only the former.

2. As soon as we know that we need a specific document or group of documents, we should proceed to acquire them. The best sources for acquisition are the same as mentioned above.

3. In addition, we need to collect data relevant to the problem. Whenever the data are available, we should try to obtain them directly from the source. This can be done by direct contact with the source or from documents published by the source. Any requests to the originator for data should be specific as to kind, type, quantity, and preferred format. Whenever data are not available, we should investigate appropriate

methods for data substitutes or data generation. Data may be generated synthetically by laboratory simulation or experiment. Synthetic data can be generated from a mathematical model, which may require the use of an electronic computer. The appropriate method to use depends on the urgency and resources available. Of course, sometimes it is not feasible to generate any synthetic data.

Example 8.3. Most models require a set of inputs that are external to the models as well as some inputs that have been generated by a previous model in the sequence of operation. For a given set of input requirements the sources of the actual parameter values to use in the model may come from the following:

1. Real-world situations, in which a common procedure is to develop scenarios of situations in order to provide the necessary inputs.
2. Hypothetical situations, which may or may not have any real-world basis.
3. Combinations of the above two.

Scenarios are frequently applied in computerized war games and business games, in which the scenarios trace a series of events relevant to the system being exercised in the model. Scenarios can be used to evaluate a given system under certain expected real-life situations. The use of scenarios has the advantage of taking real-life situations and providing actual insights into how the system will respond in actual situations. Ideally, scenarios are the best possible approach to develop inputs.

However, scenarios have disadvantages. Adequate scenarios take long to develop, and the results depend on how good the scenarios are. Unfortunately, the length of time required to develop scenarios does not necessarily ensure that a good scenario results. Often it is necessary to develop a separate transformation model simply to transform scenarios into proper model inputs. Any given scenario is applicable to a particular situation, but transfer to other situations may be difficult or impossible.

In developing hypothetical inputs there are no real-world constraints or problems associated with gathering real-world data. Thus hypothetical situations can be faster and easier to develop than real-world inputs. However, hypothetical situations are often not applicable to any real-world situation, as hypothetical situations can be so esoteric that the results may be questionable.

A combination of using real-world data along with hypothetical data can be used whenever there are some real-world inputs that are inaccessible. Because these inputs combine "fact and fancy" for inputs the results must be interpreted on that basis.

4. Collecting information can be a formidable task. However, this is only a part of the problem. Once we have collected the information we must evaluate it for relevance to the problem solution. This means making decisions as to whether a given body of information is relevant or germane to the problem. Evaluating information is usually a continuous task throughout the development of the model. We evaluate

the information on the basis of our knowledge of the problem, experience, and judgment.

5. We must also evaluate the data collected for relevance to the problem solution. This means making decisions regarding each body of data collected or generated. Usually we do not generate synthetic data unless we feel it is relevant to the problem to do so. However, when we look at and analyzc generated data, we may change our mind about its relevance.

Unfortunately, all the necessary information and data are not always available or accessible when needed. We should gather and evaluate all the information and data that we can within the problem framework. Invariably, however, we arrive at problem areas or subareas where there are voids of information and data.

ADOPT HYPOTHESES AND MAKE ASSUMPTIONS

Our next task is started upon consideration of the following factors:

1. Extent of information and data available for the problem solution.
2. Relevance of the information and data to the problem.
3. Areas lacking sufficient information and data.
4. Time frame and resources available for problem solution.
5. Expected results of the model.

Whenever concrete knowledge is lacking in some problem area, we make educated guesses about the facts. We frequently consult authorities or specialists to help us in those "gray" areas of knowledge. We design experiments to give us the necessary information, and we proceed by making hypotheses and assumptions about the problem. All hypotheses and assumptions should be clear and precise statements.

We adopt hypotheses to fill gaps in our understanding of the problem. When we lack information we hypothesize about the outcome, which we attempt to prove by experimentation. This is known as testing the hypotheses. Upon proving the hypotheses we form a more complete picture of the problem solution.

An assumption implies that the facts are unknown or unavailable and that these deficiencies in our knowledge of the problem have been taken into consideration. On the other hand, an assumption may also imply that the facts are known, but are not entirely in a form relevant to the problem solution. Therefore, certain simplifications or shortcuts are permissible in producing the expected results. Assumptions have the effect of taking unmanageable, complicated features and reducing them to simple, manageable terms.

For example, we know that airborne vehicles deviate from their fixed course in speed, heading, and altitude. These variations are due to environmental perturbations and vehicular and pilot performance errors. We can measure these deviations and determine the distribution of errors. However, for a given model in air transportation we can assume that the movement is in straight line segments provided that the deviations have no affect on the model outcomes. We have assumed the deviations out of the problem because of their negligible effects.

Statements of assumption usually begin: "We assume . . ." Assumptions should be critically examined and re-examined as to their validity and application to the problem solution.

ESTABLISH A MODEL RATIONALE

In our next task we establish a rationale for the approach we have taken in the model construction. We can develop a rationale for the mathematical model on the basis of the hypotheses and assumptions adopted. The rationale is an explanation of the underlying reasons for following a particular course in the problem solution. In establishing the rationale there are three elements to consider:

1. The real world.
2. The problem.
3. The tools to apply for its solution.

The real world consists of three distinct parts:

1. A system (or operation) designed to perform certain functions.
2. The environment in which the system performs.
3. The interactions between man and the system, man and the environment, and the system and the environment.

The real world is always the frame of reference from which the model is ultimately derived. It should always be the "wellspring" that we return to repeatedly during model development. When in doubt, always take another look at the real world. We look at that segment of the real world that affects the problem, and we organize that segment into a meaningful set of processes. This calls for an ordered logic at the selected aggregation level. We should continually relate the system to the environment and man and consider all of the interactions among the three.

There are several basic questions we must answer when considering the real-world-element during model development. We list these questions below.

What are the system functions and how are they performed?
Which functions are deterministic and which are nondeterministic?
How do we approximate these functions in the model?
What environmental factors affect system performance?
How do we approximate the effects of environmental factors on system performance?
What are the interactions between man and the system? Man and the environment? The system and the environment?
How do we approximate these interactions in the model?

Answers to these questions form the basis for establishing the model rationale. The answers depend on the characteristics of the problem. Considerations must be given to problem constraints and limitations of our resources that can be applied to the problem. These are resources in terms of manpower and money. We must consider the time frame in which we are operating, because results from a computer simulation model must be timely if the decision makers are to base their decisions on model outcomes.

We look at the real world, we look at the problem, and we decide on the necessary tools and their application to the problem. An array of analytical tools and simulation devices are available for our use in the problem solution, but we use only those tools most appropriate to obtain the solution. We are like the skilled craftsman who applies the proper implements to produce his workpiece.

By synthesizing the three elements (the real world, the problem, and the tools) we determine which approximations of the real world to derive. We determine the degree of complexity or simplification necessary to produce the required effects in the model. We derive a rationale for the model:

1. Describing the real world.
2. Giving approximations selected and reasons for their selection.
3. Describing the model concept.

This sequence is important and should be reviewed critically many times during model development.

Example 8.4. The following example illustrates the rationale for a conceptual model of a flight path programmer:

Flight path programming is the process of generating a flight path in time and space and is normally considered a human function. However, as the volume and density of air traffic increases and time is a critical factor, the mechanization of the flight path generation process is essential. Such increases in volume and density are expected with technological advances, so that there is clear need for mechanization of flight path programming in the future.

The optimum flight path between an initial point and a point of destination is that path which:

1. Is the shortest and most direct.
2. Requires fewest and least radical changes in speed, heading, and altitude.
3. Requires least fuel (or energy) consumption.
4. Is in no danger of midair collision.

Flight path programming processes are divided into two categories, static and dynamic. The *static* elements include establishing navigation fixes, selecting routes, determining height layers, and establishing geographic and political constraints. The static elements define the setting or environment in which the dynamic elements function. Those processes associated with *dynamic* elements include flight path generation and integration, coordination, and articulation of multiflight paths in a given environment. The dynamic elements involve the kinematics of flight path programming.

The total environment encompasses a volume in space that includes natural and man-made constraints. These are the mountains, valleys, plateaus, political boundaries, prohibited zones, etc. Within this environment there are certain aircraft navigation aids that define and delimit route configurations. These aids may be visual; however, they are usually electronic beacon devices.

In the air environment, routes (like roadways on the ground) are established, and rules pertaining to direction of travel by height layers and movement from navigation fix to navigation fix are determined. Enroute and terminal control procedures are determined. Rules are established for air traffic movements and collision avoidance, and emergency rules are established for abnormal situations.

For a flight i a flight path is generated after consideration is given to the geometry, constraints, traffic regulations, and requested flight parameters. The selected flight path must meet all optimum flight path criteria and must be integrated with all current flights. Each flight history must be compared against every other flight history to determine whether potential conflicts are possible.

Conflict between any two flights exists if their paths intersect in space within some ΔT time interval. This path conflict can be determined numerically by flight path extrapolation to the point of intersection. If a potential conflict occurs, a resolution is effected by alteration of some of the flight parameters, such as speed or altitude, according to some priority of conflict resolution.

The flight path programming process continues until every flight path is optimum and no spatial-temporal conflicts occur.

The flight path programmer model simulates the functions of the system. The functions are simulated by the *preprocessor, path generator,* and *conflict resolver.* The preprocessor processes all static elements, in which the elements are simulated by planes, corridors, and points in a three-dimensional coordinate system. The planes and corridors are defined by line segments extending from point to point.

The path generator generates the optimum flight path for flight i. All dynamic elements of the flight path generation are processed within the constraints established in the preprocessor. The flight path generator calculates the path by an iterative procedure until the selected path meets the optimum criteria. Whenever conflicts between two or more flights occur, the conflict resolver attempts to resolve the flight path conflicts. Conflicts are resolved by a process of flight path parameter relaxation, according to some established priority, such as alteration of requested flight speed within some specified tolerances.

If the conflict resolver cannot successfully resolve a conflict, a flight path parameter of lesser order is relaxed, and then another, until the conflict is resolved. This is an iterative process until all conflicts are resolved.

DEFINE PARAMETERS AND VARIABLES

Before we can state the mathematical model implicitly or in functional form, we must determine and define system parameters, auxiliary parameters, and input and output variables. System parameters are directly associated with the system being modeled. Auxiliary parameters (or non-system parameters) are not directly associated with the system but have an effect on sytsem performance. Variables are those quantities which may assume a succession of values, which need not be distinct. Parameters and variables are usually grouped in the following categories:

System parameters
- Kinematic
- Dynamic
- Statistical

Auxiliary parameters
- Environmental
- Kinematic
- Dynamic
- Statistical

Variables
- Random
- Controlled
- Uncontrolled

Kinematic parameters are those parameters associated with motion in the system or environment.

Dynamic parameters are those whose values change depending on the values of other parameters and variables.

Statistical parameters are those whose values affect stochastic processes and chance elements in the system or environment.

Environmental parameters are auxiliary parameters associated with the environment in which the system operates and which have an effect on system performance.

Random variables are those variables whose values are selected randomly according to a probability distribution.

Controlled variables are those variables whose values are controlled according to some established procedure.

Uncontrolled variables are not controlled by any established procedure.

After determining and defining the parameters, we must determine the significance and sensitivity of these parameters to the problem. Some parameters will have high order significance, whereas others will have little significance. Ultimately we are seeking to derive the mathematical model explicitly. In order to do this we must have an understanding of the parameters and variables and the relative significance of their effects on the system.

We should describe every parameter and variable in the model by the following items of information:

1. Definition and symbol.
2. Description.
3. Units of measurement.
4. Range of values.
5. Characteristics: e.g. single, multivalue, or coded value parameter; controlled, uncontrolled, or random variable, etc.
6. Where applied in the model.
7. Source of parameter or variable.
8. Remarks.

Example 8.45. The following are examples of system, environmental, and statistical parameters. (The examples are unrelated to each other.)

System parameters

Number of trains
Number of aircraft
Number of channels
Speed
Gallons per hour
Weight of vehicle j
Surveillance range
System bit rate
Power input
Number of employees
Peak load

Environmental parameters
- Temperature
- Wind direction
- Barometric pressure
- Terrain features
- Timber line
- Grade pitch

Statistical parameters
- Probability of correct response
- Probability of delay
- Probability of false alarm
- Probability of detection
- Probability of abort
- Probability of hit
- RMS (root mean square) navigation error
- Linear measurement error
- Angular measurement error
- Acceleration error
- Mean time interval
- Mean time between failures

The following illustrates information on a parameter:

Information	Example
Definition	Heading (HED)
Description	Vehicle heading measured clockwise from True North
Units of measurement	Degrees
Range of values	0–360°
Characteristics	Multivalue parameter
Where applied in the model	Path generator
Source	Input
Remarks	Used to calculate velocity components

For models that contain a very large number of parameters and variables, the information on each parameter and variable can be stored on punched cards as illustrated in Fig. 8.1. This illustrates a systematic procedure in which each item of information is stored on one or more punched cards. Using this procedure allows additions, revisions, or deletions to be easily made to the parameters and variables.

In the illustration we can see that all the information is punched on the left side of the card, and coded information is punched at the extreme right side of each card. For example, this parameter is numbered in the 2500 series, in which the coding to the left and the two digits on the right indicate specific items of information. This coding is used for purposes of manipulating the information in the computer if so desired.

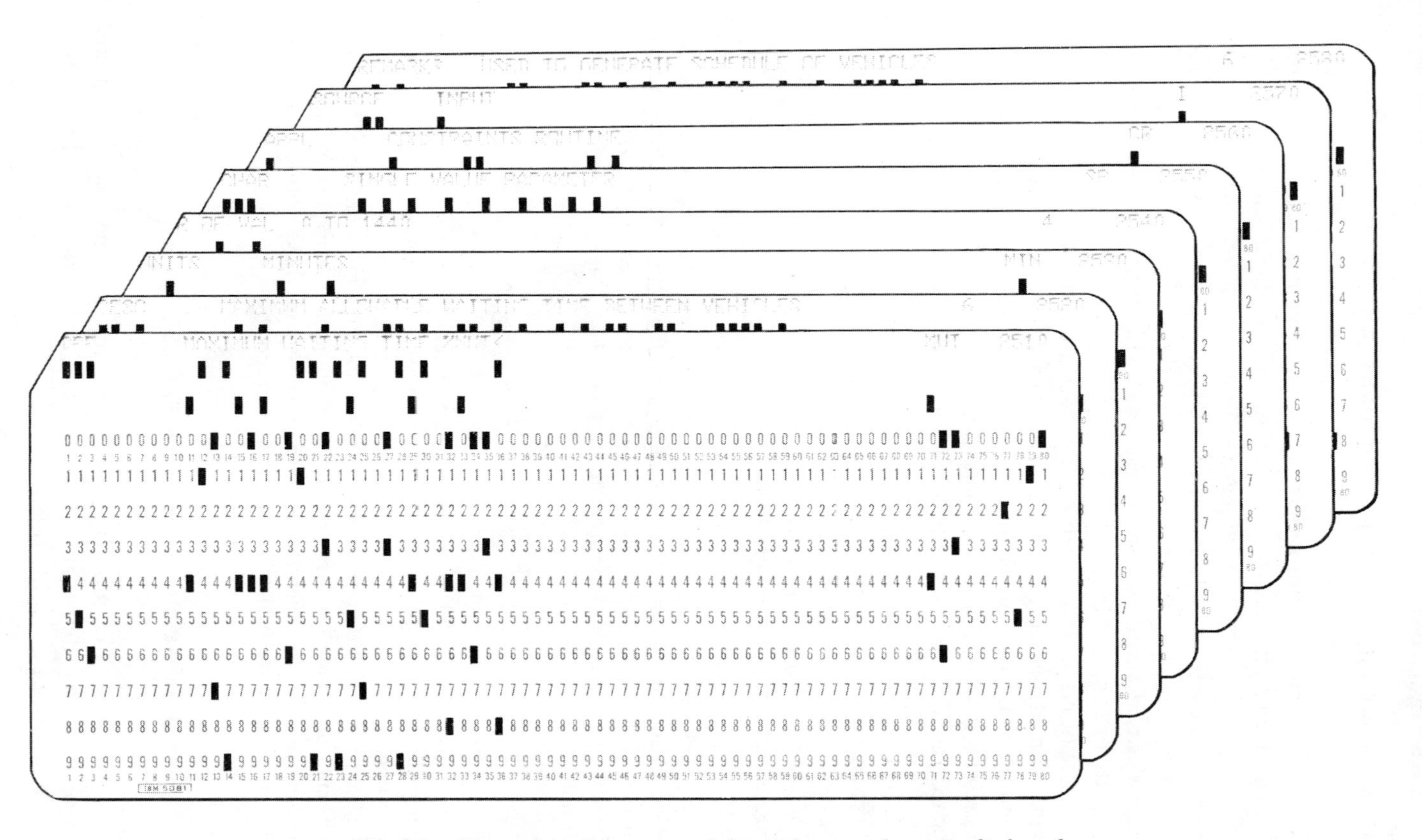

Fig. 8.1 Illustration of parameter information stored on punched cards.

DETERMINE MEASURES OF EFFECTIVENESS

We must select the appropriate set of effectiveness measures in order to obtain meaningful answers to our questions about the system. Our objective, mathematically speaking, is to derive a function that expresses system effectiveness as a function of all parameters and variables. This function describes a response surface over the region investigated, from which we can determine system response. This function can be shown analytically or graphically.

Measures of effectiveness can be expressed in various terms. The choice of expression depends on which selection gives the most meaningful representation in the problem context. Measures of effectiveness can be represented in graphical, tabular, or analytical form. Effectiveness can be expressed in any of the following terms:

1. Effectiveness indices ranging from zero to one.
2. Probability functions.
3. Scalar numbers ranging from zero to n.
4. Vectors ranging from zero to n.
5. Ratios ranging from zero to n.

Example 8.6. A promptness of performance effectiveness index I for an event E is computed by establishing maximum and minimum references in time for the event E and establishing a relationship with the actual time of occurrence of event E. Maximum and minimum time are designated by T_{max} and T_{min}, respectively. Actual time is designated by T_{act}. The index I is computed by the formula

$$I = \frac{T_{max} - T_{act}}{T_{max} - T_{min}} \qquad T_{max} \geq T_{act} \geq T_{min}.$$

The promptness index I ranges from zero to one. The closer I approaches one, the greater the promptness with which the event is performed.

For example, suppose an event E occurs in a min-max range between 4 and 10 min, respectively. In the first try the event occurs at 5 min. In the second try it occurs at 7 min, and in the third try it occurs at 6 min. What is the promptness index I for each try? Substituting in the above formula, we find that the values of I are 0.83, 0.50, and 0.67, respectively.

DETERMINE THE APPROXIMATIONS PROCEDURES

Let us consider three modeling procedures for deriving approximations of the real world: deterministic, stochastic, and expected value. What are they? When do we apply them?

Deterministic Models

In deterministic procedure there are no variations in the outcomes due to chance elements. All probabilistic elements are either nonexistent or removed from the problem because of irrelevance to the solution. Outcomes from deterministic models are always the same for a given set of inputs.

A deterministic model is represented by the function

$$x = f(\alpha, \beta, \gamma, \ldots), \tag{8.1}$$

where α, β, γ, . . . are nonrandom parameters and variables. Deterministic procedures are applied whenever chance perturbations, such as random errors, have negligible effects on the outcomes.

Let us illustrate with a trivial example. Suppose N trucks go from point A to point B and each truck can carry X pounds of cargo. What is the total cargo weight per mile carried by the trucks? The solution is determined by a deterministic model, for there are no chance elements introduced in the problem.

We apply deterministic procedures whenever (a) chance elements have no effects on the desired results or (b) chance elements are irrelevant to the problem.

An example of an implicit deterministic model is illustrated in the flow chart in Fig. 8.2.

Stochastic Models

In stochastic procedures, also called randomization or nondeterministic, we sample from probability distributions to determine specific outcomes in the model. For any given trial an outcome is determined by Monte Carlo, in which the outcome is not always the same for a given

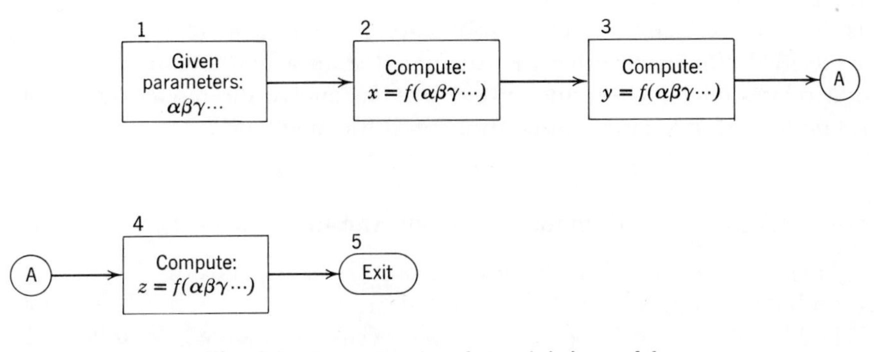

Fig. 8.2 Example of a deterministic model.

set of inputs. The effect of each outcome is introduced in the simulation process, which continues until completion. Randomization implies that replications are necessary in order to assign statistical confidence measures to the results. Outcomes determined by randomization are associated with *system reliability, system effectiveness, event occurrence, functional operation time,* and *measurement error.* Each is described below.

System Reliability. Reliability is expressed as a function of time. It is a decaying exponential function that expresses the probability that a system, subsystem, or component can operate without failure for a specified period of time. For example, one measure of reliability is given by MTBF (mean time between failures). Randomized reliability is introduced whenever system, subsystem, or component failures have an effect on the model outcome.

System failure is gamed by sampling from the reliability function R, in which time is a parameter. The system fails at time t if the inequality

$$R \leq U \tag{8.2}$$

exists at time t, where U is a uniform random variate between zero and one. Otherwise, the system does not fail.

Example 8.7. Reliability may be expressed by the functional

$$R = e^{-\lambda t},$$

where t is time and λ is a system parameter or a mathematical function that relates several parameters.

System Effectiveness. System effectiveness is expressed by the probability that a system performs at a certain level of effectiveness. Each system has a unique function or set of functions to perform. In a randomized model Monte Carlo is used to determine whether a system performs its function effectively. The probability P_e that a system performs at a specified effectiveness level is calculated from a mathematical function that relates effectiveness and system parameters. In the model the system is said to perform some unique function if the inequality.

$$P_e \geq U \tag{8.3}$$

exists, where U is a uniform random variate between zero and one.

Event Occurrence. A stochastic event E is expected to occur with a probability P_E, where P_E is derived from a mathematical function. Whether the event does or does not occur is assumed to follow the

Bernoulli distribution, which is a discrete distribution function. An event E may be associated with the system, the environment, the human, or any interactions among the three. In a Monte Carlo simulation containing Bernoulli events, event E occurs whenever the inequality

$$P_E \geq U \tag{8.4}$$

exists, where U is a uniform random number between zero and one. Otherwise event E does not occur.

The occurrence of event E is Bernoullian; however, the parameter P_E can be determined by a different function, which may be deterministic or nondeterministic, so that P_E may be expressed functionally by

$$P_E = f(\gamma, \lambda, \ldots), \tag{8.5}$$

where $(\gamma, \lambda, \ldots)$ are input variable of P_E may be expressed as a function of a random variable. In place of a function single- or multiple-value parameters may be used arbitrarily.

Example 8.8. Determine at random whether an event that has a 0.45 probability of occurrence will or will not occur.

SOLUTION. We generate a uniform random number, such as 0.73378, and apply (8.4). We apply the inequality test and observe that $0.45 \ngeq 0.73378$ is the result. Therefore, we conclude that the event will not occur.

Functional Operation Time. Functional operation time is expressed by the probability that the time for a given system or environmental function to operate is a certain time duration. The time interval is usually expressed by an exponential function or probability distribution, such as lognormal. A random time interval δT which has been identified as being distributed according to the lognormal can be computed from the expression

$$\delta T = \exp\left[\overline{\ln \delta t} + R\sigma_{\ln \delta t}\right], \tag{8.6}$$

where t is a parameter and R is a normal random variate sampled from the standard normal probability distribution.

Example 8.9. Determine a random time interval that is distributed according to the lognormal probability distribution with a mean time of 5.42 and standard deviation of 1.41.

SOLUTION. We generate a normal random variate, for example, 0.8, and apply (8.6).

$$\delta T = \exp\left[\ln 5.42 + 0.8(\ln 1.41)\right]$$
$$\delta T = \exp\left[1.69010 + 0.8(0.34359)\right] = \exp\left[1.96497\right] = 7.17.$$

Therefore the random time interval is 7.17.

Measurement Error. Measurement error is expressed by the probability that a given error will not exceed a certain measurement value. Measurement error may be univariate, bivariate, or multivariate; that is, it may have one, two, or more dimensions. In the model the magnitude of the error is determined by sampling from the error probability distribution. For normal measurement error in one, two, or three dimensions the sampled values are determined by the following three sets of equations:

$$X = \bar{X} + R_1\sigma_X \tag{8.7}$$

$$\begin{aligned} X &= \bar{X} + R_1\sigma_X \\ Y &= \bar{Y} + R_2\sigma_Y \end{aligned} \tag{8.8}$$

$$\begin{aligned} X &= \bar{X} + R_1\sigma_X \\ Y &= \bar{Y} + R_2\sigma_Y \\ Z &= \bar{Z} + R_1\sigma_Z, \end{aligned} \tag{8.9}$$

where $\bar{X}$, $\bar{Y}$, and $\bar{Z}$ are mean error and σ_X, σ_Y, σ_Z, are standard deviation of the error in X, Y, and Z, respectively. R_1, R_2, and R_3 are normal random variates sampled from the normal probability distribution.

Whenever in the bivariate case, or two-dimensional error, $\bar{X}$ and $\bar{Y}$ both equal zero, $\sigma_X = \sigma_Y$, and $\rho = 0$, the error follows the circular normal distribution. Whenever in the trivariate case, or three-dimensional error, $\bar{X}$, $\bar{Y}$, and $\bar{Z}$ equal zero, $\sigma_X = \sigma_Y = \sigma_Z$, and $\rho = 0$, the error follows the spherical normal distribution.

Example 8.10. Find a random linear measurement that is normaly distributed with a mean of 4 units and standard deviation of 0.1 unit.

SOLUTION. We generate a normal random variate, for example -1.95, and apply (8.7). We obtain

$$x = \bar{x} + R\sigma_x = 4 - 1.95(0.1) = 3.805.$$

Therefore the random measurement is 3.805 units.

Randomization procedure is applied in modeling whenever (a) the random features associated with *reliability, effectiveness, event occurrence, functional operation time,* or *measurement error* in the system or environment affect the model results; (b) it is necessary or desired to know individual outcomes, rather than aggregated results; or (c) it is desired to derive the distribution functions of the results and to compute the variance in addition to the mean.

Let us illustrate randomization procedure with an example. Suppose trucks N_1, N_2, N_3—with associated reliabilities R_1, R_2, R_3—go from point A to point B. Suppose they travel at mean speeds $\bar{S}_1$, $\bar{S}_2$, $\bar{S}_3$—with normal error distributions σ_1, σ_2, σ_3, respectively. Suppose the mean time and standard deviation in log normal for repair in case of breakdowns are $\overline{\ln \delta t_1}$, $\overline{\ln \delta t_2}$, $\overline{\ln \delta t_3}$—and $\ln \sigma_1$, $\ln \sigma_2$, $\ln \sigma_3$—, respectively. Establish an arrival queue at point B if all trucks leave point A at predesignated times. The solution is determined by randomization procedure, in which Monte Carlo is applied to determine occurrence of failure, time required for repair, and time in travel.

An example of an implicitly stated randomized model is illustrated in the flow chart in Fig. 8.3.

Example 8.11. Computerized games of conflict, war games, and business games are usually constructed as Monte Carlo simulations. In these simulations a series of events is simulated by exercising the model with randomized variables. Monte Carlo is also applied in models that involve traffic flow, message flow, and randomized allocation. In these simulations the amount of flow or allocation is randomized during model exercise.

Reliability, system effectiveness, event occurrence, functional operation time, and *measurement error* can be inputs to the model, intermediate

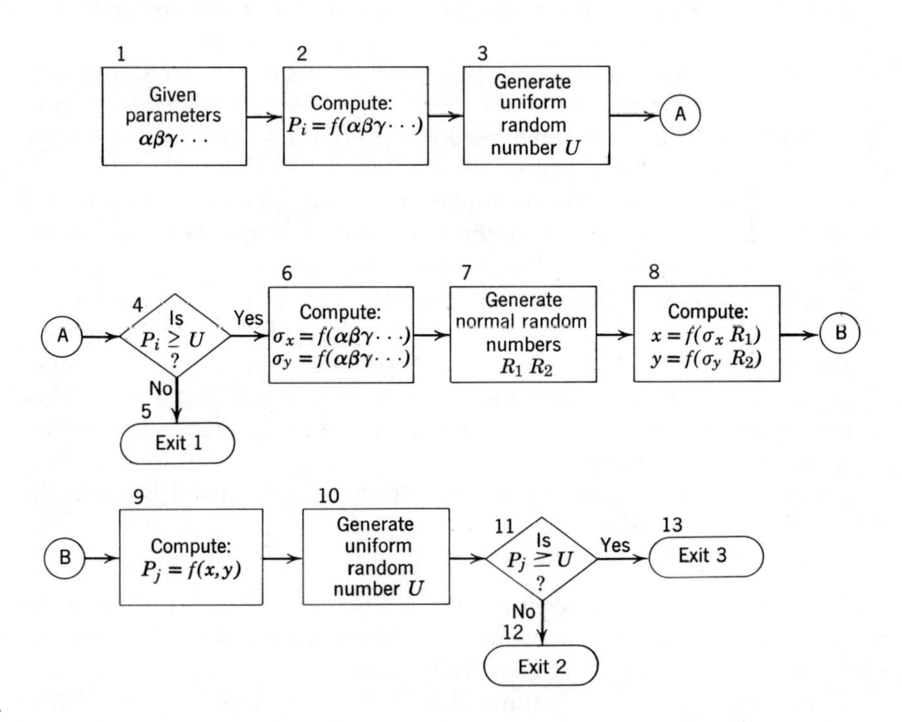

Fig. 8.3 Example of a randomized model.

computations, or outputs from the model. For example, a given model may require reliability as inputs, whereas in another model reliability may be an output. Model inputs and outputs are dictated by model requirements and the answers we are trying to obtain from model results. We make this point because there are no features that are exclusively inputs or exclusively outputs. The inputs and outputs depend on the particular problem being solved.

Expected Value Models

In expected value (or mean or average value) procedure, model outcomes are characterized by an aggregate of results. Individual results within the model are not determined as in randomization procedure; rather, the expected effects on a sample population are determined. In expected value procedure we assign mean values to the chance parameters and assign zero variance. The chance parameters may include reliability, system effectiveness, event occurrence, functional operation time, or measurement error. No variance of the results is determined, and no distribution function of the results is determined.

Monte Carlo procedure is not necessary and is not applicable in a model that is entirely expected value. Monte Carlo procedure would be redundant and if used would only produce results similar to expected value and at a greater cost. However, for a hybrid model containing both expected value and randomization procedures internally, we could apply the Monte Carlo to both.

Expected value procedure is applied whenever (a) the aggregate outcome is sufficient for problem solution, and it is not germane to the problem to know individual outcomes; (b) the model results are not affected by the variations of individuals; (c) it is not necessary to determine the distribution function and variance of the model outcomes.

Let us illustrate the expected value procedure with a trivial example. Suppose N trucks with reliability R go from point A to point B. How many trucks can be expected to break down? The solution is determined by expected value procedure.

An example of an implicitly stated expected value model is illustrated by the flow chart in Fig. 8.4.

Let us contrast the three procedures.

1. In deterministic procedures the results are always the same for a given set of inputs. There are no chance elements, and so chance elements have no effects on the desired results.

2. In randomization procedure the results vary depending on chance elements. The procedure is applied whenever chance elements affect

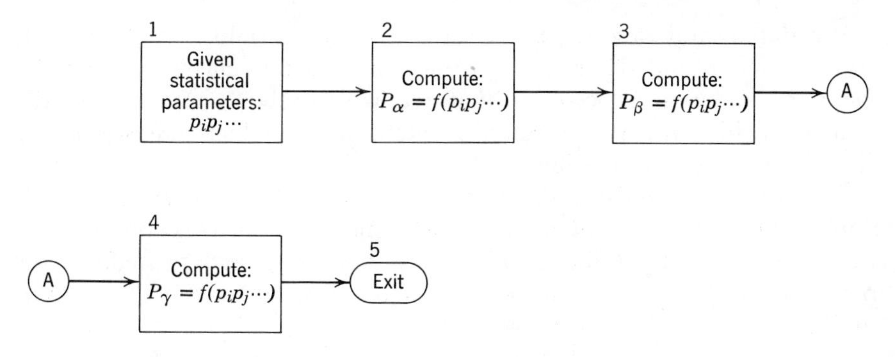

Fig. 8.4 Example of an expected value model.

the desired results and whenever it is desired to determine information on the probability distributions of the outcomes.

3. In expected value procedure the chance elements are assigned the mean or expected value. The procedure is applied if no information on the probability distributions of the outcomes is desired.

All three procedures are applicable in computer modeling and simulation, and all three can be used in the same model where appropriate. Most computer simulations are hybrids of all three procedures. The rationale for selecting a given procedure to model a given function must be explicitly stated.

In review, when is deterministic procedure applied? Randomization applied? Expected value applied? The answers are largely a matter of applying the right procedure at the right place in the model. We look at the real world; we study the problem; we examine the expected results of the model; we look at our resources and time schedule for the problem solution. These factors should give us an indication as to the appropriate procedure most feasible to apply.

DESCRIBE THE CONCEPTUAL MODEL IN ABSTRACT TERMS AND CONCEPTS

At this point of development of the conceptual model we can describe and define the model in abstract terms and concepts. We can show our analysis and how it led to the model concept. We state our assumptions and hypotheses explicitly. We give the rationale explaining the underlying approach, in which we proceed from the real world, to approximations, to a model of the real-world situation.

We define and describe the parameters and variables in the model, and we define and describe the measures of effectiveness. We describe the approximation procedures that we will apply to the model. We state explicitly which features are deterministic, which are stochastic, and which are expected value.

All these characteristics describe the conceptual model which we will implement in Phase 2 of model construction. In the conceptual phase we have reflected on the problem; we have discussed procedures for problem solution, and we have decided upon the described the conceptual model.

Example 8.12. The following example illustrates a brief description of a computer simulation model of a management information system:

Management Information System (MIS) is a computer model of a management information system that handles all management tasks associated with the flow of information in a large business complex. MIS stores in memory all relevant information introduced in the system. MIS sorts data according to several prescribed formats and traces the flow of information through the systems. MIS retrieves information when interrogated and performs all required arithmetic and logical operations necessary in the storage, flow, and retrieval of data.

MIS is a large integrated model consisting of many functional blocks in a modular design. The modularity is characterized by many routines, each planned to execute a specific function. Each routine is independent of every other routine and is used only when required in the operation of the model.

The MIS basic modes of operation include initiate, change, update, and interrogate. The *initiate mode* is that mode of operation in which new data and information are introduced into the system. The *change mode* is that mode of operation in which changes or revisions are made in the data or information existing in the system. The *update mode* is that mode of operation which cycles through the system and updates all dynamic information. The *interrogate mode* is that mode of operation in which MIS is externally interrogated for the retrieval of required information or data processed by the system.

The intiate and change modes involve very simple processes, such as read and write data or information. The update and interrogate modes include processes such as read, write, and sort in addition to arithmetic and logical operations of the data. Interrogations are preprogrammed in the form of definitive questions. Each question is all-inclusive, with explicit restraints on the limits of interrogation. Each question elicits a specific response from the system. Each question sets in motion a unique process that has been designed to obtain the appropriate answer from the system.

At the heart of MIS is the "activity word." The activity word is a coded designator that identifies the relevant features of an activity. An activity is all-inclusive and applies to items of data or information coming into the system. An activity may include data or information on a document, letter, telephone call, conference, chain of directives, etc. For each activity introduced into the system, an activity word is defined and stored in the system. The activity word contains coded information of type of activity, source, history, status, order of flow, cross-references, and special or miscellaneous information. Each activity word is appropriately tagged for addressing purposes.

The MIS model contains an N-dimensional code bank. The code bank provides the necessary information to correlate with the coded designations in the activity word. The code bank is the dictionary that defines each item of coded information.

An activity word may flow through the system deterministically or nondeterministically. An activity may flow along a routine path in which delays in the flow may be random or nonrandom, or an activity may flow through the system along random paths with random delays. The choice for randomness or nonrandomness is made by the user, depending on the activity.

MIS operates for both scheduled and unscheduled operations. In the scheduled operation MIS handles all routine procedures in the system in some basic time unit in a cyclic manner, such as daily. Unscheduled operations include nonroutine procedures in the system that have sufficient priority to pre-empt the system of any operations of lesser priority. MIS outputs include status reports of system operations at critical times in the processes of the management information system.

The effectiveness of the system is determined by the efficiency with which information or data flow through the system with minimum delay, correct routing, and quick retrieval. Queues, delays, losses in the system, etc., can all be observed in the exercise of the MIS model.

CHECK THE VALIDITY OF THE CONCEPTUAL MODEL

After our conceptual model is defined and described and we have established a model rationale, we should make some validity checks on our model concepts before continuing into the next phase of model construction. Checking model concepts is rather difficult because we are attempting to validate a concept stated in abstractions. However, we can apply some validation techniques with a fair degree of success.

One technique is similar to checking numerical calculations. We know that a common procedure in checking numerical calculations is to reverse the process. For example, we use addition to check subtraction problems. In model construction the conceptualization phase is mainly a reasoning process. We start with a problem definition and reason through to a conceptual model which we describe at the conclusion of Phase 1. We look at the real world; we make approximations; then we define our model. As in checking numerical calculations, we can check the validity of the model by tracing the reasoning by reverse process.

Essentially, by reverse reasoning, we would look at the model, trace back to the approximations, and finally trace back to the real world.

Such a reverse reasoning procedure would involve the following steps, in which each step is associated with the previous steps.

1. Examine and review the model concept and the model rationale.
2. Relate the model concept and rationale to the deterministic, randomization, and expected value features in the model.
3. Examine the above approximations in relation to the real world.
4. Review measures of effectiveness, parameters, and variables.
5. Examine the assumptions and hypotheses.
6. Relate items 4 and 5 above to the real world. Examine the system, system environment, and man. Examine the interactions among the three.
7. Check the validity of information and data and their sources applied in the problem.
8. Review the entire procedure in relation to the problem definition.
9. Review the problem statement.

Even though the reverse reasoning process is not foolproof as a validity check, it does afford a complete re-examination from a different viewpoint. Weaknesses that otherwise might not have been readily apparent may be made evident by reverse reasoning.

Another validity-checking technique to apply to the conceptualization phase is to review the whole process with outside, disinterested parties. Outside parties can take a more detached, objective look at the problem and identify weaknesses in the reasoning process that may have escaped our attention.

A re-examination of the entire model concept is highly desirable and necessary before proceeding to the implementation phase. It is easier to redefine and revise in Phase 1 than to attempt concept changes during the implementation phase. Even though the concepts behind a model may be judged satisfactory, implementation should not proceed unless the conceptual model is defined and described completely and accurately. A very good conceptual model may exist in someone's mind, but unless he can adequately communicate this concept, implementation of the model is not possible.

DOCUMENT THE CONCEPTUAL MODEL PHASE

Documentation at the conclusion of the conceptualization phase should appear in the form of a concept paper or concept document. The documentation should include the following information:

1. Comprehensive problem statement.
2. Analysis of the problem.

3. Parameters, variables, and effectiveness measures.
4. Hypotheses and assumptions.
5. Model rationale.
6. Model description in general terms and abstractions.
7. Expected results and model applications.

SUMMARY

In the conceptualization phase of model construction, we determine and formalize the broad plan and design of the model. We examine the real world; we determine the approximations to use; and we define the model concept. The rationale for the model is explained. We check the validity of our conceptual model, and we document our results in a concept paper or concept document.

PROBLEMS

8.1 Select a model described in Chapter 2 and prepare a brief problem statement appropriate to the model.

8.2 Select a model described in Chapter 2 and prepare a likely list of parameters and variables for the model.

8.3 What are some reasonable effectiveness indices for the following models?

A model to simulate the flow of traffic at an intersection.
A corporate business game.
A model of a conceptual computer.
A model of a communications network.
A model of a satellite in orbit.

8.4 Distinguish among deterministic, stochastic, and expected value.

8.5 Illustrate with some examples models that are deterministic, stochastic, or expected value.

8.6 Prepare a brief description of the conceptual model of some real-world system.

8.7 Summarize the "conceptualization" phase of model construction.

8.8 Prepare a brief problem statement of one of the following problems.

Handling air traffic congestion at a busy airport.
Assigning telephone calls to outgoing trunk lines.
Handling inventory control of 10,000 items.
Determining buyer response to market fluctuations.
Eliminating receiver noise in an electronic environment.
Designing a business game in a competitive market.
Designing a war game of a global conflict.
Designing a system to regulate the flow of peak hour traffic.
Establishing a data bank of land values for a given region.

8.9 What might be the bad consequences of a poorly conceptualized model?

8.10 What are the characteristics of a well-conceptualized model?

8.11 Develop a simple conceptual model of a mail system. Describe incoming and outgoing mail in addition to internal handling.

8.12 Develop a simple conceptual model of a retail outlet that handles three items. Describe some of the simple functions, such as buying, stock control, and selling. Illustrate with a simple flow chart.

8.13 Develop a simple conceptual model of a transportation sytsem that carries passengers from *A* to *B*. Consider scheduling, origin/destination flows, and peak load only.

8.14 What salient features should appear in a document that describes a conceptual model?

9

MODEL IMPLEMENTATION

In the second phase of model construction—implementation—we translate the abstract model concept defined in Phase 1 into a concrete, tangible model. Phase 2, which represents about 40% of the total effort in model construction, is the "action" phase, in which ideas and concepts are implemented explicitly and made operational. The model concept is translated into a logical flow chart of the system or operation. We derive the mathematical equations explicitly; we translate the logical flow chart into the program flow chart; and we program and check out the model for the appropriate computer. During Phase 2 we perform at least three major validity checks on the procedures.

At the conclusion of Phase 2 we document the work we have done in the implementation of the model. We discuss and describe the procedures and tasks of model implementation below.

DEVELOP THE LOGICAL FLOW CHART

Let us consider the organizational structure of the model as implemented in the logical flow chart. We should direct our attention to this feature as soon as we begin to implement the conceptual model. A modular approach to model construction is the recommended procedure for model implementation. Modularization is efficient, logically sound, and easy to implement and revise. By modularization we can build the model by adding integral blocks to the over-all structure by an iterative process in which we refine the model at each iteration.

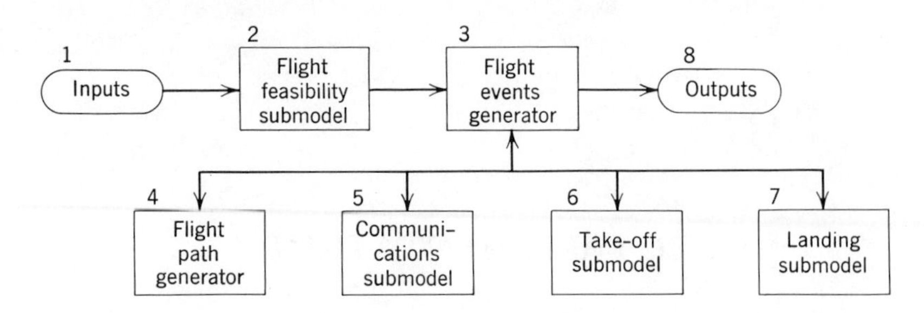

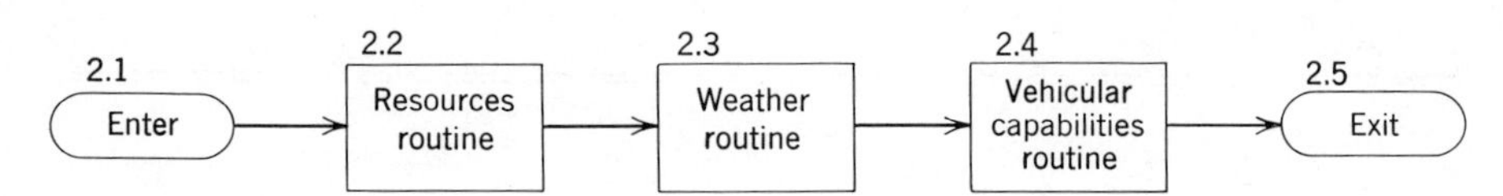

Fig. 9.1 Illustration of modularization technique. Model and submodel levels.

The modular concept of model construction allows for flexibility of model exercise during implementation and the production runs. Modules or blocks can be revised without affecting the growth and development of other modules.

Example 9.1. Modular concept is a rather common phenomenon in human activities, and we could cite many examples of modular design in the structure of human organization. Consider a few examples at random.

1. Biology classifies the animal kingdom according to the following ranking categories: animal kingdom, phylum, class, order, family, genus, species. The plant and mineral kingdoms are also classified by ranking categories.
2. The railroad system is modular. The railroad car is the basic module, which, when combined with other modules, forms a train. More than one train can be joined to form a section. Continuing through the organizational structure ultimately leads to the total railroad system.
3. Military organization is modular in structure; for example, squads group into platoons, platoons group into companies, companies group into battalions, and so on through military hierarchical structure.
4. Office buildings consist of offices connected by corridors into wings; wings form floors; and several floors comprise the office building.

Applications of modular design in computer simulations are as useful as the applications of the modular concept in all other human activities.

In constructing a modular model, we divide the model functions into logical subfunctions of the next order level of detail. We continue this process of division of modules into submodules to whatever level of detail is necessary. Each subdivision represents a module at some level of detail. Thus we divide the *model* into functional *submodels.* We divide each *submodel* into functional *routines,* and we divide each *routine* into functional *subroutines.* Usually going down to the subroutine level of detail is sufficient.

We have illustrated modularization technique at four levels of detail in Figs. 9.1 and 9.2. In these figures we have applied modularization to the logical flow chart of a hypothetical air traffic control model. We have taken one submodel and expanded it into routines. We have taken one of the routines and divided it into subroutines, and we have expanded one of the subroutines. Also note how we have numbered the individual blocks at each level of detail. By some numbering scheme, such as the one illustrated, we can systematically relate every module to every other module.

Modules are of two types: system or auxiliary. *System modules* simulate a specific function in system (or operation) logic. A system module represents some part of the system. For example, a detection routine in a radar model is a system module that simulates the detection function

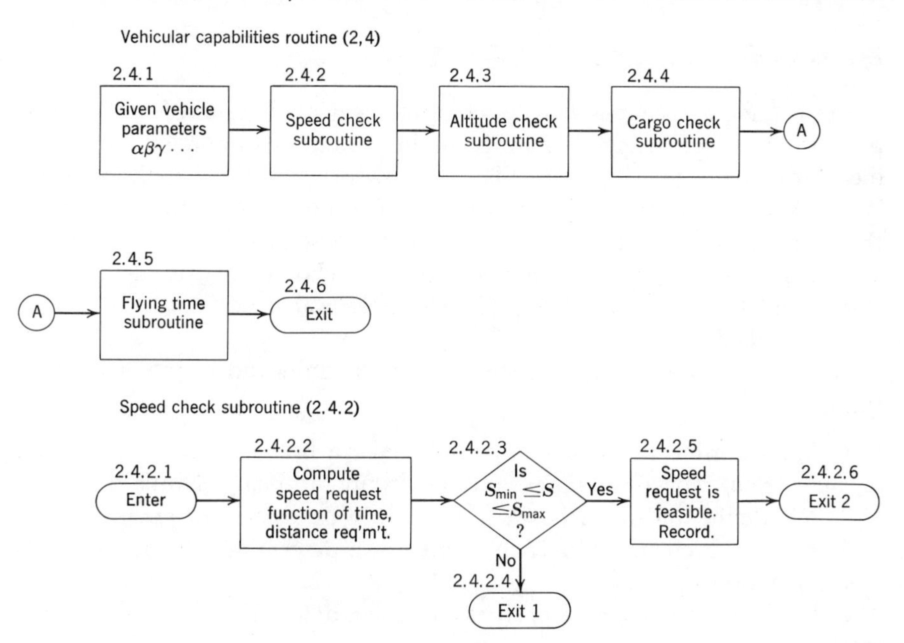

Fig. 9.2 Illustration of modularization technique. Routine and subroutine levels.

of the radar. *Auxiliary modules* are an integral part of the model, but do not represent a system function directly. Auxiliary modules are non-system modules and are not necessarily unique to any given model. For example, a random statistical variates generator routine is an auxiliary module that may be applied in any stochastic model to generate random numbers when needed in the model processing.

We now describe several *auxiliary modules* that are applicable in the development of the logical flow chart.

Model Processor

Each model requires a central model processor module (or executive routine) to integrate the activities of the model modules. The model processor is the model mechanism or generator that logically drives the model through the orderly processes of model logic and computations. The model processor integrates all deterministic, random, and expected value procedures in the model. Each unique model activity initiates a unique flow or cycle through model logic. On completion of the activity, control of the model returns to the model processor. The next ordered activity is selected for processing according to a predetermined procedure. This process is repeated continuously until the model run is complete.

Events Generator

Many model activities can be characterized by a series of events that proceed in a prearranged manner or in a random manner. An events model processes a series of events that may occur with or without regularity. We can implement an events generator routine that performs the events model processor function. The purpose of the events generator is to generate and store events in what we choose to call the "events store" and to process the events in chronological order until the model run is finished.

We describe the general procedure for designing an events generator routine.

1. We examine the real world and make a list of all relevant events in the system (or operation) and environment being simulated.
2. We define and describe each event E in the system or environment.
3. For the occurrence of each event E we determine all possible real-world reactions.
4. For nonoccurrence of each event E we determine all possible real-world reactions.

5. We determine what deterministic or nondeterministic functions initiate the occurrence of event *E*.

6. We translate real-world reactions into a logical flow chart showing the subsequent logic for occurrence and nonoccurrence of event *E*.

7. We determine what succeeding event or events, if any, will follow the occurrence or nonoccurrence of each event *E*, and we translate this process into the logical flow chart.

8. We determine what latencies (or delays) may occur between an event *E* and the subsequent associated event or events.

9. We determine the mathematical procedure for computing each delay. We determine whether the function is deterministic, random, or expected value.

10. We select an appropriate event format for storing the events in the events store, in which each event requires the following items of information: (a) time of anticipated occurrence, (b) event code (an event identifier), (c) identity of object or objects associated with the event, and (d) action statements defining event-processing logic and computations and subsequent actions. The time of anticipated occurrence indicates when a given event is a candidate for processing. If the event is deterministic it will always occur at the anticipated time. If the event is nondeterministic it will occur only if it passes the Bernoulli events test, which compares the probability of occurrence with a uniform random number to make the decision. A Bernoulli events generator subroutine is described later in this chapter. The event code is an event designation code or event identifier that we arbitrarily assign each event in order to distinguish one event from another. Usually the code consists of alphabetic characters, which may be descriptive of the event name, such as SELL. The identity of objects associated with the event indicates the specific object or objects, such as Aircraft X33B, which initiates the event. The action statements designate all the internal model responses to the event occurrence. The logic and calculations, as well as all subsequent actions, are specified. For example, the action statement for a hypothetical event *E* might state the following: "Go to subroutine TRIM. Test TRIM results against factor Q. For *yes* decision generate event EBB and store. Write TRIM results in XYES and exit. For *no* decision write TRIM results in XNO and exit."

11. We determine procedure for storage and retrieval of events in the events store. The most efficient procedure is to store newly generated events in chronological order. The most recent event in the events store is retrieved and processed. Any new events initiated by the last event are generated and stored in the events store in chronological order. The

next most recent event is retrieved and processed, and so on. This process continues until all events have been processed.

We illustrate an events generator in Fig. 9.3.

Example 9.2. The following example illustrates the processes of the events generator shown in Fig. 9.3.

Step 1. Search the events store. Locate most recent event *E*. Time: 9:52 A.M.
Step 2. What event number is event *E*? Event DEPCH.
Step 3. Go to appropriate event subroutine. Call in DEPCH routine.
Step 4. Process event *E*. Process event DEPCH.
Step 5. Record desired output information. Store value of IFMR in STRN, and store SLVC in YTRN.
Step 6. Generate any appropriate new events. Generate event WEPCH.
Step 7. Store new events in events store chronologically. Store WEPCH at time 11:36 A.M. immediately following event SPOKE at time 11:34 A.M.
Step 8. Are any events left in the events store? If so, return to Step 1.

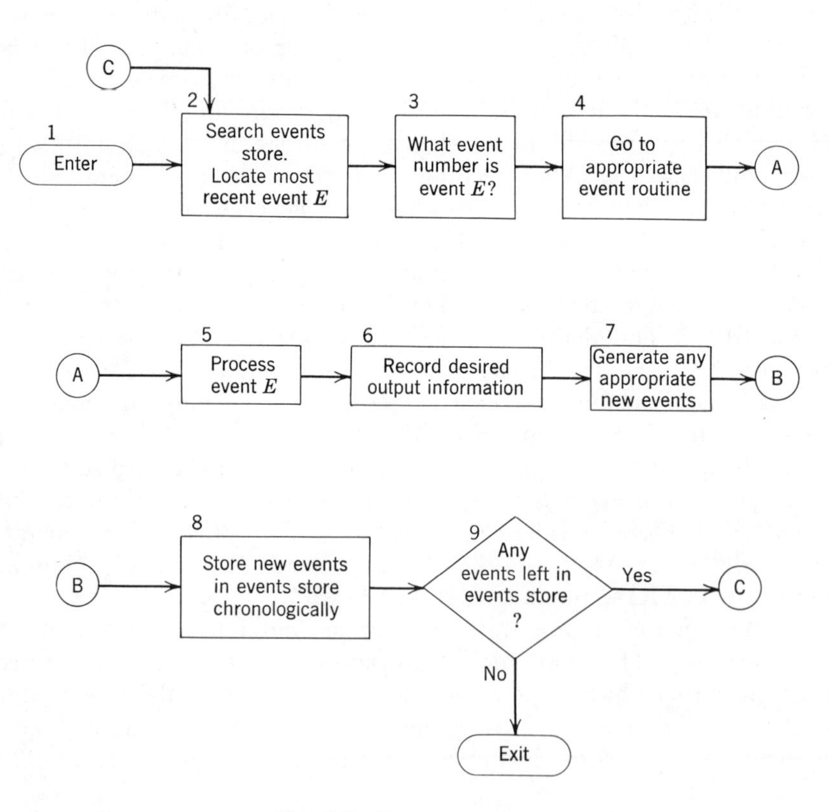

Fig. 9.3 Events generator.

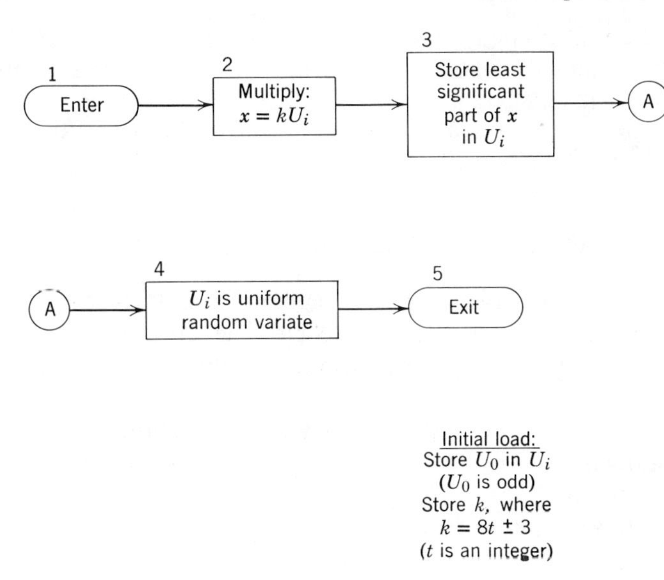

Fig. 9.4 Uniform random variates generator.

Uniform Random Variates Generator

The uniform random variates generator is a subroutine to generate uniform pseudorandom numbers. There are several methods available to generate random numbers, but whatever method is selected must be statistically reliable and capable of being efficiently implemented for the computer. In stochastic simulation models the random number generator is exercised repeatedly in the model processes. Thus a highly efficient random number generator decreases computer running time over an inefficient generator.

We illustrate a uniform random variates generator in Fig. 9.4. This random number generator applies the power residue method for generating random numbers. The internally generated random number is in binary form; thus, if the number is to be used externally it must be converted to decimal.

Example 9.3. The following example illustrates the generation of a uniform random number using the procedure given in Fig. 9.4. In the calculations we illustrate equivalent binary, octal, and decimal values.

Step 1. Multiply KU_0.

	Binary	Octal	Decimal
K	001011001	131	89
$\times U_0$	$\times$ 000100000	$\times$ 40	$\times$ 32
X	000000101100100000	5440	2848

Step 2. Store least significant *part of* X in U_0: 100100000.

Step 3. The uniform random number is the new value of U_0: 100100000 in binary, 440 in octal, or 288 in decimal.

Note: The next uniform random number is computed by multiplying 001011001 by 100100000.

Non-uniform Random Variates Generator

All nonuniform random variates generators must first generate one or more uniform random numbers. Next, one of several techniques is applied to transform the uniform random number (or numbers) into a nonuniform random number. Nonuniform random numbers come from either discrete or continuous probability distributions. Nonuniform random numbers may be only positive or only negative, or symmetrical or nonsymmetrical about zero.

To generate nonuniform random numbers from discrete or continuous probability distribution functions with only one nonzero parameter and with density functions that contain only positive or negative values or are symmetrical about zero, the most direct and efficient technique of transformation is table lookup. For multi-nonzero parameters or for density functions that are nonsymmetrical about zero, we recommend using other methods, such as we illustrate for binomial and Poisson distributions later.

Let us examine table lookup method. By this method we store the probability distribution function (or cumulative) and use a select portion of a uniform random number as the argument to look up the tabular value. However, we must remember that the internal number systems in computers are binary-octal. Binary and octal number systems are interchangeable. The binary-octal feature can be used to our advantage, but some initial decimal-octal conversions are required.

The table arguments must be in the octal number system because the computer memory address system is in octal and the uniform random number is in binary. This places constraints on the table size selected. The table size can only be some number that is an integral power of 2, such as 32, 64, or 128. The tabular values must be arranged in proportional parts of the total table size.

Usually published probability table arguments are in the decimal number system. Traditionally our everyday number system has been decimal. Since the introduction of electronic digital computers, however, we have found application for number systems other than decimal. Thus, to store probability tables we must transform the tabular values from decimal to octal indexing for compatibility with the octal number system. To perform this task we apply a transformation technique. We illustrate a transformation in Table 9.1. The function is linear and the range of tabular values is 0–3.6. The functions are identical; the values shown in the two halves of the table are different because we have applied a different scale to the argument. We have shown 10 values transformed to 16 values. Note that the tabular values are in decimal in both halves of the table, but that the arguments are in decimal in one half and octal in the other.

For table lookup we use as many bits from the uniform random number as is necessary to encompass the total table size. For a table size of 128 values, we need 7 bits (2 raised to the 7th power = 128) from the uniform random number to address all 128 tabular values. We take that portion of the uniform random number in binary to address the octal memory location for the appropriate nonuniform random number tabular value.

We illustrate an example using Table 9.1. Suppose the uniform random number generated is 01001101001 in binary. We take the last 4 bits because our octal table size is 16. The last 4 bits are 1001, or 11 in octal. We now use $K + 11$ as our argument for the table lookup, where K is the octal address of the location of the first value in the table. In our example $K = 0$, so that the corresponding tabular value

Table 9.1 Illustration of Transformation from Decimal to Octal Arguments

Decimal Arguments—Decimal Table		Octal Arguments—Decimal Table	
0	0	0	0
1	0.4	1	0.24
2	0.8	2	0.48
3	1.2	3	0.72
4	1.6	4	0.96
5	2.0	5	1.20
6	2.4	6	1.44
7	2.8	7	1.68
8	3.2	10	1.92
9	3.6	11	2.16
		12	2.40
		13	2.64
		14	2.88
		15	3.12
		16	3.36
		17	3.60

is 2.16. The value of K must be zero or some multiple of the table size. In the example K could be 0, 20, 40, 60 in octal, etc. K is selected by the computer programmer, depending on where in computer memory he stores the table.

We illustrate the flow chart for a nonuniform random variates generator in Fig. 9.5. This example uses table lookup method, in which the table has been stored in 128 memory locations. We have arbitrarily selected a table size of 128 because it is large enough to give good representation of the probability function and small enough to store in computer memory without occupying too much space. However, the size of the table could be doubled or cut in half very easily by changing the number of bits and reallocating the table.

The above discussion generally applies only to all positive or all negative tabular values. If we apply table lookup method to a probability distribution whose density function is symmetrical about zero, we must use another bit from the uniform random number to randomly assign plus or minus to the tabular value. We have an equal chance of getting 0 or 1. Therefore the random values generated will be symmetrical about zero. However, in order to eliminate bias, the bit used to determine the sign cannot come from the portion of the random number that

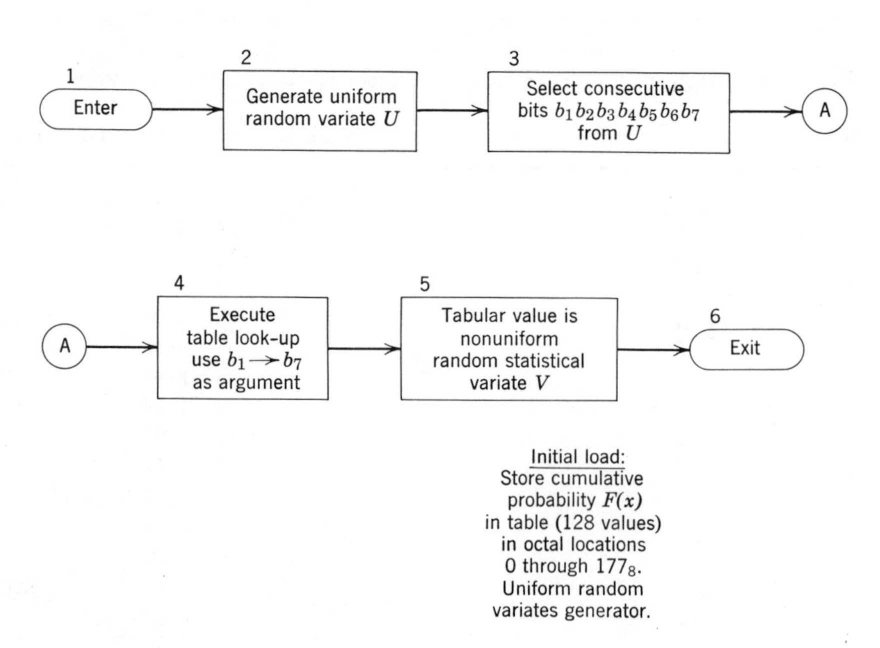

Fig. 9.5 Nonuniform random statistical variates generator.

we use to address the table. The sign for each tabular value would be predetermined and thus not random. We leave it up to the reader to rationalize this bias.

Table lookup method can be used for either discrete or continuous distribution functions provided that we can represent the table in one dimension. For example, the cumulative for the standard normal distribution has only one nonzero parameter, which is the standard deviation. The mean is always zero. Therefore table lookup works quite well for the normal distribution. However, for distributions containing more than one nonzero parameter, such as binomial or Poisson, we recommend using other methods than table lookup. Although efficient table lookup could be used by a very careful arrangement of the table in memory banks, we are still inclined to stand by our recommendation. Likewise, for density functions not symmetrical about zero, we recommend using other methods.

Normal Random Variates Generator

The normal random variates generator is a special case of the nonuniform random number generator. Since it is the most frequently used it warrants special attention. Various techniques can be used to generate normal random numbers. However, we recommend the table lookup method rather than a generative technique. We have performed a decimal to octal transformation for the cumulative normal distribution, and we have shown this transformation in Table D.5.

Normal random number generation lends itself to table lookup because the table is one-dimensional and the density function is symmetrical about zero. Other methods generally require more computation time.

Normal random numbers are applied to determine random measurement errors in one, two, or three dimensions that follow the normal measurement error. Transformed normal random numbers are also used to determine the random time intervals that follow the log normal probability distribution. We illustrate this later in our discussion of the log normal time interval generator.

Example 9.4. The following example illustrates the generation of a normal random number using the procedure shown in Fig. 9.6.

Step 1. Generate a uniform random number U: 001101001100011.

Step 2. Select bits 2 through 8: 0110100.

Step 3. Execute table lookup using the value from Step 2 as the argument; 64 in octal is the argument.

Step 4. Choose the sign from bit 1. If 0, use plus. If 1, use minus.

Step 5. Normal random number is tabular value plus sign: + 0.54.

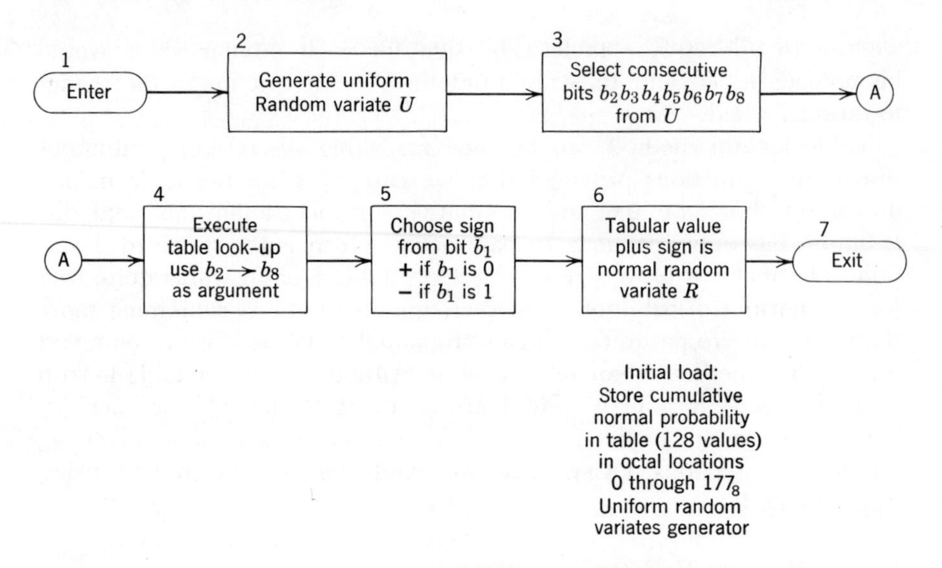

Fig. 9.6 Normal random variates generator.

Binomial Random Variates Generator

To generate a binomial random variate s a generative technique is recommended rather than table lookup. The binomial distribution has more than one nonzero parameter. The random variate s is the expected number of successes to apply in a random binomial trial for given n and p. We illustrate the flow chart to generate the binomial random variate s in Fig. 9.7, in which we generate n uniform random numbers

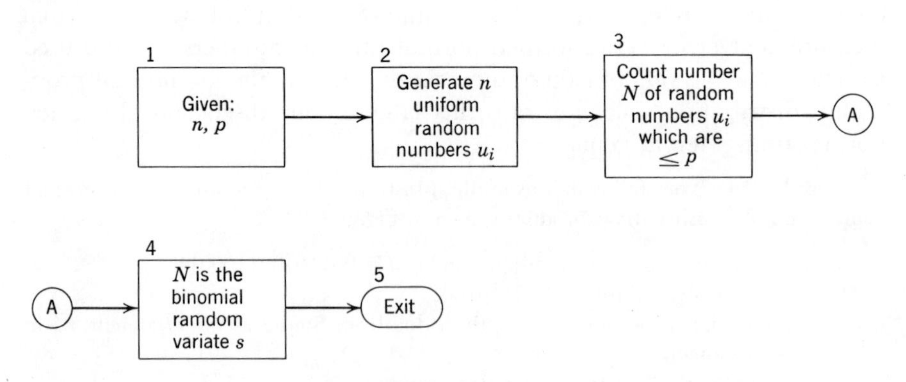

Fig. 9.7 Binomial random variates generator (for small n).

and compare them with p. From the comparison we determine the variate s.

Example 9.5. The following example illustrates the generation of a binomial random number using the procedure given in Fig. 9.7.

Given: $n = 5$, $p = 0.4$.
Step 1. Generate five uniform random numbers: 0.34261, 0.76322, 0.02376, 0.41699, 0.89324.
Step 2. Count the number of random numbers that are $\leq p$. We observe that $0.34261 \leq 0.4$ and $0.02376 \leq 0.4$.
Step 3. Step 2 determines the value of the binomial random variate s: $s = 2$.

Poisson Random Variates Generator

To generate a Poisson random variate s we recommend a generative technique rather than table lookup. The Poisson distribution has more than one nonzero parameter. We illustrate the flow chart for the Poisson random variates generator in Fig. 9.8, in which the number of uniform random numbers that we generate varies depending on the results of certain tests performed in the process.

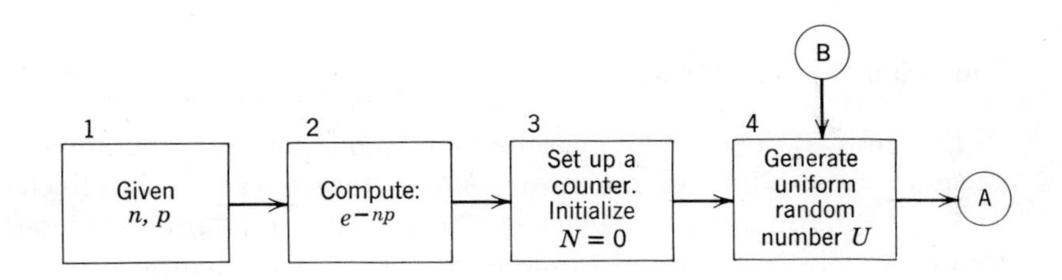

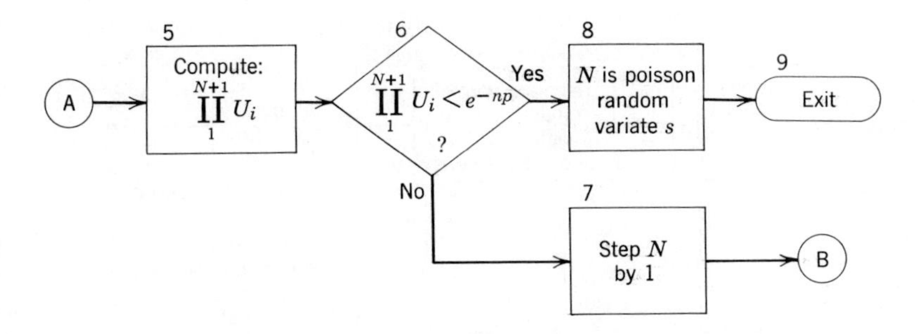

Fig. 9.8 Poisson random variates generator.

Example 9.6. The following is an illustration of the application of Poisson random variates in computer modeling and simulation:

Suppose customers at a toll booth are expected to arrive according to the Poisson probability distribution. During toll booth operation there is a 0.2 probability that one customer will arrive every 20 sec. Simulate the number of arrivals in 10-min intervals from 8 A.M. to 12 noon.

SOLUTION. We apply (3.167) every 10 min of simulated time. There are thirty 20-sec intervals in each 10 min. Therefore $n = 30$ and we have given $p = 0.2$. For the 4-hr period we generate 24 Poisson random variates for $np = 6$. We obtain the following results:

8:00– 8:10	6	10:00–10:10	5
8:10– 8:20	7	10:10–10:20	9
8:20– 8:30	5	10:20–10:30	6
8:30– 8:40	6	10:30–10:40	4
8:40– 8:50	8	10:40–10:50	8
8:50– 9:00	7	10:50–11:00	7
9:00– 9:10	8	11:00–11:10	6
9:10– 9:30	6	11:10–11:20	5
9:20– 9:30	4	11:20–11:30	7
9:30– 9:40	6	11:30–11:40	6
9:40– 9:50	5	11:40–11:50	7
9:50–10:00	7	11:50 12:00	6

Univariate Normal Measurement Generator

The univariate normal measurement generator is a routine used to calculate a one-dimensional measurement that is randomly affected by univariate normal error. Given the mean and standard deviation, the routine generates a normal random number and calculates the measurement for the one trial. We illustrate the flow chart for the univariate normal measurement generator in Fig. 9.9. For measurements in more

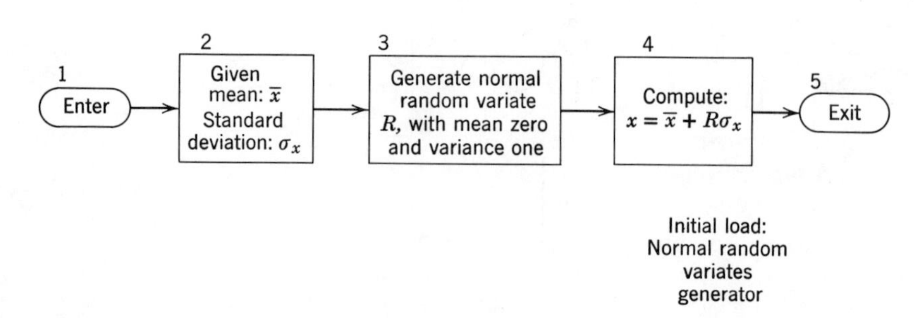

Fig. 9.9 Univariate normal measurement generator.

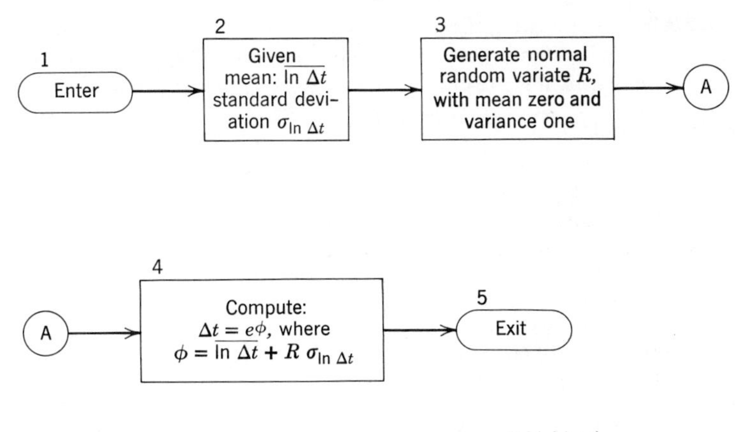

Fig. 9.10 Log normal time interval generator.

than one dimension, we merely apply the routine for each measurement using the appropriate mean and standard deviation for each measurement. This routine can be used to determine the measurement in X, Y, or Z.

Example 9.7. The following example illustrates the generation of a measurement X that is randomly distributed according to the normal probability distribution. We use the procedure shown in Fig. 9.9.

Given: $\bar{X} = 10$ ft
$\sigma_X = 2.2$ ft.

Step 1. Generate a normal random variate R: $R = +0.60$.
Step 2. Compute: $X = \bar{X} + R\sigma_X$

$$X = 10 + (0.60)(2.2) = 11.32 \text{ ft.}$$

Log Normal Time Interval Generator

The log normal time interval generator is a routine that calculates a time interval distributed according to the log normal probability distribution. Given the mean and the standard deviation of the logarithm, the routine generates a normal random number and calculates the time interval. We have illustrated the routine by the flow chart shown in Fig. 9.10. This routine is similar to the normal measurement generator except that a log transformation is applied.

Example 9.8. The following illustrates the generation of a time interval T that is randomly distributed according to the log normal probability distribution. We use the procedure shown in Fig. 9.10.

Given: $\overline{\ln \Delta T} = 2.00$

$\overline{\sigma_{\ln} \Delta T} = 0.60$

where ΔT is in seconds.

Step 1. Generate a normal random variate R: $R = -1.1$.

Step 2. Compute: $T = e^{\phi}$

where $\phi = \overline{\ln \Delta T} + R\sigma_{\ln \Delta T}$

$\phi = 2.00 - (1.1)(0.60) = 1.34$

$\Delta T = e^{1.34} = 3.819$ sec.

Bernoulli Events Generator

The Bernoulli events generator is a routine that we use to determine the occurrence or nonoccurrence of an event distributed according to the Bernoulli (or binomial) probability distribution. Given the probability P of occurrence, we make a Bernoulli test to determine which results are "go" or "no-go." We illustrate the routine by the flow chart shown

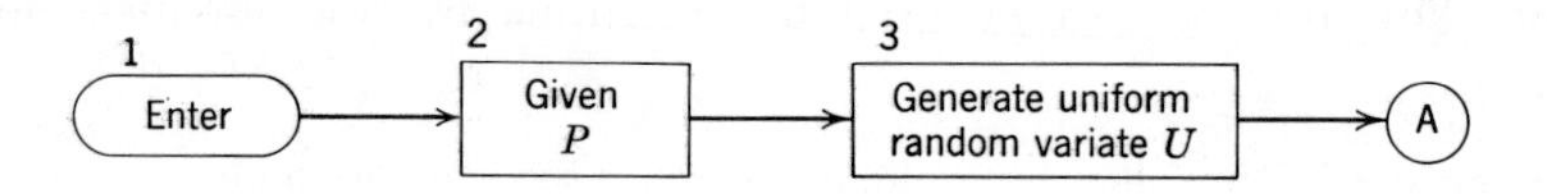

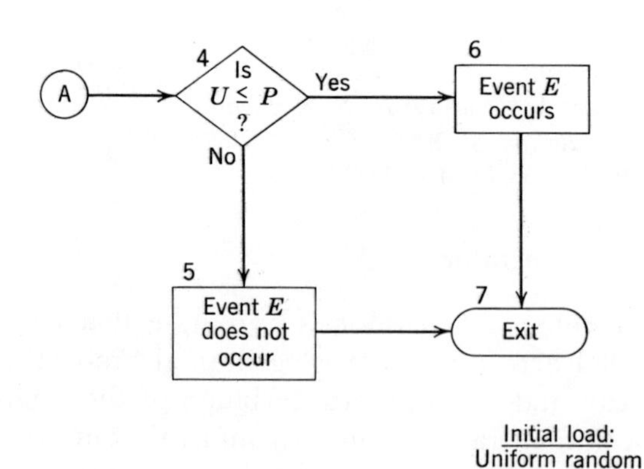

Fig. 9.11 Bernoulli event E generator.

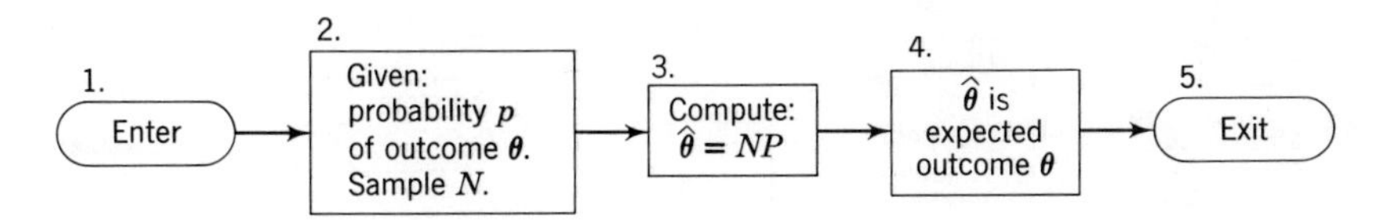

Fig. 9.12 Expected value generator.

in Fig. 9.11, in which a simple test is made comparing P and U to determine the outcome, which is always discrete.

Example 9.9. The following example illustrates the generation of a Bernoulli event E using the procedure given in Fig. 9.11.

Given probability of occurrence of event E: $P = 0.75$.
Step 1. Generate uniform random number U: 0.68345.
Step 2. Compare U and P. Is $U \leq P$? Is $0.68345 \leq 0.75$? YES.
Step 3. If the answer is YES event E occurs. Therefore event E occurs.

The above routines are all applicable in randomization procedures in model processing. However, some are more frequently applied than others, depending on the given problem. Next we examine routines that are applicable to expected value and deterministic procedures.

Expected Value Generator

In expected value procedure the outcome is determined by using the mean value with variance zero. With no variance we eliminate any random processes in the computations, as the value never deviates from the mean value. For probabilities associated with reliability, we determine the outcome on a population N by multiplying by the mean value probability. For probabilities associated with effectiveness and event occurrence, we determine the outcomes in a similar manner. For probabilities associated with functional operation time and measurement errors, we use the mean values.

We illustrate the flow chart for a generalized expected value model in Fig. 9.12. This routine, however, is only applicable to expected value procedures involving reliability, effectiveness, or event occurrence. For time intervals and measurement errors the procedure is even simpler than the example shown in Fig. 9.12. We just use the average values.

Deterministic Function Generator

A deterministic function contains no chance elements; thus for a given set of parameters and variables the computational results are always

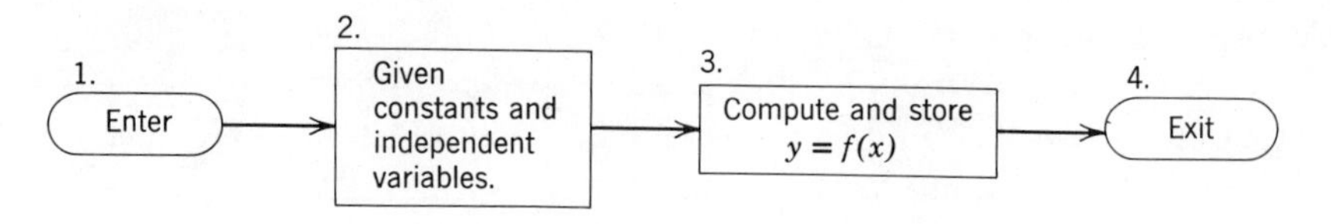

Fig. 9.13 Deterministic function generator.

the same. We illustrate the flow chart for a generalized deterministic function generator in Fig. 9.13.

Summary

We now summarize the applications of our discussion in the implementation of the logical flow chart. We have discussed modularization and described several auxiliary modules, and we have illustrated them with flow charts. We have characterized modularization as efficient, logically sound, and easy to implement and revise. It is an additive procedure in which we build the model by the addition of modules or blocks.

The statements contained in the logical flow chart must be explicitly stated and must use consistent symbology. The statements must be clear and concise, yet contain sufficient information that the user can understand unequivocally what is said and intended. For example, statements such as the following are quite explicit:

"Transfer to ELIT routine."
"Compute sine X."
"Generate normal random number R."

These statements tell exactly what to do and thus create no doubt for the programmer in transforming the logical flow chart into the program flow chart.

As modules or subunits are implemented each module should be given a descriptive title, like the titles we have used in our descriptions of auxiliary modules. The level of model structure should also be indicated, such as routine or subroutine. The function of each module in the model should be explicitly stated. The direction of logic flow should be very clear. We should be able to trace through the logic tree easily. The conditional flow, such as decision test nodes, should also be clear.

The initial implementation of the logical flow chart should progress in a form similar to what we have illustrated in Figs. 9.1 and 9.2.

We prefer to begin at the grossest level and then refine each module at the next level of detail. This refinement continues until we have adequately drawn the complete flow chart of the model.

In order to maintain some continuity and show relationships among the modules, we should adopt some consistent module numbering system. We have illustrated a numbering system in Figs. 9.1 and 9.2. A numbering system helps to illustrate the model structure and organization. We can easily determine where each element belongs in the hierarchical structure of the model. For example, from the previous figures we can determine that the speed check subroutine 2.4.2 is part of routine 2.4. If a given subroutine is used in several routines, we can assign the subroutine several numbers that refer to the various routines.

DERIVE THE MATHEMATICAL EQUATIONS EXPLICITLY

Concurrently with the implementation task of the logical flow chart, or prior to it, we should derive the mathematical equations as explicit functions. During the conceptualization phase of model construction it is adequate to express the mathematical functions implicitly. Since in Phase 1 we may not yet know what the explicit functions are, in Phase 2 we have to derive the functions analytically or by regression analysis of empirical data.

Example 9.10. We give an implicit expression of the flexural modes of vibration.

$$p = f(s, q, \rho, c, a).$$

The explicit expression is given by

$$p = \left[\frac{1}{4}\,\frac{s^2(s^2-1)^2}{1+s^2}\,\frac{q}{\rho}\,\frac{c^2}{a^2}\right]^{1/2}.$$

As we derive the mathematical equations, we implement them in the flow chart. The equations are then an integral part of the flow chart. The flow chart should represent the complete implementation of the model concept. The completed chart should contain the following features:

1. All modules (routines, subroutines, etc.) adequately detailed and properly titled.
2. A module reference numbering system.
3. Model logic explicitly shown.
4. Clear direction of activity flow.
5. All mathematical equations in explicit form.

Example 9.11. The following are examples of mathematical models that would be implemented in the flow charts of specific computer simulation models:

1. Total direct operating cost:

$$C = I_c + C_c + M_c + S_c,$$

where C = total direct operating cost
I_c = insurance cost
C_c = crew cost
M_c = maintenance cost
S_c = service cost.

2. Braking resistance of a moving vehicle:

$$B = C_0 + C_1 V + C_2 V^2,$$

where B = braking resistance of a moving vehicle
C_0, C_1, C_2 = resistance coefficients, all positive values
V = velocity of vehicle.

3. Linear movement:

$$X_1 = X_0 + R \sin \alpha$$
$$Y_1 = Y_0 + R \cos \alpha,$$

where $R = S\tau$
$\tau = t_1 - T_0$
S = speed
α = heading measured from true north
τ = time interval
X_0, Y_0 = X, Y at time t_0
X_1, Y_1 = X, Y at time t_1.

4. Work trip generation:

$$W_{ij} = \frac{(Q_j/R_{ij})(P_i)}{\sum_{j=1}^{m} Q_j/R_{ij}} \qquad (i = 1, 2, \ldots, n)(j = 1, 2, \ldots, m),$$

where W_{ij} = number of one-way work trips between i and j
Q_j = number of jobs available at j
P_i = number of workers living at i
R_{ij} = straight-line distance between i and j.

5. Linear program formulation of an allocation problem:
Minimize

$$\sum_{i=1}^{m} \sum_{j=1}^{n} C_{ij} x_{ij}$$

subject to

$$x_{ij} \geq 0$$

$$\sum_{i=1}^{m} x_{ij} = A_i$$

$$\sum_{j=1}^{n} x_{ij} = B_j,$$

where C_{ij} = coefficients
X_{ij} = variables
A_i = supply at ith location
B_j = capacity at jth location.

6. Aerodynamic drag:

$$D = \tfrac{1}{2} C_D A \rho V^2,$$

where D = aerodynamic drag
C_D = drag coefficient
ρ = air density
A = cross-sectional area
V = velocity.

7. Trajectory equations:

$$\frac{d\theta}{dt} = \frac{g \cos \theta}{V}$$

$$\frac{dV}{dt} = -\frac{D}{M} + g \sin \theta,$$

where $d\theta/dt$ = rate of change of angle θ
dV/dt = rate of change in velocity
g = gravity constant
θ = angle between trajectory and horizontal
D = aerodynamic drag
M = mass of projectile
V = velocity.

8. Probability of detection:

$$P_D = 1 - e^{-np},$$

where n = number of attempts at detection
p = probability of a single detection
P_D = probability of detection.

9. Fuel consumption of an aircraft:

$$F = W_0(1 - e^{-kS}),$$

where F = weight of fuel consumed in flying
W_0 = initial gross weight of plane, including fuel
S = distance of flight
k = fuel consumption constant.

10. Determination of system availability:

$$A = \left(1 + \frac{\text{MTTR}}{\text{MTBF}}\right)^{-1},$$

where A = system availability
MTTR = mean time to repair
MTBF = mean time between failures.

11. Energy loss in the flow in pipes:

$$h = \frac{32lv^2}{\text{R}dg},$$

where h = energy loss
l = length of pipe
v = average velocity
R = Reynolds number
d = pipe diameter
g = gravity constant.

12. Radar power formula:

$$P = \frac{AGP_tK}{(4\pi)^2R^4},$$

where P = received power at receiver
A = effective cross-section of receiving antenna
G = power gain of feeder and radiating antenna
K = reflection coefficient
R = distance from radar to target
P_t = power at transmitter.

13. Reverberation time:

$$T = \frac{kV}{a},$$

where T = reverberation time
k = constant of proportionality
V = volume of room
a = absorption.

14. Archimedes' buoyancy principle:

$$F = \rho g V,$$

where F = buoyancy force
ρ = fluid density
V = volume of body
g = gravity constant.

15. Intensity of sound wave:

$$E = 2\pi^2 \rho f^2 a^2,$$

where E = sound energy
ρ = density of medium
f = frequency of vibration
a = amplitude.

16. Total incremental cost equation (inventory model):

$$\text{TIC} = \frac{C_1 Q}{2} + \frac{C_2 R}{Q}$$

where TIC = total incremental cost
C_1 = inventory holding cost
Q = lot size
C_2 = preparation cost
R = annual requirements.

CHECK MODEL VALIDITY

We come to the *first* major validity check during model implementation. Once the model has been derived it must be validated so that it corresponds closely to the real world and measures what it is supposed to measure. A model is an approximation to a real-world situation in which the model is valid within certain confidence limits. Unless validity is proven, we never know with confidence that the model measures what it is supposed to measure.

There are many classical physical models, such as the equations of a free falling body, whose validity has been proven and which are accepted as valid. Valid models can be incorporated as submodels in the mathematical model where appropriate. Each valid submodel contributes to total model validity. However, one nonvalid submodel can destroy total model validity, and so it is still necessary to determine over-all model validity.

Determining model validity may very well be the single most significant problem in computer modeling and simulation. Unquestionably, the confidence attributed to the model results depends on the model validity. The proof of model validity is the burden of the model builder, and so he must rationally describe the validity of the model within specified confidence limits.

On completion of the model logical flow chart we have arrived at a major milestone in model construction. We have essentially defined the model explicitly, except for programming. Before proceeding to the programming task, we should re-evaluate the entire procedure up to this stage of development. The model concept should be reviewed in relation to the logical flow chart and the mathematical equations. We should ask the following questions about the model:

1. Is the concept of the model appropriate?
2. Does the logical flow chart accurately represent this concept?
3. Is the logical flow chart complete and free of inconsistencies?
4. Are the mathematical equations correctly stated?
5. Are the mathematical equations correctly applied?

All these questions must be answered in the *affirmative* before we can consider that we have a valid logical flow chart. Question 1 was really answered at the conclusion of Phase 1. However, a critical review of the conceptual model is necessary if we are to answer Question 2. We should review each function in the conceptual model and determine whether the function is appropriately implemented in the logical flow chart. As we check the accuracy of implementation in Question 2, we should also check for completeness and consistency in Question 3. We should check that the logical flow chart includes all the necessary information in sufficient detail. The logical flow chart should be explicit, and nothing should be implied in the final version of the logical flow chart.

Quite separate from the logic, we must also check the validity of the mathematical equations. For Question 4 we should check that all mathematical equations are correct. If the equations were derived from empirical data, we can check some test points in the equations for reasonable agreement with the empirical data. If the equations were derived theoretically, we can calculate some test points for reasonableness of results. An additional check on the equations is to perform a dimensional analysis. We should check that all dimensional units, such as feet per second, are appropriate and that the scaling is correct. We should check that all the dimensional units balance in the equations.

For Question 5 we should check that all mathematical equations are correctly applied in the logical flow chart. We must be sure that the right equation appears in the right calculation box in the logical flow chart. We must also be sure that the results of the calculations are applied correctly in the model process.

The validity checks at this stage of model construction are quite critical. It is easier if errors and mistakes in the logical flow chart are detected and corrected now rather than later. Unfortunately, some errors can be difficult to detect, but this is all the more reason why we should diligently check for errors in logic and mathematical equations now. It is foolish to continue in the model development unless we are reasonably sure that the above five questions have been answered affirmatively.

The following is a suggested checklist as an aid in establishing validity of the logical flow chart:

Compare each conceptual model function with its logical flow chart implementation.

Check for completeness of flow.

Check for impedances in the flow and for any illogical flow.

Trace the flow for arrows going in the correct direction.

Check decision points for correct follow-on.

Check connector points for correctness.

Check language for explicitness, precision, and accuracy.

Check routines and subroutines for completeness.

Check inputs and outputs used in routines and subroutines.

Check that subelements are placed in the appropriate hierarchical structure.

Check that the flow chart has a "start" and an "exit."

Trace all loops. Be sure there is a way into each loop and a way out of each loop.

Examine all modification boxes for proper modifications.

Check the numbering scheme for consistency.

Check flow chart information for sufficient depth in detail, accuracy, and completeness.

Compare actual model outputs against desired model outputs.

Check the application of all mathematical equations for appropriateness.

Check equations for correctness.

Check dimensional units in all equations.

Check the sources of inputs to all equations.

Check the utilization of outputs from all equations.

Check equation constants for correctness.

Check for correctness of sources of constants, parameters, and variables.

Check all mathematical and logical symbology.

Check for correctness of higher derivatives.

Check subscripts, superscripts, and indices for correctness.

Check all scalars and vectors.

Check for errors in function generators, such as trigonometric and exponential routines.

Check for errors in statistical random variates generators. Check for randomness in each generator.

Check initial values of all parameters and variables.

Check parameter tables for completeness.

Check all mathematical equations for correct implementation.

SELECT THE COMPUTER

We are now at a stage of model development in which we must make the final decision on computer selection. The decision could have been made earlier, but to postpone it now will only delay the completion of the model. Upon completion of the logical flow chart we have a tangible realization of the magnitude of the model. We know the extent of computations required, and we know what the inputs and outputs will be. We can apply the criteria for computer selection described in Chapter 6. We summarize the criteria.

1. Ease of programming.
2. Least expense.
3. Computer accessibility.
4. Fastest results.
5. Computing requirements.

DRAW-UP PROGRAM SPECIFICATIONS

Before the computer program is actually written we must have already selected the computer, and we should draw up some program specifications to guide ourselves in writing the program. Program specifications specify the estimated size and magnitude of the computer program and programming effort. Program specifications should indicate the following:

1. Appropriate computer.
2. Approximate number of computer instructions.
3. Programming system and programming language.
4. Approximate storage size.
5. Desired computer running time per model run.
6. Desired programming and "debugging" time.

These specifications should be drawn up on the basis of our understanding of the problem, model requirements and an appreciation for programming problems. The specifications provide a perspective and fix the context of the programming effort to the total problem. The specifications are guidelines for the programmer in programming the model for the computer.

Example 9.12. The following are program specifications for a computer simulation model called the TRANS model:

The TRANS model will be programmed for a computer of at least 32,000 core. The auxiliary memory should contain tables and model inputs and outputs. contain a maximum of 15,000 program instructions. Active program elements, which include the program, executive routine, specific tabular values, scratch memory, and the monitor system, should be stored in the main memory of 32,000 core. The auxiliary memory should contain tables and model inputs and outputs.

Computer running time per model pass should be a maximum of five minutes on a large-scale computer or equivalent. Computer programming and program checkout should be completed within three calendar months from the start date and should cost less than six man-months.

PROGRAM THE MODEL FOR THE COMPUTER

Given a valid model and the program specifications, we can proceed to program the model for numerical solution on the computer. Programming includes all the procedures required to transform the logical statements and mathematical formulations of the model to computer statements. The following procedures are involved:

1. Modularization of the model in a programming context, in which the model is subdivided into logical units and subunits.
2. Construction of flow chart diagrams that represent the program flow of the model.
3. Coding of the program for the appropriate computer.
4. Checkout of the computer program using test cases to check the validity of the program.
5. Making necessary revisions.
6. Estimation of computer running time per model run as a function of the number of inputs.
7. Preparation of input and output data formats.

Programming is one of the major tasks in the implementation phase of model construction. During the conceptualization phase we gave some initial attention to programming. In preanalysis we determined the computer system and programming system to use, program specifications, and program checkout methods.

We also selected the most expedient programming system applicable to the model and the computer. We decided when to use the basic machine language and when to use synthetic languages, such as ALGOL or FORTRAN, or whether to use a simulation language, such as SIMSCRIPT. We estimated the number of computer instructions. We estimated the storage requirements. We estimated computer time per run. Finally, we determined the methods we will apply to program checkout. We determined what elements of the program can be checked separately, how we will check out the integration of these elements.

Example 9.13. How do we decide whether or not to use a simulation language? How do we decide which language, such as GPSS, SIMSCRIPT, or SIMPAC, to use?

We can suggest an approach to the decision. First, examine in detail the system or operation being simulated. Determine the general and specific features of the system. Next, determine what requirements are imposed by these general and specific features of the system. Next, locate a simulation language that can fulfill these requirements. Determine the feasibility, availability, and costs of using the simulation language. If the language appears appropriate, then we will use it. If the language appears inappropriate we should explore other alternatives until we have found the best solution.

We list below some features of GPSS, SIMSCRIPT, and SIMPAC as briefly summarized by Tocher [258].

	GPSS	SIMSCRIPT	SIMPAC
What computers can be used?	IBM 7090	IBM 7090, CDC 3600	IBM 7090
What is the basic computer language?	Machine	FORTRAN	SCAT
What are the dominant types of activities?	Transaction	Transaction	Transaction
How is the system represented?	Flow chart	General	Flow chart
Are magnetic tapes used?	Yes	Yes	Yes
What uniform random number generation technique is used?	Multiplicative	Multiplicative	Multiplicative
How many random number generators are available?	Indefinite	1	1
Is there uniform sampling?	Yes	Yes	Yes
Is there normal sampling?	No	No	Yes

	GPSS	SIMSCRIPT	SIMPAC
Is there Poisson sampling?	No	No	Yes
Can there be sampling from an input histogram?	Yes	Yes	Yes
Is there any statistical collecting in histogram form?	Yes	No	Yes
Can the mean be computed?	Yes	Yes	Yes
Can the standard deviation be computed?	Yes	Yes	Yes
What is the limit on the number of distributions?	100	None	None
Can arithmetic tests be performed?	Yes	Yes	Yes
Can set inclusion tests be performed?	No	Yes	No
Can logical tests be performed?	No	No	Yes

Our first major task in program implementation is to translate the logical flow chart into the program flow chart. This task is primarily a transformation of format but not activity content of the model. For each logical flow chart activity a programming procedure is selected and implemented in the program flow chart. Often several alternative procedures may be possible, depending on the programming system chosen. We usually select the most efficient procedure in terms of economy of number of instructions, storage space, and computer running time. However, the selection of programming procedures is generally the responsibility of the programmer.

The program flow chart does not necessarily look like the logical flow chart. However, the difference between the two should be in appearance only. The model content and computational and logical processes must remain the same as implemented in the logical flow chart. The logical flow chart indicates the flow of processes in the model. The program flow chart indicates "how" these processes will be done in the computer. There is an interface problem between logical flow charting and program flow charting, and we should give this interface problem very careful attention in order to prevent errors from being introduced into the model.

We illustrate an example of the transformation of the logical flow chart activities to a program flow chart in Fig. 9.14. The example selected is a trivial one, but it illustrates the transformation.

CHECK THE VALIDITY OF THE PROGRAM FLOW CHART

We come to the *second* major validity check during model implementation. The completion of the program flow chart is another milestone in model construction, and we do not want to proceed beyond the previous task unless the program flow chart accurately represents all logical flow chart activities.

We suggest a reverse process for the validity check of the program flow chart; in other words, we take the program flow chart and trace each feature back to the logical flow chart. We compare each program flow chart activity for agreement with the corresponding logical flow chart activity. We compare the program flow for agreement with the logical flow. For example, we take the illustration in Fig. 9.14 and trace the program flow chart activity for agreement with the corresponding activity in the logical flow chart.

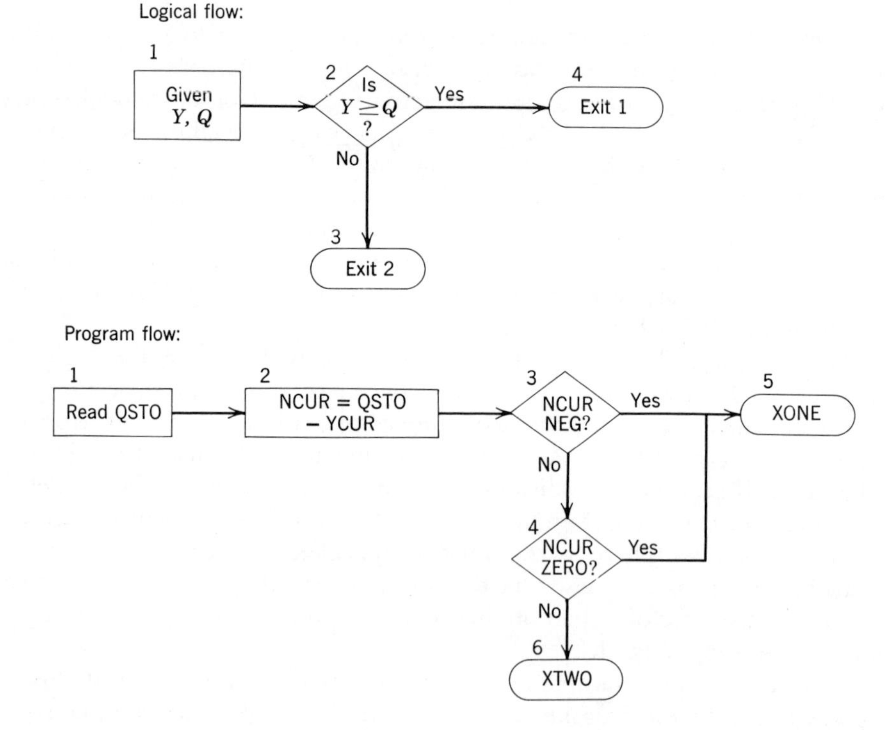

Fig. 9.14 An example of transformation from logical flow to program flow chart.

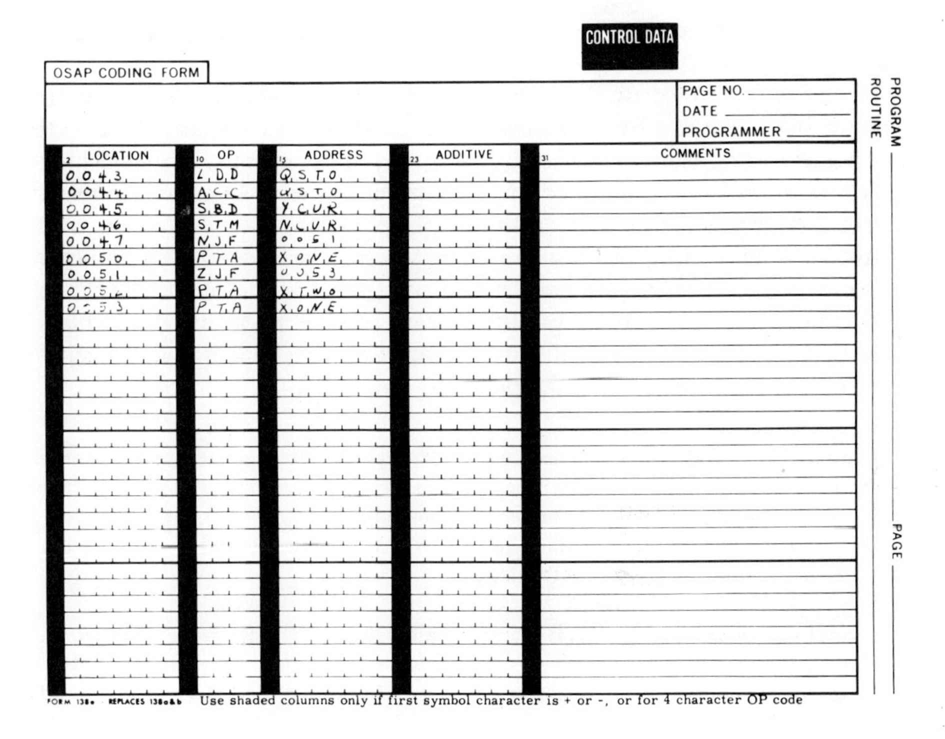

CONTROL DATA

OSAP CODING FORM

PAGE NO. ______
DATE ______
PROGRAMMER ______

PROGRAM ______ ROUTINE ______ PAGE ______

2 LOCATION	10 OP	15 ADDRESS	23 ADDITIVE	31 COMMENTS
0043	LDD	QSTO		
0044	ACC	QSTO		
0045	SBD	YCUR		
0046	STM	NCUR		
0047	NJF	0051		
0050	PTA	XONE		
0051	ZJF	0053		
0052	PTA	XTWO		
0053	PTA	XONE		

FORM 138a REPLACES 138a&b Use shaded columns only if first symbol character is + or -, or for 4 character OP code

Fig. 9.15 Hypothetical example of computer coding.

CODE THE PROGRAM

With a sufficiently detailed program flow chart, which accurately represents logical flow chart activities, we now proceed to the task of coding the program. Coding is a fairly straightforward and routine task if we have an adequate program flow chart. An adequate program flow chart is one that should enable a competent programmer to code the program with minimum assistance and guidance from the analyst.

In Fig. 9.15 we illustrate a hypothetical coding example for the program flow chart segment shown in Fig. 9.14.

CHECK THE VALIDITY OF THE CODED PROGRAM

We come to the *third* major validity check during model implementation. At the completion of the coding we have reached another milestone in model construction. The validity check of the coded program should be done at *three* levels.

First, by a reverse process we take the coded program and trace the coding back to the program flow chart, so that we compare the coded program for agreement with the program flow chart. This checking method is preferably handled by two programmers. One programmer uses the program flow chart, and the other programmer uses the program listing or the coding. In this reverse process the second programmer verbally translates program code into a program flow chart version while the first programmer retraces the process on the program flow chart. The coding is considered valid at this level of checking if the retracing is consistent with the flow in the program flow chart.

Example 9.14. The following example illustrates the dialogue in a sample case of validity checking by reverse process. The first programmer is following the flow chart and the second programmer has the coding.

Second programmer: "Add the value of SBAR to YBAR and store the sum in SYBAR. Compare SYBAR to SOBAR."

First programmer: "Correct."

Second programmer: "If SYBAR is greater than SOBAR, store SYBAR in SOBAR and call in FRAM routine."

First programmer: "Incorrect; the flow chart indicates TRAM routine instead of FRAM."

Second programmer: "O.K., I've noted the change in coding. Next, if SYBAR equals SOBAR, decrease the value of TALLY by one."

First programmer: "Correct."

Second, we select integral subelements in the program and check the logic and computations by running sample test cases on the computer. The sample test cases should be simple and straightforward. In test cases we predetermine the calculations and logic to test on the computer. If the program subelement results from the computer agree with our predetermined results we conclude that the program subelement is valid, and we have finished the checkout for that subelement. We continue with this process until we have checked out every subelement separately.

Third, we integrate all the subelements and checkout the entire model. Again we use sample test cases to check out the entire program. Usually several test cases may have to be run in order to exercise the entire model thoroughly. One test case usually only exercises a portion of the program, and we must devise other test cases to exercise the remaining portions of the program. These test cases should be designed to exercise the calculations and logic in the program.

Example 9.15. The following example illustrates computer program checkout using calculations from a sample problem: $z = 2x^2 + y^2$.

	Code	Operation	Results
122	LDD	$X = 3$	
123	ACC		3 in accumulator
124	MTP	3×3	9
125	STM		Store 9
126	MTP	2×9	18
127	STM		Store 18
128	LDD	$Y = 4$	
129	ACC		4 in accumulator
130	MTP	4×4	16
131	ADD	$16 + 18$	34

Once the computer program is checked out to the satisfaction of the responsible persons the program is considered operational and ready for production runs. At this point we should re-examine our original estimates of computer time per run. Program checkout may shed some new light on our original estimates. It would be quite useful, especially for the user of the model, also to derive a simple mathematical approximation of computer time per run as a function of model input quantities.

DOCUMENT THE IMPLEMENTATION OF THE MODEL

Documentation at the conclusion of the implementation phase should include the following items:

1. The complete logical flow chart, including the explicit mathematical equations.
2. A substantiative statement of the validity of the logical flow chart and equations.
3. A description of the program indicating programming system and program specifications.
4. The complete program flow chart.
5. The complete program listing or coding.
6. A substantiative statement of the validity of the computer program.
7. Input/output format with descriptions, such a units, scaling, range of values, and headings.
8. Instructions on running the program.
9. Estimated time per computer run.

SUMMARY

In the implementation phase of model construction we translate the abstract model concept into a concrete, tangible model. We organize the model structure into a logical flow chart, and we explicitly derive the mathematical equations. We translate the logical flow chart into the program flow chart, and we code the program for the computer.

During the implementation phase we should perform three validity checks on the model. First, we review the model concept in relation to the logical flow chart for accuracy of implementation. Second, we check the validity of the program flow chart for agreement with the logical flow chart. Third, we check out the coded program.

At the conclusion of Phase 2 we document our work completed during the implementation phase, and the model is now ready for production runs.

PROBLEMS

9.1 What are the chief advantages of modular construction?

9.2 Select a model in Chapter 2 and make up a list of likely "events" applicable in the model.

9.3 Generate three uniform random numbers using the flow shown in Fig. 9.4 for $K = 7912$ and $U_0 = 4189$.

9.4 Is it possible to duplicate a series of uniform random numbers in two different runs? Explain.

9.5 Translate the logical flow of one of the random variates generators illustrated in this chapter into a detailed program flow chart.

9.6 Select a real or hypothetical computer and code the routine in 9.5 for computation.

9.7 Design a sample test case to check out the coding in 9.6.

9.8 Generate a binomial random number using the procedure in Fig. 9.7 for $n = 4$, $p = 0.3$.

9.9 Generate a normal random variate using the procedure in Fig. 9.6 for $\bar{X} = 5$ and $\sigma = 1.2$.

9.10 Select a classical formula from physics. Show the formula as an implicit function and as an explicit function.

9.11 Select five items from the list beginning on page 215. Explain and illustrate how you would apply each item.

9.12 Design a small segment of a model of a hypothetical (or real) system. Illustrate with a logical flow chart, program flow chart, and coding of the segment.

9.13 Prepare your own supplemental checklist of validity checks during the implementation phase.

9.14 Briefly summarize the "implementation" phase of model construction.

9.15 Briefly explain how to proceed in implementing a conceptualized model.

9.16 Locate and study a programmed uniform random number generation routine. What generation method is used? What is the computer? What are the restrictions on the starting number? What randomness test was used to check out the routine?

9.17 Locate and study a programmed normal random number generation routine. What generation method is used? What is the computer?

9.18 Select a model given in Example 9.11. Suggest a way to implement that model.

9.19 What salient features should appear in the documentation of the implementation phase?

9.20 What implementation problems might arise from a poorly conceptualized model?

9.21 Suppose there are three computer candidates from which to make a selection. Discuss how you would justify the final choice.

10

MODEL RESULTS

In the third or final phase of model construction—results—we execute the production runs on the computer. We analyze computer results and draw conclusions. We make recommendations and report on the findings. Phase 3, which represents about 40% of the total effort in model construction, is the evaluating-summarizing-recommending phase of model construction. In Phase 3 we reach the final objective in the solution of the problem, and we investigate future applications and potential growth of the model. Finally, we terminate the project.

However, before we start on the final phase, we should have done some careful planning during the previous phases of model construction. When to begin certain tasks in modeling is not always clear. We may only know when the tasks should be completed. This is applicable to certain analysis tasks. For example, by now we should have a plan for a purposeful and statistically valid experimental design. We should have a plan for handling the production runs on the computer. We should have a plan for the output analysis, and we should have a plan for illustrating expected model outcomes.

FINALIZE THE EXPERIMENTAL DESIGN

Prior to making production runs on the computer, an experimental design should be constructed giving the parameter levels and combinations of parameters to be incorporated in the production runs. The choice of the experimental design depends on the results expected from the simulation. A properly constructed experimental design should yield a maximum amount of information with a minimum amount of computational effort. Statistical techniques are utilized in the experimental design to yield the most efficient and economical design.

Example 10.1. The following are examples of parameters with various levels shown for each:

Speed: 50, 100, 200, 500, knots.
Altitude: 1000, 5000, 10,000 ft.
Number of aircraft: 1, 5, 8.
Flying time: 2, 3, 5 hr.
Wind velocity: 10, 15, 20 mph from N, E, W, S.
Probability of false alarm: 0.02, 0.04, 0.06.

DETERMINE COMPUTER AVAILABILITY

As far in advance as is feasible we should determine computer availability and request computer time. We should indicate how much time we will need and when we will need it. We should indicate any special peripheral equipment that may be needed and whether any unusual demands are expected for the computer or operating personnel.

From the experimental design we can determine the requirements for the production runs on the computer. We can determine the quantity of input data required and estimated running time. When we know the computer requirements, on one hand, and computer availability, on the other, we can draw up a schedule of production runs. The schedule should show when the inputs will be prepared and when the computer runs are scheduled. We should monitor the schedule closely to observe any deviations from it. If circumstances change we must update the schedule for the new conditions.

EXECUTE COMPUTER RUNS

Once the program is operational and the experimental design has been determined we can proceed with model computations on the computer. Normally the production runs on the computer involve the following procedures:

1. Preparation of input data sheets.
2. Transcription of input data to computer inputs, such as punched cards or input tapes.

3. Verification of computer inputs.
4. Executing computer runs.
5. Retrieving computer outputs.

Simulations should usually be run in *two* phases: pilot runs and production runs.

We conduct pilot runs to check out the model and to determine sensitivity of results to changes in level of inputs. Checkout of model validity is primarily to authenticate the model; that is, we determine that the model does what it is supposed to do. Sensitivity analysis is a procedure to determine the sensitivity of output variables due to incremental variations in the input parameters. There are several methods of conducting a sensitivity analysis.

One method of sensitivity analysis is to use a statistical design, such as random balance or fractional factorial experiments, of input parameters, and to analyze the variations in the outputs. Another method is to take the partial derivatives of each variable in each equation. The calculation of the partial derivatives of each variable yields formula sets for the rate of change of each output variable with respect to each input variable.

When we execute the production runs we first prepare data inputs for the computer. The inputs are prepared on data sheets in the appropriate input format for the program. We should verify the data sheets to be sure the data are correct. Next we transcribe the data from the data sheets to computer inputs, such as punched cards or punched tapes. We should always verify the computer inputs against the data sheets to be sure no errors of transcription have been made.

Input data errors are not uncommon and can be a nuisance. Even small errors can delay the schedule unnecessarily. Suppose computer runs have been scheduled to run only once daily. Any error that disrupts the scheduled computer run causes a one-day delay in the schedule. The time we spend in verification of the inputs is worthwhile if it eliminates potential delays in the schedule. Some computing facilities contain peripheral equipment for verification of inputs, such as a card verifier. We should take advantage of this equipment whenever we can.

Computer centers or installations are either "open shop" or "closed shop." In open shop anyone with a program to run comes in during his scheduled time and runs the program on the computer himself. In closed shop the facility accepts the program and input data, runs the program with its own operators, and returns the completed output package.

If the production runs are to be made in closed shop we must make up complete and explicit instructions for the computer operators. We should indicate what input/output devices and programming system to use, as well as special library routines, reference tapes, tape drives, etc. We submit the run for computer processing, and upon completion we obtain the computer outputs and examine them for reasonableness.

We examine to make sure we have the correct outputs for our program run. We review the outputs for correct format and expected quantity, and we examine the outputs for reasonableness and completeness (Fig. 10.1).

If our experimental design calls for a feedback loop before the next run we should perform whatever output analysis is necessary to feed back the information. Even if the feedback is not a part of the plan it is always wise to examine the outputs, if possible, before submitting the next run. There might possibly be some significance from an output for subsequent runs. We continue the production runs according to our schedule until all the runs in the experimental design are completed.

In order to assure that the production runs proceed according to schedule we should direct our attention to three stages of the computer runs. These are (a) input preparation, (b) program run, and (c) output retrieval.

During input preparation we must be sure we have the right data and that they are correct. The inputs should be prepared, validated, and submitted for computer runs according to schedule. We should always be sure that we do not fall behind schedule in input preparation. If we do fall behind schedule the other two stages of computer runs are affected.

During program run we must be sure the program is properly executed and the input data properly applied to the computer program. At output retrieval we must be sure we have the corresponding outputs and inputs. We must be sure the outputs are valid and complete. We must remember that the computer records and saves only those results for which it has been programmed. If feedback is necessary before the next run we must carry the task out within the schedule.

During production runs, if we are to proceed according to schedule, we must have all the routine mechanics planned, such as where, when, and by whom the inputs are prepared, the verification of the inputs, when and by whom the inputs are submitted for computer processing, handling output pickup, and analysis, storage, and filing of the outputs. Production runs can be one of the busiest times in the whole process of model construction, as there are so many clerical tasks to be performed in addition to output analysis. During production runs more persons usually become involved in the operation than at any other time, thus

SUM REV	AT 1/2 U	AT 2* U	COST	COST/PM	ENT COST	SCALE INC	NREV END
119405.55	238811.10	59702.77	109000.00	2.81	5.00	1.00	-10405.54

STATION I	STATION J	DISTANCE	PASS LD	REVENUE	FARE	PMILE COST
10	11	3.40	19037.	2855.55	15.	4.41176
8	9	3.80	2222.	333.30	15.	3.94736
9	10	4.10	1739.	347.80	20.	4.87804
6	7	4.30	3785.	757.00	20.	4.65116
5	6	4.40	729.	145.80	20.	4.54545
4	5	5.00	1594.	318.80	20.	4.00000
7	8	5.10	3161.	632.20	20.	3.92156
1	2	6.90	20547.	5136.75	25.	3.62318
9	11	7.50	16768.	5030.40	30.	4.00000
5	7	7.70	417.	125.10	30.	3.89610
8	10	7.90	64.	19.20	30.	3.79746
7	9	8.90	220.	77.00	35.	3.93258
4	6	9.40	4611.	1613.85	35.	3.72340
8	11	11.30	5478.	2191.20	40.	3.53982
1	3	13.40	40991.	18445.95	45.	3.35820
4	7	13.70	488.	219.60	45.	3.28467
3	6	14.50	52.	26.00	50.	3.44827
7	11	16.40	1302.	716.10	55.	3.35365
1	4	18.50	41402.	24841.20	60.	3.24324
3	7	18.80	154.	92.40	60.	3.19148
1	5	23.50	8769.	6576.75	75.	3.19148
1	6	27.90	19850.	16872.50	85.	3.04659
1	7	32.20	13735.	13735.00	100.	3.10559
1	8	37.30	5075.	5582.50	110.	2.94906
1	11	48.60	8768.	12713.60	145.	2.98353

Fig. 10.1 Sample of a computer printout.

creating problems of supervision and coordination of personnel and work efforts. For large models it is quite useful to have an expediter to dispatch all the production tasks.

ANALYZE THE OUTPUTS

In order to perform an output analysis effectively we must know what to do with the computer results and how to interpret these results. This presupposes some preliminary analysis during the previous phases of model construction. We should have planned the extent to which we will use the computer to perform the output analysis. From the experimental design we have determined the quantity of outputs required and how we will analyze the outputs.

We should have an adequate computer printout that contains both summary and detail information. A carefully planned format greatly facilitates the handling of computer outputs.

In order to study and analyze the computer results we must analyze outputs versus inputs. The computer printout should contain a listing of input parameters and variables and a listing of the corresponding outputs. All inputs and outputs should be appropriately labeled and have correct dimensional units. The results can be presented in the printouts in tables, graphs, charts, diagrams, etc.

Usually computer printouts are in language representations using alphabetics and numerics. However, computers can also be effectively used to produce pictorials, such as charts, graphs, and diagrams. Pictorial outputs require more specialized handling of the output processor than language printout only. However, we should explore the possibility and feasibility of pictorial printouts if they are appropriate to the illustration of problem results. For example, many computer routines already exist to print out an *X–Y* graph. These are available in some computer libraries.

Example 10.2. The following plotting routines are available through IBM branch offices:

"EAI Data Plotter Subroutine Package," File No. 7090-3040COPLTP.

"7090/94 Plotting Routine for EAI Data Plotter Model 3034 C/D," File No. 7090-3134WHPLT4.

"Automatic Graphic Package," File No. 7090-3172AMGRPH.

"Plotting Routine for Functions of 1 or 2 Independent Variables," File No. 7090-3140OURTBN.

The following are examples of some commercially manufactured data plotters that use card or tape inputs:

CDC 165 Data Plotter, made by Control Data Corporation.

Concord Digital Coordinatograph, made by Concord Control Inc.

EAI Data Plotters, Models 3034, 3120, 3130, 3440, and 3500, made by Electronic Associates Inc.

A FORTRAN routine for plotting two dimensional graphs is given in [403].

The computer can be used effectively to compute statistics of the outputs in the output processor. We can easily implement the output processor to compute any of the statistics, such as mean, variance, analysis of variance, regression analysis, and χ^2 test. We should use the computer to compute these statistical functions whenever it is feasible. Computer programs have already been written and checked out to perform statistical analyses. Many of these programs are available from program-sharing libraries.

How much of the output analysis task should we assign to the computer?

We should assign to the computer as much output analysis as it can perform, as much as is feasible in our schedule, and as much as we can afford within the budget. Computer costs go up as we give the computer more to do, and manpower costs for output analysis go down. There is less chance for human error if we assign a bigger role to the computer. We can be confident that the computer will perform as we instruct it to perform, and the computer performs almost without error.

Example 10.3. Prepared computer routines are available for use in the analysis of computer results. Most computer manufacturers maintain reference libraries of routines that are available to users of the computers. The following are examples of analysis routines available through IBM branch offices:

"Multivariate Regression Program" File No. 7090-3104AMRGNL.

"General Purpose Analysis of Variance Program," File No. 0709-3027 NOANAV.

"Curve-Fit of Second Degree Simultaneous Differential Equations," File No. 7090-3173AMHOVA.

"Stepwise Multiple Regression Procedure," File No. 7090-3143ERMMPR2.

"Least Squares Regression Fit to Sum of Two Exponentials," File No. 7090-3014TYELS2.

"A Least Squares Iteration," File No. 0709-3024NOLSQ.

The following are examples of computer programs developed for biomedical research but also applicable in other disciplines. These programs are available from the Health Sciences Computing Facility, University of California, Los Angeles.

"Factor Analysis," BMDO3M.
"Canonical Analysis," BMDO6M.
"Simple Linear Regression," BMDO1R.
"Stepwise Regression," BMDO2R.
"Multiple Regression with Case Combinations," BMDO3R.
"Polynomial Regression," BMDO5R.
"Asymptotic Regression," BMDO6R.
"Analysis of Variance for One-Way Design," BMDO1V.
"Analysis of Variance for Factorial Design," BMDO2V.
"Analysis of Covariance for Factorial Design," BMDO3V.

ILLUSTRATE MODEL RESULTS

We now discuss some visual methods for presentation of model results. We can illustrate the results by tables, graphs, response surfaces, charts, or diagrams. We should select whichever method is most appropriate to illustrate the results to the user.

Tables are very convenient for listing results. We should give each table an appropriate title, define the headings correctly, and indicate the proper units. The format should be clear, and each table should be designed to convey only one major idea. Attempting to convey several concepts in one table leads to confusion in its interpretation.

Each table should be appropriately referenced to the corresponding computer runs and to other tables or graphs.

Graphs illustrate functions more vividly than tabular values. Tables do not readily show how a function behaves. Plotting data on graph paper illustrates their behavior. When we plot a graph we must select the appropriate dependent and related independent variables. Traditionally the dependent function is plotted along the vertical axis and the independent function on the horizontal axis. The graph illustrates how the dependent function varies as the independent functions change.

Each graph should be correctly titled and identified according to the appropriate parameters. Each graph should be referenced to the proper computer output, tables, or other graphs. We should label the vertical and horizontal axes appropriately and clearly. We should indicate the dimensional units. We should identify each curve with the appropriate parameters, and if data points are shown we should explain the symbology in the legend. The legend should contain precise information describing the graph.

In plotting graphs of tabular values we must select the most suitable scale for plotting. The vertical and horizontal axes may use the same or different scales. We can plot data on straight, semilogarithmic, logarithmic, or probability scales. We have illustrated examples of the first three scales in Figs. 10.2, 10.3, and 10.4, respectively. We have illustrated two examples of continuous probability scales for normal and log normal in Figs. 10.5 and 10.6, respectively. The probability plots represent the cumulative functions of the distributions. Even though we have

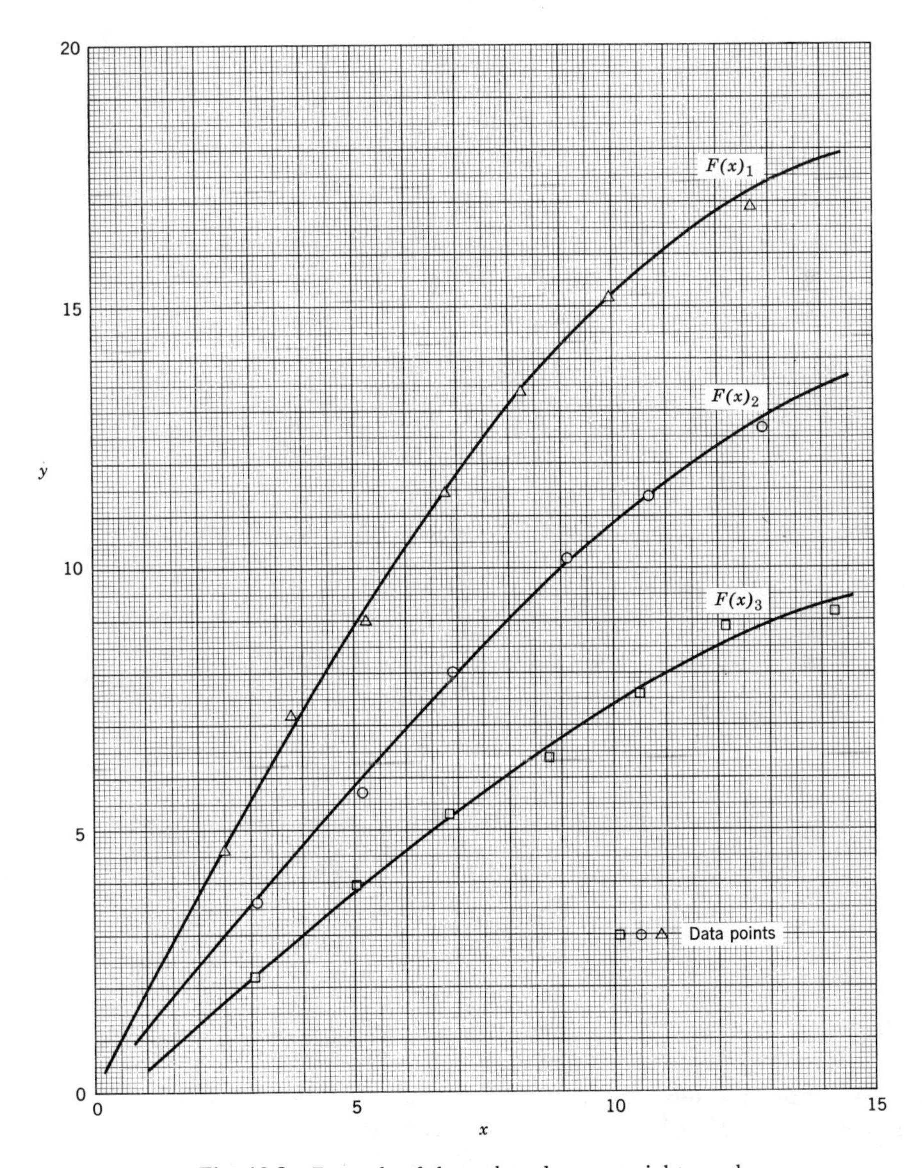

Fig. 10.2 Example of data plotted on a straight graph.

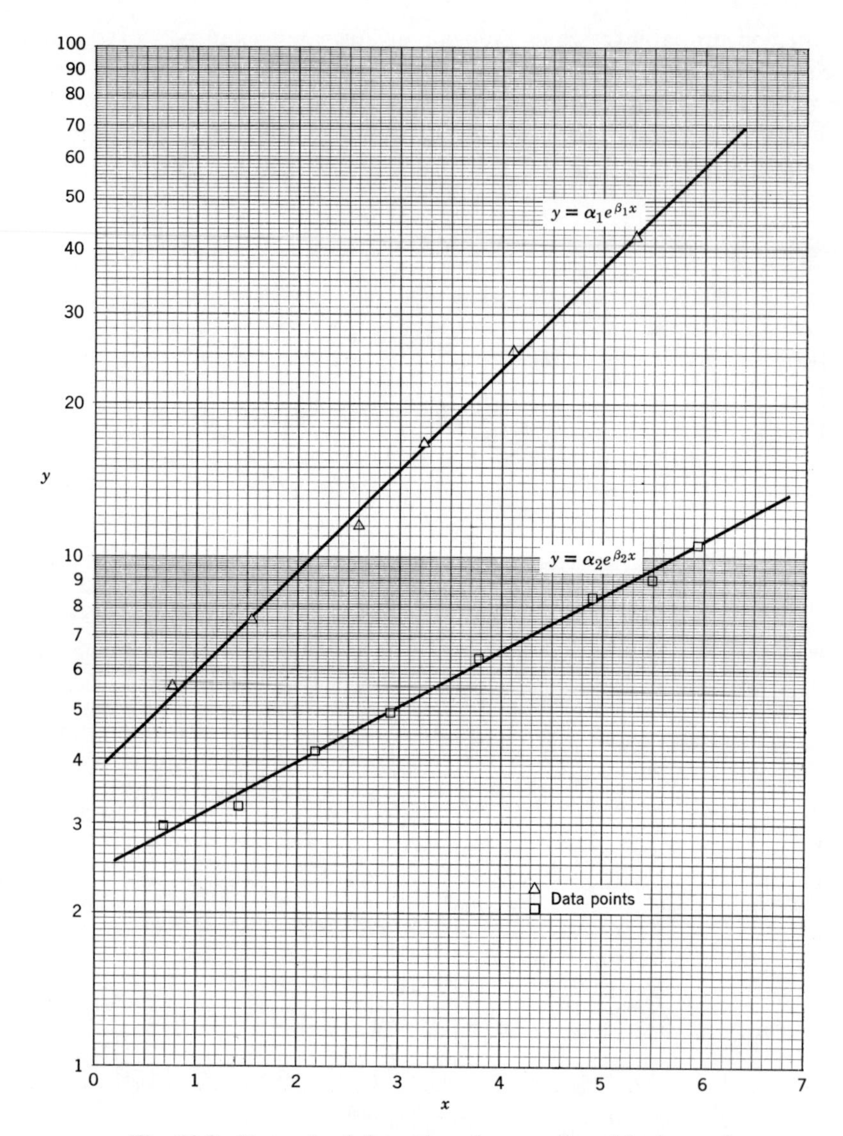

Fig. 10.3 Example of data plotted on semilogarithmic graph.

chosen to illustrate only continuous probability distributions, we can also plot graphs of discrete distributions, such as binomial or Poisson.

We select the most suitable graph, depending on which scale is most representative of the function. If we know the correct function beforehand we can immediately select the appropriate scale. If we do not

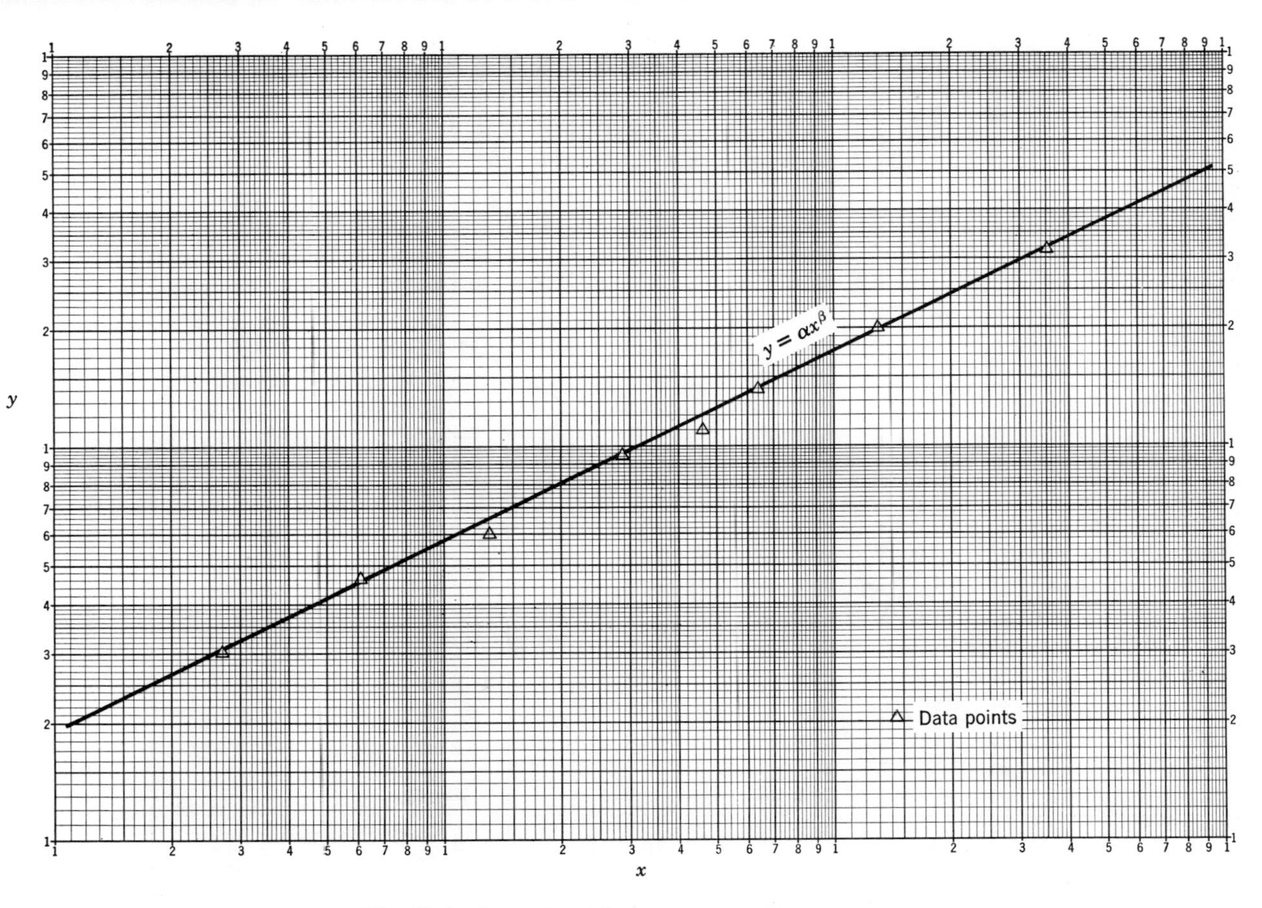

Fig. 10.4 Example of data plotted on logarithmic graph.

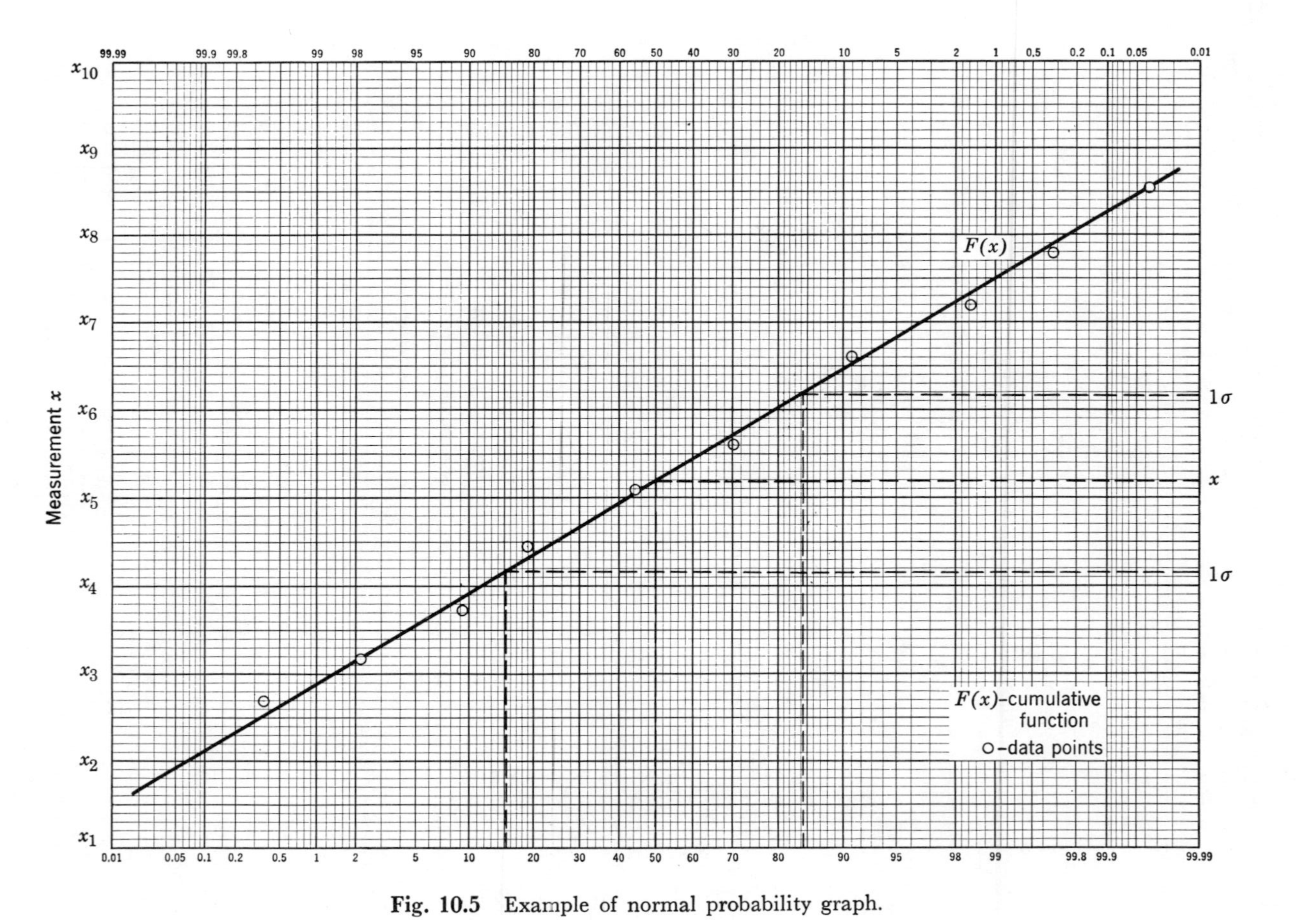

Fig. 10.5 Example of normal probability graph.

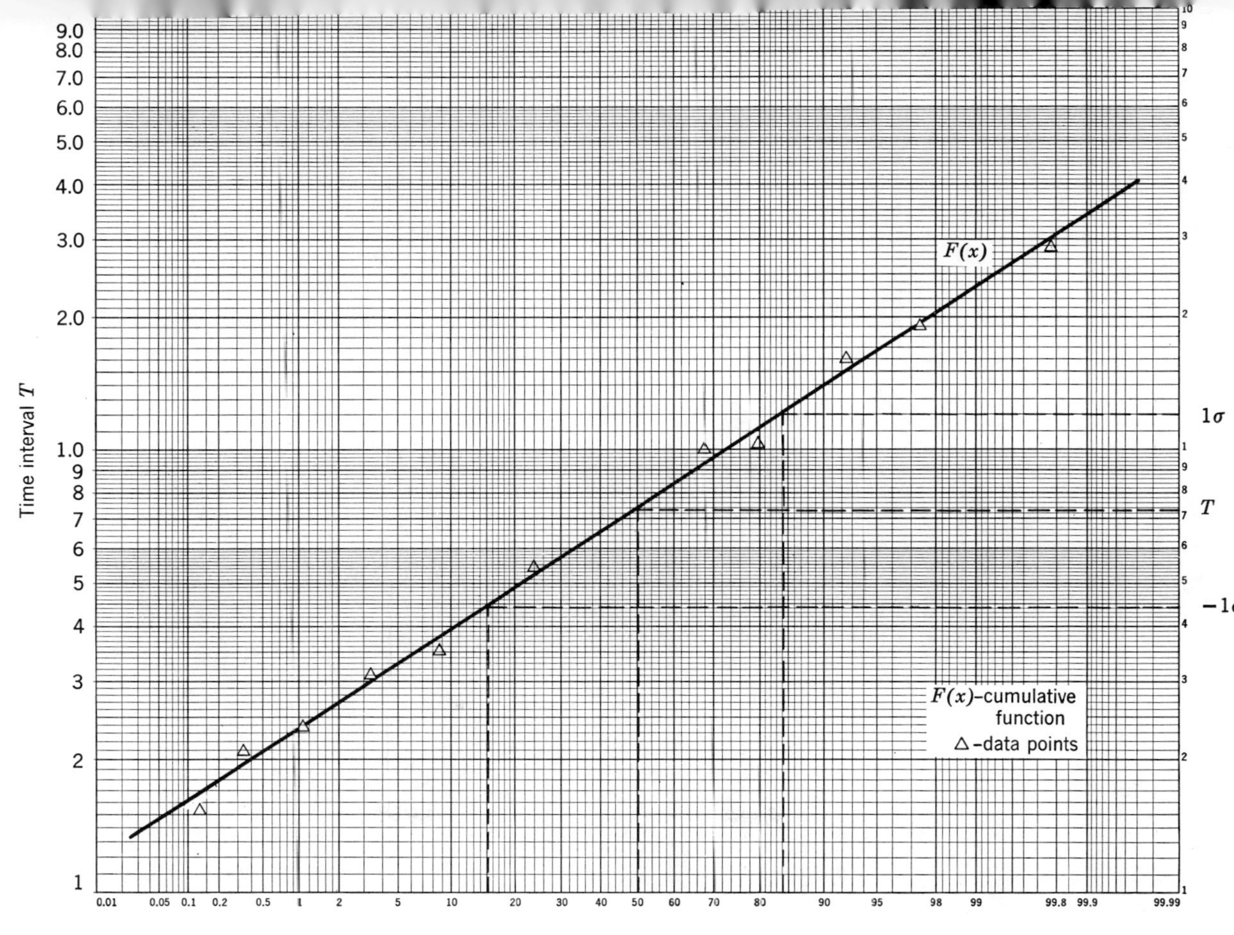

Fig. 10.6 Example of log normal probability graph.

know the function we can experiment with various scales to see which seems to fit the data best. If possible we usually choose that scale in which the data points are most nearly linear.

By using any of the scales mentioned above, we can illustrate measures of effectiveness for the response surface of the system or operation. We can illustrate response surface in two or three dimensions. For a small number of parameters and variables the response surface can be easily illustrated. In Fig. 10.7 we illustrate a response surface using linear scales, in which three variables α, β, γ are illustrated by response surface contours in two-dimensional graphs. The response surface can also be illustrated in perspective or by a three-dimensional model, such as a plaster of Paris model.

However, as the number of parameters and variables increases, it becomes increasingly difficult to illustrate graphically or by a physical model. It is very difficult for us to illustrate a multidimensional response surface consisting of four or more dimensions with the conventional three-dimensional space. We can illustrate four variables or more by an extension of the illustration in Fig. 10.7. However, it is difficult to interpret the results unless we choose the representation very carefully.

In addition to graphic representation or in place of it, we can represent

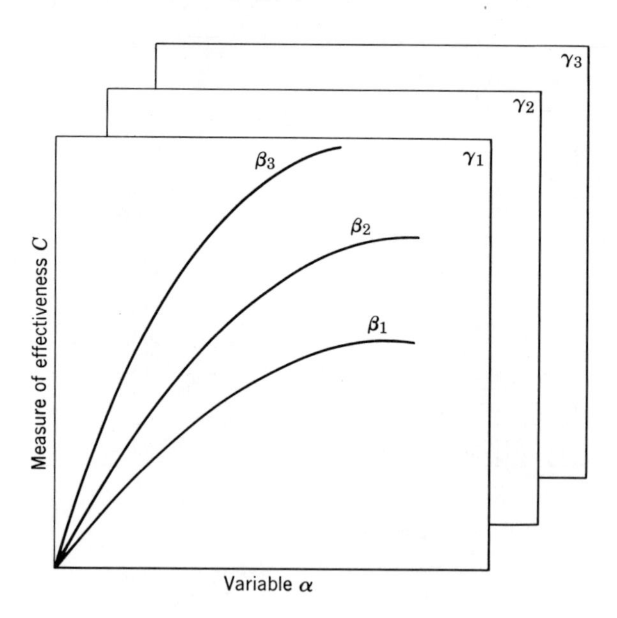

Fig. 10.7 Measure of effectiveness C shown as a function of variables and parameters α, β, γ.

the response surface analytically by response surface equations. Response surface equations are the analytical representations of the relation between the response of two or more parameters. We apply standard numerical curve-fitting techniques to the data in order to derive the response surface equations:

$$C = f(\alpha, \beta, \gamma \cdot \cdot \cdot), \tag{10.1}$$

in which the measures of effectiveness C are given as functions of α, β, γ . . . .

We can also derive the response surface equations from the graphs of the data. By inspection we can determine the slope and intercepts of the plots and determine the constants for the functions. This method is less accurate than numerical techniques, but nevertheless useful.

We can use charts and diagrams to illustrate the results more pictorially than in graphs. We can also use charts and diagrams to illustrate the results by a less technical presentation than graphs. Chart or diagram presentations should be very clear and simple. We should illustrate only a few salient features and only one major idea in each chart or diagram. We can put our point across more easily by clearness and simplicity of content than if we attempt to show too much.

A good rule for the choice of representation is to select that method of presentation which best illustrates the results to readers.

EVALUATE THE RESULTS

When we have analyzed the results we are able to evaluate them in relation to the problem solution. Evaluation of results proceeds easily if we have adequately preplanned our output analysis. With proper planning we should have already determined the expected results. We should already know how we plan to interpret and evaluate these results. Let us illustrate by citing results from an example based on a real system: an air traffic control device.

We seek to optimize the system parameters of an air traffic control device. This is a device that processes *X-Y-H* positional data of aircraft under surveillance by radar and compares the dynamic data with preplanned flight path parameters. The device continuously attempts a correlation of the right aircraft radar returns with the right preplanned flight path.

The method of correlation is by geometry, in which certain tolerances in three-dimensional space are permitted between radar returns and

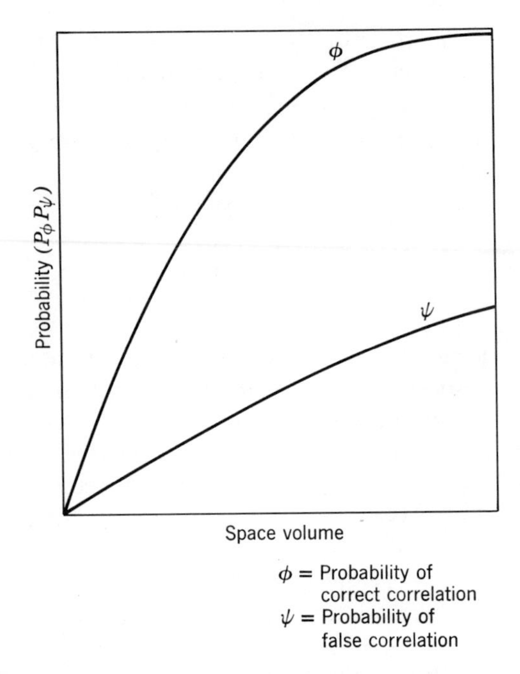

Fig. 10.8 Effects of volume tolerances on correlation probabilities.

each preplanned flight path. Each aircraft radar video return that continuously correlates with a given flight path is identified as that specified flight path. The amount of tolerance permitted between actual and planned flight is a system parameter. If the tolerance is very small the probability of establishing correct correlation between aircraft and flight plan is small. If the tolerance is increased the probability of establishing correct correlation also increases. However, the probability of incorrectly correlating with other aircraft in the vicinity and the probability of false alarm also increase.

The question posed is: How large a tolerance should be permitted to obtain the highest probability of correct correlation and the lowest probability of false alarm? The optimum parameters are determined from the results of a computer simulation model that uses empirical data from field testing as inputs. An example of the results is shown in Fig. 10.8, in which actual values are omitted. The appropriate tolerance parameters can be selected from the graphs by applying criteria for decision, such as performance effectiveness requirements, permissible false alarm rate, and costs.

SUMMARIZE THE RESULTS

When we have analyzed and evaluated the results we should summarize them briefly. We should summarize results for individual computer runs. We should indicate significant and salient features of the analysis and evaluation. We should indicate the relationship of the results with the experimental design, and we should indicate observable trends in relation to previous computer runs. The computer output, the analysis and evaluation, and the summary of results can be bound or packaged together for convenient filing or storage.

When all results are in we should analyze, evaluate, and summarize the complete results. Next we derive an over-all analysis, evaluation, and summary of the entire model results. We should indicate significant and salient features of the results for the entire experimental design. Upon completion we have two sets of analyses, evaluations, and summaries: for individual model runs and for over-all model results.

DRAW CONCLUSIONS

When all the results are in, analyzed, evaluated, and summarized we can draw certain conclusions from the experiment. We can test the hypotheses, and we can draw some inferences. These conclusions are based on results produced over a select range of values of input variables and parameters. These are values that were selected from the experimental design, in which our conclusions must relate to the results.

We should state the conclusions explicitly and substantiate them by the findings of the model results. It should be very clear and evident that we arrived at certain conclusions because the interpretation of the results logically leads to these conclusions. Any other conclusions should be inappropriate.

Example 10.4. The following are examples of conclusion statements:

"We conclude from modeling results analysis that installing one additional height-finder radar to the present configuration and situated one mile in any direction from the approach runway will increase the present number of tracking channels by 10% and increase height information accurately by 70%."

"We conclude that increasing green signal timing by 10% along route *A* during specified peak loads will permit an additional flow of 1000 cars per hour over the present amount with an additional delay for the cross traffic across route *A* of 50 cars per hour."

"We conclude that installing one additional checkout stand for every 50 customers will reduce customer waiting time by 5%."

MAKE RECOMMENDATIONS

On the basis of the model results and the conclusions we make certain recommendations relevant to the problem. The recommendations are not restricted to the problem alone. The recommendations should indicate follow-on problems and problem areas and how to handle these follow-on problems.

The recommendations should be explicitly stated and clearly presented, and the outlook of the statements should be objective. We should present the conclusions and recommendations in such a manner that management decisions can be made wisely on the basis of the accumulated knowledge from the computer simulation model efforts and results.

Example 10.5. The following are examples of specific recommendation statements:

"We recommend that for the predicted traffic flows on Sweetwater Bridge shown in Table 5 at least 2 toll booths and not more than 5 should be operational between 7 A.M. and 7 P.M. in order to permit the most efficient traffic flow."

"We recommend one additional surveillance radar be added to the network for every 5000 square miles to efficiently process the expected air traffic in 1975."

"We recommend further study to determine if the present communication network can handle the projected message traffic in 1975."

"We recommend additional studies be planned to determine the feasibilty of purchasing teaching machines for advanced algebra instruction."

DOCUMENT THE RESULTS

We should report on the findings as soon as possible upon completion of model computations and analysis of results. We should report the results clearly, accurately, and completely. We should use a clear and attractive reporting format, and we should make our presentation in a meaningful manner.

Documentation at the completion of the results phase of model construction should include the following:

1. The experimental design.
2. Abstract of computer run inputs.
3. Summary of computer outputs by individual runs.

4. Summary of the outputs from all the computer runs.
5. Analysis and evaluation of results.
6. Summary of results.
7. Conclusions and their substantiations.
8. Recommendations.
9. Future potential growth and applications of the model.

The complete documentation of the entire model project should include documentation from each of the three phases of model development. The documentation of the entire project is the final product. The final document should be attractive, and it should convey the complete story clearly and accurately.

Example 10.6. Modular report writing is an example of an efficient report-writing technique. A *modular report* consists of modules that are arranged in a logical, systematic manner, and each module is an integral unit in the report structure. A modular report is written in the following steps:

1. Construct a content outline in which all the materials are organized in a logical sequence and in modular design. Carry the outline to whatever level of detail is necessary to cover the contents of the report completely. For example, the modules may be arranged as follows:

1.0 Certain concepts are common to all transportation.
  1.1 There are time-spatial relationships.
  1.2 There are movable items.
    1.2.1 People move.
    1.2.2 Goods move.
  1.3 There are origins and destinations.
2.0 Motivational forces initiate movement.

2. Check the outline with all contributors for agreement in content, logical flow, completeness, and adequacy of coverage.
3. Revise the outline where necessary.
4. Take each module, such as 1.0, 1.1, 1.2, 1.2.1, 1.2.2, 1.3, and 2.0 shown above, and write a short essay completely covering the content of that module at the appropriate level of detail. For example, 1.0 is general in coverage, whereas 1.2.1 is at a finer level of detail. Whenever it is practical, illustrate a module with a figure, diagram, chart, or graph.
5. Arrange all the essays and illustrations in the same order as the content outline.
6. Rearrange and revise the report where necessary.

Modular report writing is especially useful whenever there are several contributors to the report, because the content is determined before the actual writing, and the level of detail of each module is established. It is easy to make revisions to the content outline, and it is easy to revise the report even after it has been written. A well-thought-out modular design covers the content completely and at the appropriate level of detail.

Example 10.7. The following is a suggested checklist to check the over-all documentation of a computer simulation model:

1. Check the text for completeness of thought, thoroughness of presentation, clarity, consistency of expression, substance, organization, language syntax, redundancies and omissions.
2. Check the spelling, punctuation, grammar, sentence structure, and verb agreement.
3. Check all mathematical equations for correctness, appropriateness, consistency and clearness of symbols, and appropriate units.
4. Review all examples and illustrations for accuracy and relevance in the text.
5. Check all figures and illustrations for correct titling and proper referencing in the text.
6. Check glossaries, bibliographies, table of contents, etc., for accuracy and clarity.
7. Check over-all format for attractiveness and esthetics.

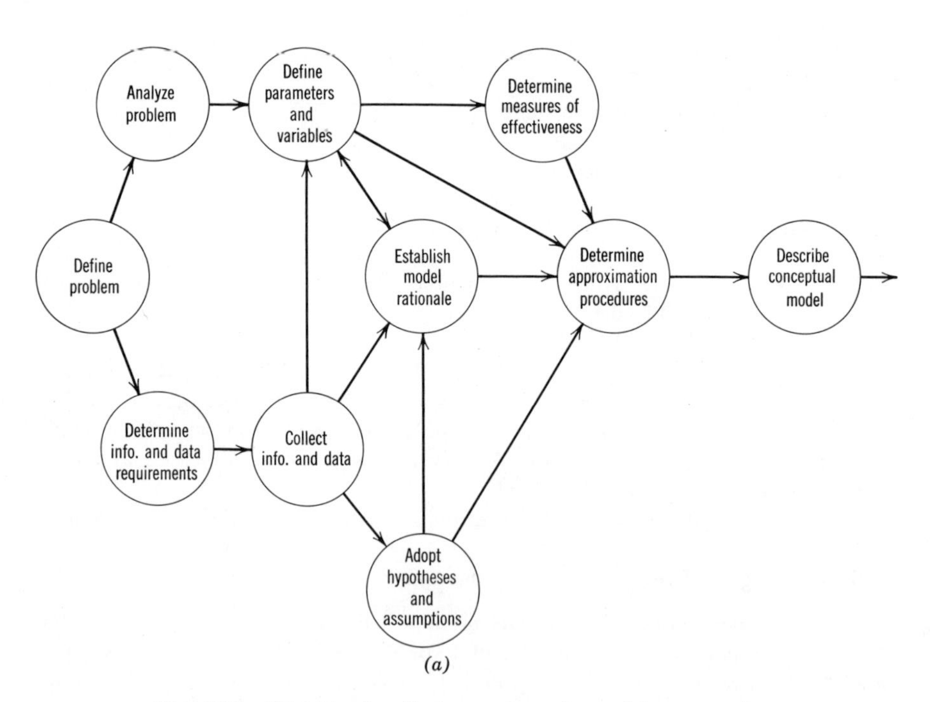

(a)

Fig. 10.9 "Bubble chart" of procedures in model construction.

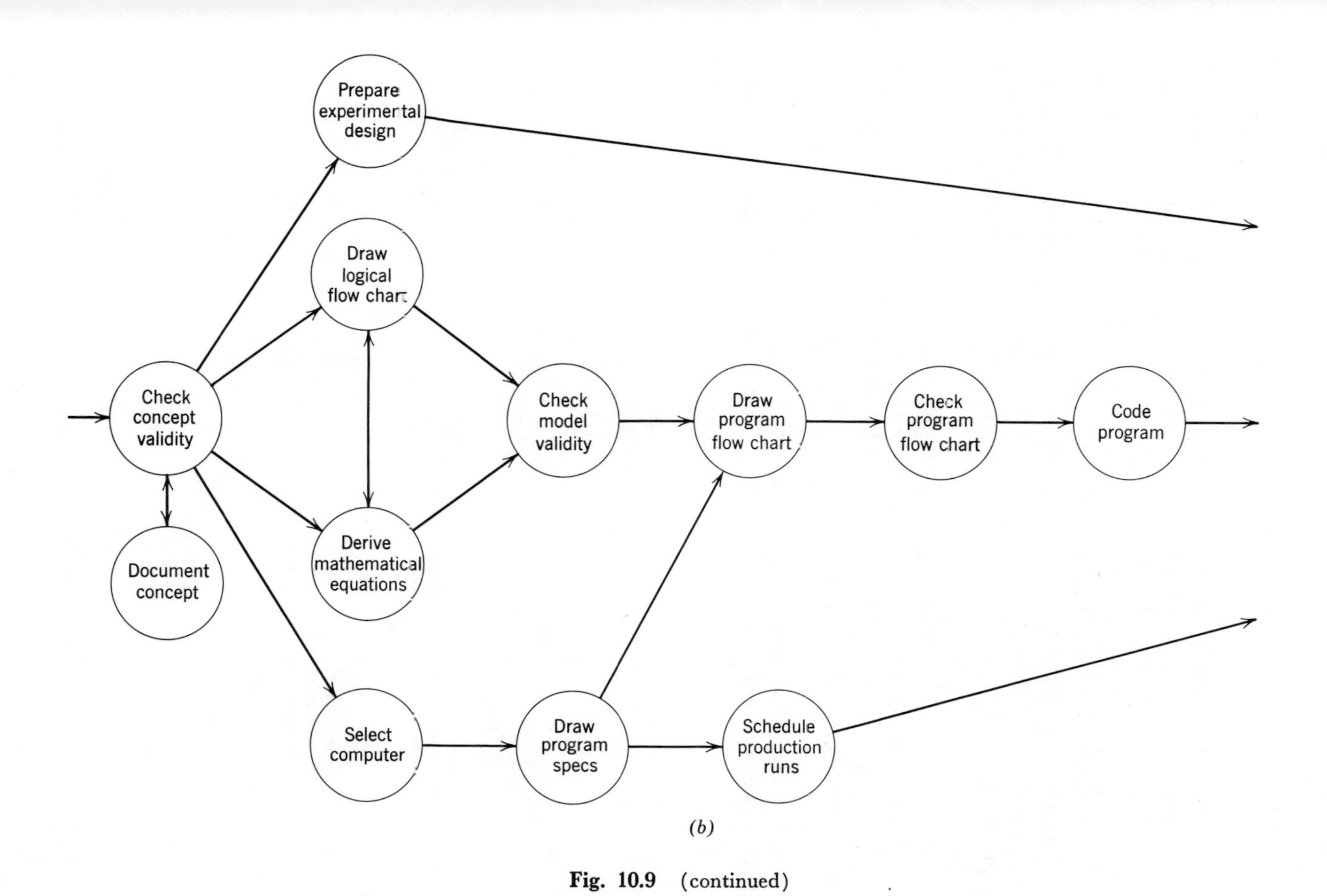

(b)

Fig. 10.9 (continued)

SUMMARY

We now summarize the tasks of model construction. We have grouped the tasks into three sequential major phases and described each phase in a separate chapter. In the *conceptualization* phase we examined the real world; we determined the approximations to use, and we defined the conceptual model. This phase is the "thinking and planning" phase of model construction. In the *implementation* phase we translated the abstract model concept into an explicit model. This is the "action" phase of model construction. We represented the model in the logical flow chart by logical-mathematical representation. We programmed the model for the computer, and we checked out the computer program. In the *results* phase we executed the computer runs and analyzed and evaluated the results. We summarized the results, drew conclusions, and made recommendations, and reported the findings.

In Fig. 10.9 we summarize the step-by-step procedures in model construction. We have used a simple pictorial representation in which each task is shown. In the so-called "bubble chart" we have enclosed

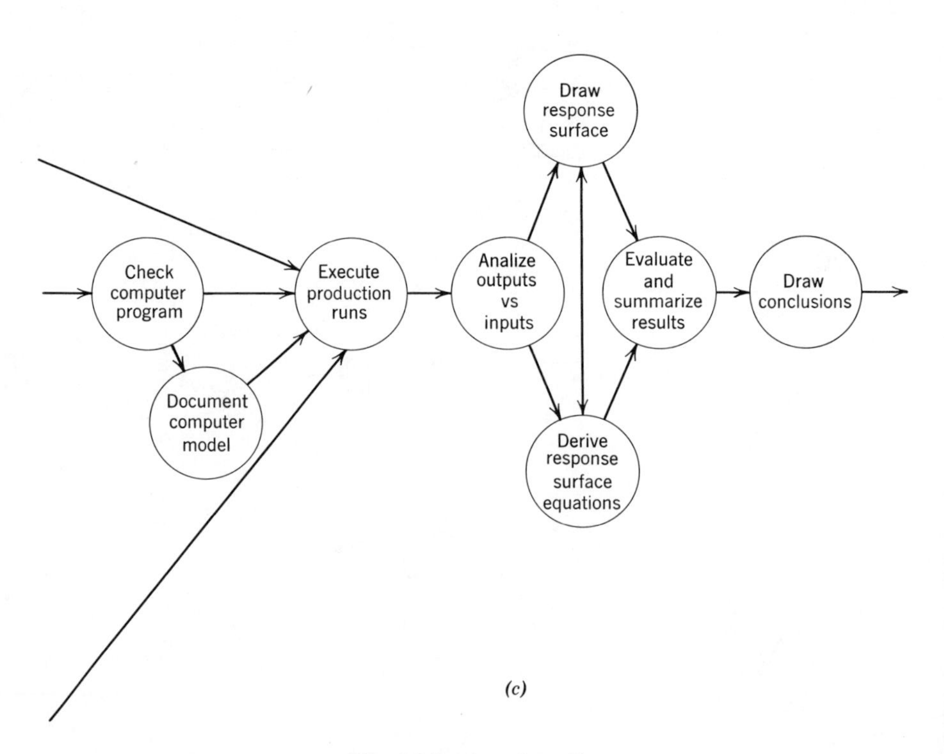

Fig. 10.9 (continued)

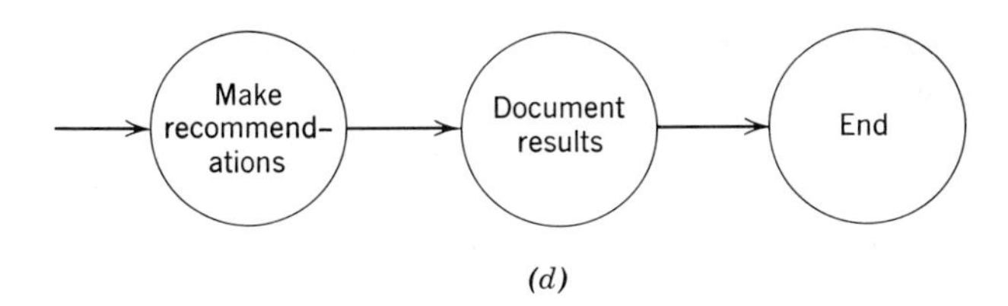

(d)

Fig. 10.9 (continued)

each major task in a circle or bubble. We have shown the logical sequence of tasks from beginning to end.

Normally the sequence follows the direction of the arrows. Usually any task can effectively be started only upon completion of all tasks with arrows directed to that task. Some tasks have interactions with other tasks. These we have illustrated with two-way arrows, such as the tasks of drawing the logical flow chart and deriving the mathematical equations. Some tasks proceed sequentially, and some tasks proceed in parallel.

The preparation of and adherence to a bubble chart assures us that we proceed in a logical manner and include all the major tasks in their proper sequence. In Part Four we have given some guidelines on construction of a model. Each problem is unique and requires unique handling, and so deviations from these procedures are often necessary. But if we interpret these guidelines broadly, we can find application to any model. We feel that with proper application the model builder is equipped to design and apply effective models in all research and analysis activities.

PROBLEMS

10.1 Plan a field trip to a nearby computer facility. Inquire about computer availability, costs, procedures for program submission, turnaround time, services available to the user, computing equipment, and peripheral equipment.

10.2 Given *X-Y* data, design a simple routine to plot the data on an off-line printer from a set of punched cards.

10.3 Select a model described in Chapter 2. Suggest and illustrate model results.

10.4 Prepare a brief report stating conclusions and recommendations based on results of a hypothetical modeling project. Draw some graphs to substantiate the findings.

10.5 Prepare an outline for the final report document of a hypothetical modeling project. Report in three phases.

10.6 For a project, design and develop a model of a real-world system or operation. State the problem. Develop a rationale. Implement the model and show expected results from computer runs. Follow the procedures shown in Fig. 10.9.

10.7 Briefly summarize the "results" phase in model construction.

10.8 Discuss what appear to be strengths and weaknesses in modular report writing.

10.9 Discuss the importance of clear presentation of results.

10.10 How elaborate should the presentation of results be?

10.11 Select a writeup or a document of a computer model. (a) Write a critique of the model. (b) Write a critique of the style of reporting on the model.

10.12 Select a model, such as one described in Chapter 2. (a) Determine what the expected results might be. (b) Illustrate how the results might be presented.

10.13 Select a document of a computer model. Prepare an outline of a modular report of the model using material from the present document.

10.14 Three candidate systems *A, B,* and *C* have been evaluated by computer simulation. Simulation results have been analyzed; conclusions and recommendations have been made. Postulate an outcome; then write a brief report giving conclusions and recommendations only.

10.15 Study the model described in Appendix B. Prepare an outline of a different reporting style that could have been used.

10.16 Expand and improve upon one of the following concluding statements.

We conclude that system *A* operates faster than system *B*.

We conclude that we have inadequate models to predict stock market trends.

We conclude that ground clutter effects in radar video returns can be decreased.

We conclude that increased air traffic over International Airport will create safety hazards.

10.17 Study the model described in Appendix B. Suggest possible revisions for the second-generation model.

10.18 Discuss the role of the model builder in making conclusions and recommendations based on model results.

10.19 Discuss the role of the model builder in the decision-making processes.

10.20 Show another way of presenting the following results.

$\gamma = 5$					
α_1	β_1	α_2	β_2	α_3	β_3
$\frac{1}{2}$	3	1	2	1	1
1	5	2	4	3	3
2	8	3	6	5	5
$\gamma = 10$					
1	2	2	2	2	$\frac{1}{2}$
2	5	4	3	4	$1\frac{1}{2}$
3	7	5	$4\frac{1}{2}$	7	$2\frac{1}{2}$
$\gamma = 15$					
2	$2\frac{1}{2}$	2	1	2	$\frac{1}{2}$
3	4	4	$2\frac{1}{2}$	4	1
5	6	6	$3\frac{1}{2}$	7	2

Appendix A

GLOSSARY

Aggregation. The process of considering groups of persons or things rather than singly.
Algorithm. A symbolic technique or method used in mathematical disciplines.
Analog. A representation by analogous method, e.g., a representation of numbers by physical magnitudes.
Analysis. Methods of determining how a system behaves when subjected to command inputs. Analysis takes a given system and determines its behavior.
Analysis of Variance. A statistical method of making inferences from an experiment designed to investigate the effects of several factors (or parameters) on a variable of interest.
Analytical Model. A mathematical model in which all functional relationships can be expressed in closed form and the parameters fixed in advance.
A Posteriori Probability. A probability determined afterwards. Empirical probability.
A Priori Probability. A probability set purely by the definition of a system. Mathematical probability.
Assembler. A computer routine that converts symbolic addressing to computer addressing.
Bar Graph. Same as histogram.
Block Diagram. A display of a system or operation.
Blocks. The horizontal or row designations in a matrix in the analysis of variance.
Central Limit Theorem. The theorem that states that the normal is the limiting distribution as the number of samples approaches infinity.
Coefficient of Correlation. A measure of the relative importance of the dependent variable to the independent variable in a linear relationship.

Coefficient of Determination. A measure of the relative closeness of a linear relation.
Compiler. A computer routine that converts programming language to machine language. A translator.
Compound Probability. The probability of an event having properties of two or more events, each of which has independent properties, is given by the product of the probabilities of each event. An application of the multiplication law.
Computer. An electronic system that can be programmed to solve numerical problems.
Concept. A thought. An idea. A mental image of an action or thing.
Conditional Probability. A probability computed under some assumption of the outcome of the events.
Confidence Level. The probability with which values can be expected to fall inside a specified spread about the mean.
Control Personnel. Persons who monitor and assess results of players in games, such as war games.
Coordinator. Person who serves as a common link between players and computer in a game.
Correlation. A relationship of two or more variables.
Covariance. Connection between correlated variables.
Cubature. Integration of $f(X, Y)$ over a rectangular area in the X-Y plane.
Cumulative Frequency Graph. A graph showing the number of cases along the vertical axis in all categories which fall below and including a specified amount. See Appendix E.
Cumulative Percentage Graph. A cumulative frequency graph in which the vertical axis is given in percentage. A graph of the probability distribution function $F(X)$. See Appendix E.
Cumulative Probability. The probability distribution function $F(X)$. A function giving the probability of a measurement occurring less than or equal to some specified number.
Curve Fitting. Representing a body of data by mathematical equations.
Curvilinear Regression. An analysis of the association among several variables in which a variable is approximated by a curvilinear function.
Cycle. A normal sequence of events.
Data Analysis. The process of extracting meaningful results from a mass of data.
Data Generation. The process of generating synthetic data that can be used in a system operation.
Data Reduction. The process of regrouping or reorganizing a mass of ungrouped data.

Degree of Freedom. The number of independent measurements that are available for estimating a statistical parameter. Abbreviated df.
Density Function. A function giving the frequency of specified measurements. Same as frequency function $f(X)$.
Dependability. The probability that a system will operate when needed.
Design of Experiment. The logical structure of an experiment.
Deterministic. Analytical, nonstochastic representation.
Differentiation. The process of finding the instantaneous rate of change of a function. The reverse of integration.
Digital. A representation by a clearly defined number.
Distribution. A systematic arrangement of numerical data. A distribution may be discrete or continuous.
Distribution Function. The integral of a density function or frequency function. The cumulative probability.
Effect. The change in response produced by a change in the level of a factor.
Effectiveness. The capability of producing a result.
Empirical Probability. The value of a probability that has been arrived at from accumulated data.
Entity. An object of which a system is composed.
Error. The difference between the *approximate* value of a quantity and the *exact* value.
Error Type I. False rejection of the hypothesis.
Error Type II. A hypothesis that is in fact false, but has been mistakenly accepted.
Event. A noteworthy occurrence in systems or operations processes.
Experimental Error. An error that tends to be distributed according to the normal error distribution.
Experimental Unit. The primary sampling unit.
Factorial Design. A systematic arrangement of a number of different factors.
Factorial Experiment. An experiment that studies the effects of a number of different factors on some observable quantity by varying two or more of the factors simultaneously.
Flow Chart. An orderly representation of a process. A graphic illustration in which activities are defined and their interrelationships are illustrated.
Frequency Function. Same as density function.
Frequency Polygon. A bar graph in which the midpoints of the tops of successsive bars are joined by lines and the bars are not drawn in. See Appendix E.
Function. A relationship between variables.

Game. A simulation of a situation of competition or conflict in which opposing players decide on a course of action to follow. For example, war games, business games.

Graph. A device for presenting visually the relationship between two or more variables.

Greco-Latin Square. An experimental design made of Greek and Latin letter designations.

Group Frequency Distribution. A histogram or frequency polygon in which the data are grouped in intervals of equal size. See Appendix E.

Histogram. A graph of frequency versus measurement presented in bar form. See Appendix E.

Index of Correlation. A measure of the relative importance of the dependent variable to the independent variable in a curvilinear relationship.

Index of Determination. A measure of the relative closeness of a curvilinear relation.

Integration. The process of finding a function when its derivative is given. The reverse of differentiation.

Interaction. An interaction exists if the effect of one factor is dependent on the chosen level of another factor.

Invariant. A constant.

Iteration. Repetition.

Joint Probability. Relative frequency with which two events occur.

Kurtosis. The relative flatness or peakedness of a frequency distribution curve. Fourth moment about the mean.

Latin Square. An experimental design utilizing Latin letter designations.

Law of Large Numbers. The estimate of the mean approaches the true mean as the number of samples approaches infinity.

Least Squares Method. A mathematical method of curve fitting.

Leptokurtic. A tall and thin frequency distribution curve.

Level. The fixed value of a factor (or parameter) examined in a factorial experiment.

Linear Programming. A method of maximizing or minimizing a function subject to contraints.

Linear Regression. An analysis of the association among several variables in which a variable is approximated by a linear function.

Markov Process. A stochastic process in which the conditional probability of a future state of a system is unaffected by the past history of the system.

Mathematical Model. The mathematical representation of a process or operation for which solutions can be obtained for a set of input variables.

Mean. The expected value of a random variable. The moment of central tendency. The average. The first moment about zero measurement on the frequency distribution curve.

Mean Deviation. The averaged, absolute value of the summation of the deviations from the mean.

Mean Square Deviation. The variance or measure of dispersion about the mean. The second moment.

Measure of Response. The measure of the result for a particular treatment.

Measurement Error. Error introduced by inaccuracies of the measuring device.

Median. The number that occupies the middle position.

Mesokurtic. A medium-sized frequency distribution curve.

Modality. Description of statistical data that occur the most frequently.

Mode. The number that occurs most frequently.

Modeling. A simulation technique for the analysis of operations and systems.

Modular. Logical, systematic compartmentalization of an operation.

Modules. Functional substructures of the total model.

Moments. Measurements of characteristic features of the probability density function.

Monte Carlo. A device for studying an artifical stochastic model of a physical or mathematical process.

Mutually Exclusive Events. If any particular event occurs on a specific occasion, it is not possible for a mutually exclusive event to occur on the same occasion.

Nondeterministic. Stochastic, probabilistic.

Nonuniform Random Number. A number selected at random from a nonuniform probability distribution. A random statistical variate.

Null Hypothesis. A hypothesis that assumes that the apparent difference between two means is due solely to random fluctuations, and that the true difference is zero.

Observation Unit. The ultimate subdivision of the primary sampling unit.

Operation. A process, a specific action.

Operations Research. A discipline, a methodology applied to the study of systems or operations. The basic methods are akin to the methods of life and physical sciences.

Orthogonal Polynomials. A mathematical technique for estimating the degree of a polynomial fit.

Parameter. An unknown quantity that may vary over a certain set of values.

Permutation. An arrangement, usually restricted to arrangements of things taken without replacement.
Phenomenon. Any observable fact or event.
Platykurtic. A flat frequency distribution curve.
Population. A complete group, a complete aggregate of individuals.
Positions. Horizontal or row designations in a matrix in the analysis of variance.
Probability. A quantitative measure of the chance or likelihood of an event occurring. The probability of a certain event is 1.0. The probability of an impossible event is 0.
Probable Error. Includes 50% of all cases about the mean in the normal distribution.
Program. A sequence of step-by-step operations performed by a computer in order to solve a given problem.
Quadrature. Direct, numerical integration of $f(X)$.
Quantum. A basic measurement unit.
Random. A sequence of trials in which the results follow no recognizable pattern.
Rardom Sample. A sample such that each individual has an equal and independent chance to be included in the sample.
Random Variable. A variable that has an equal and independent chance to be included.
Regression. Deals with the nature of the relation between variables.
Regression Analysis. The analysis of the association among several variables.
Reliability. Accuracy, constitutes confidence. Probability that a system will be able to meet operational requirements for a given interval of time.
Replication. The repetition of the whole or part of an experiment a number of times in order to establish accurately the effect of a given treatment. The repetition of an experiment or experimental unit.
Residual. The difference between *observed* values and *estimated* values.
Resolution. The basic unit of a measurement used in a simulation.
Response. The numerical result of a measurement made for a particular treatment.
Response Surface. The geometrical representation of the relation between the response of two or more factors.
Root Mean Square. The standard deviation or square root of the variance.
Routine. An integral subdivision of the program that performs a specific function or activity.

Sample. An individual selected from a population. An incomplete group.
Sensitivity Analysis. A procedure that determines the sensitivity of output variables due to variations of the input parameters.
Sequential Analysis. A procedure that leads to a statistical inference. The procedure indicates when sufficient observations have been made.
Significance Level. The measure by which a result is unlikely to be obtained by chance.
Simulation. An artificial representation of a phenomenon, concept, system, or operation by analog or digital representation, usually programmed for solution on a computer.
Simulation Language. Synthetic programming language especially appropriate for computer simulations.
Skewness. The asymmetry of a frequency distribution curve. Third moment about the mean.
Standard Deviation. The root mean square deviation from the arithmetic mean. The square root of the variance.
Standard Error of Estimate. A measure of the closeness or accuracy of the estimate of the relation of the dependent variable to the independent variable.
Statistical Probability. The expectation of the outcome of future events.
Stochastic. Nondeterministic. A process is stochastic if it includes random variables whose values depend on a parameter, such as time.
Stochastic Mode. A mathematical model in which one or more of the functional relations depend on chance parameters, i.e. a value selected from a probability distribution.
Submodel. A subset of a model.
Subroutine. A subset of a routine.
Sum of Squares. The sum of the squares of the deviations between individual measurements and the mean of the measurements.
Summation. Formation of sums.
Synthesis. Procedure for determining the best way of selecting many elements and combining them into a system. Synthesis creates a system that will behave according to a certain desired pattern.
System. A series of processes. An organic or organized whole. A complex of men and machines.
Systems Analysis. A method or procedure. A procedure that encompasses and utilizes the knowledge of all traditional disciplines and adds concepts not normally considered by conventional approaches.
Transaction. Basic unit that moves through a system.
Treatment. The set of levels of all factors used in a given trial. Also the different procedures whose effects are to be measured.

Uniform Random Number. A number selected at random from a uniform probability distribution, in which there is an equal likelihood that any number within a specified interval may occur.
Validity. The degree with which a device measures what it is supposed to measure.
Variable. A quantity to which an unlimited number of values can be assigned in an investigation.
Variance. The measure of dispersion about the mean or the second moment about the mean. The square of the standard deviation. The mean value of squares of the deviations of a set of observations from their arithmetic mean.
Variate. A variable for which a distribution function exists.

Appendix B

EXAMPLE OF A COMPUTER SIMULATION MODEL

The model described below is a condensed version of a "demand model," in which significant highlights of the model are given. This model description has been included for purposes of illustration and to provide a more comprehensive example than the models described very briefly in Chapter 2.

Complete documentation of a computer simulation model would normally contain all the information on conceptualization, implementation, and results phases of model construction. Such documentation would consist of published and unpublished reports and fugitive materials, such as punched cards and computer printouts. Obviously, for most models the complete documentation could be quite voluminous.

PROBLEM STATEMENT

We observe a certain orderliness and regularity in man's patterns of behavior and the institutions, industries, and activities he creates. Man organizes his behavior consistent with customs and mores of society, and he designs his artificial environment with certain symmetry and continuity. Yet, within this framework of regularity, man continually changes his behavior patterns and his environment. However, orderliness and regularity are the features on which we capitalize when making a systematic investigation of the problems of man and his society. These features form the basis for our investigation of demand for movement.

Demand for movement refers to the quantity of tripmakers (people or goods) that will move from an origin to a destination to satisfy a specific purpose.

The problem is to determine the demands for movement in terms of "who-where-when." "Who to move" applies to movable items, which may range in description from iron ingots to canned goods, or from domestic workers to senior naval architects. "From where to where to move" may be across the street, across the city, or across the nation. "Where to move" implies that there are origins and destinations. "When to move" may be daily, weekly, or yearly and may be on a regular or irregular basis. "When to move" implies departure and arrival times.

The demand for movement problem is an interdisciplinary problem that cuts across geographic, political-legal, demographic, economic, and psychosocial disciplinary structures. All these disciplines bear an impact on some part of the problem, and demand for movement must synthesize all the implications of these disciplines.

We consider man's needs and his institutions, industries, and activities. We examine how these elements relate to demand for movement, and we establish relationships that can be expressed by mathematical abstraction. The functional relationships describe the mathematics of movement whereby numerical calculations of the demand for movement can be made.

For a given problem in demand for movement we ask: What is the locale? What is the time frame? What is the appropriate level of aggregation? What are the origin and destination nodes? What are the aggregations of people and goods between these nodes? What are the criteria for movement for specific trip purposes? Which criteria are represented by deterministic functions, and which by nondeterministic functions? Answers to these questions provide input information to generate the demands for movement.

For a given problem of multiple origins and destinations, the solution requires thousands of data items and thousands of calculations. Many arithmetic and logic manipulations of raw data and input parameters are necessary in order to generate demand for movement from the *i*th origin to the *j*th destination. Some of the functions are deterministic and some are nondeterministic.

All these features suggest that the problem be solved by designing a computer simulation model of demand for movement, a model that provides the user with a valid tool to generate movement demands for problems ranging from the local level through the national level. In the following sections we describe the conceptual model and discuss model implementation and expected results from model computations.

MODEL RATIONALE

There are certain basic concepts that are applicable to all transportation problems regardless of scope, scale, or aggregation. Whether our problem is at the national, regional or local level we observe that *all transportation problems involve temporal-spatial relationships between people (or goods) and places in which certain motivational forces initiate demands for movement.*

We operate on these temporal-spatial relationships and motivational forces to generate demand for movement in terms of "who-where-when" to move. From the rationale we seek to develop the mathematics of movement, which expresses the functional relationships that generate demand for movement between the *i*th origin and *j*th destination.

Transportation problems may be spatially bounded at the local through national boundaries. The problems may exist in any time frame from the present through the future. Increments in time and in space may range from minutes through years and from square feet through square miles, respectively, where the appropriate increments depend on the scale of the specific problem.

Tripmakers (or movable items) may be people or goods. We can aggregate people movements ranging from the individual through groups of people, and we can aggregate goods ranging from the individual unit through carloads. We can categorize person trips by purpose, such as work trips or recreation trips, and we can categorize goods into shipping, economic, or other categories, such as liquid bulk and dry bulk.

The origins and destinations (O/Ds) have characteristics that affect movement generation for certain types of tripmakers over given trip periods. A trip period is the time from the beginning of one trip to the beginning of the next associated with trip type. Underlying all these features is a rationale for movement, which describes the movement in a random or in a deterministic procedure.

In the context of the movement problem a large number of combinations is possible. For example, we could categorize a given problem as being bounded at the local level, existing in the present time frame, involving work trips, and so on. Therefore the demand model must be sufficiently general and flexible to have application at any level of aggregation, at any locale, and at any time period in the present or future, yet it must be sufficiently flexible to have specific application. The demand model must be both general and specific. Therefore the model should be modular in structure in order to permit rearrangement of its elements (or blocks) for any given application. A modular approach also has other distinct advantages. We can make revisions, changes, or additions to the model with ease. We can allow for future growth by starting at a simple level and proceeding to a more complex and sophisticated level in future generation models.

There are many mathematical functions that we combine to define the demand model. Basically these functions involve *time-space* relationships. Some functions are applied in series because the inputs of one function depend on outputs from one or more other functions. On the other hand, some functions are applied in series only because it may be computationally expedient to do so. Depending on the logic, in one instance it may be desirable to generate the functional value when needed, and in another instance it may be desirable to use a function table and select a tabular value directly.

Some functions may have been explicitly stated and can be applied directly in proper context in the demand model. Other functions may have been only implicitly stated and are replaced by parameter values until the appropriate mathematical functions have been derived theoretically or empirically. The features of using explicit functions or parameter values and of generating functions or using a function table are built into the demand model. Such features permit us to exercise and apply the demand model in its more simple form whenever the explicit functions have not been derived.

The manner in which we combine the various functions used in the demand model generally depends on trip purpose. A specific trip purpose may require a specific combination of trip-generating functions. This may or may not be a unique combination.

We look at the real world of demand for movement and recognize that certain features are common to all problems. These features are the elements with which we operate in the demand model exercise. We study the movement rationale and derive a set of rules for movement of people and goods. These rules establish specific demand movement relationships between a tripmaker at origin i and destination j at time t. These rules are relevant to the level of aggregation applied in the problem solution. They are movement rules that establish relationships among "who," "where," and "when" to move by purpose.

We describe the movement rationale by specific rules as a function of trip purpose and tripmaker characteristics. We translate these rules into a set of algorithms that define and describe demand model procedures. Ultimately, the demand model consists of a set of algorithms that allocate tripmakers from the ith origin to the jth destination according to a specified movement rationale.

MODEL DESCRIPTION

The purpose of the demand model is to generate trip demands for movement of people and goods. As conceptualized, the model is both general and specific. The model contains a general structure applicable to all demand for movement relationships. The model contains special substructures that are applicable only to specific problems. Thus it can be applied to a wide spectrum of time-space situations, ranging from the present time frame to the future and extending from local boundaries to national boundaries.

For movement at any level of resolution or aggregation in the model, time and space increments are controlled variables whose values are dictated by temporal and spatial boundaries. ΔX, ΔY, and ΔT are model inputs that are selected for any given problem and their values remain constant during the model exercise.

Origins and destinations are placed at the nearest grid node, as we are using ΔX and ΔY as the spatial quanta. Origins and destinations are classified by types and subtypes, in which we select classifications appropriate to the problem. We represent O/D types and subtypes by Boolean designations, in which we define types of O/Ds at the grossest level and then subdivide the classifications into finer descriptions carried to the desired level of detail. A grid node may contain several types and subtypes of origins and destinations.

Tripmakers, which include people or goods, are classified by types and subtypes that represent the classes of people or goods that create trip demands between the *i*th origin and *j*th destination. We represent tripmaker types and subtypes by Boolean designations similar to O/D designations. Trip demand relationships exist only between certain classes of tripmakers and certain classes of origins and destinations. Thus the movement for a tripmaker is restricted to certain specified origin and destination classes only. For example, clerical workers may only move about origins and destinations associated with their work and their home.

The demand model generally allocates trips in two parts. In the *first* part all the spatial distributions of trips for tripmakers from origin to destination are determined, in which the spatial distributions are determined according to some specified policy. Depending on the policy, the appropriate trip generative routine is called in to determine the allocation. The demand model is not restricted to any single allocation technique, as we realize that several applications are possible.

Spatial distributions can be made as follows:

1. By using deterministic distribution techniques, in which spatial allocations are made on the basis of rational movement criteria in a nonrandom manner.
2. By using nondeterministic distribution techniques, in which spatial allocations are made in a randomized procedure.

3. By using empirical distribution models, which require empirical data to calibrate the constants in the model before spatial allocations can be made.

In the *second* part all the time distributions of trips for tripmakers from origin to destination are determined. The temporal distributions are made according to some specified policy. Depending on the policy, the appropriate time distribution routine is called in to determine the allocation. The algorithm for the routine must specify the distribution function and the trip period by purpose. For example, trip departure or arrival may be designated by a negative exponential function whose periodicity covers a specified number of ΔT intervals beginning at time T.

Temporal distributions can be made as follows:

1. By using empirical techniques based on empirical data.
2. By using deterministic techniques.
3. By using nondeterministic techniques.

In Part 1 "who" moves "where" is determined by the appropriate technique. In Part 2 "when" the move takes place is determined. However, the demand model is sufficiently flexible so that procedures other than those described above can be applied. All the mathematical functions applicable to trip demand generation are in routine form and are used in the model processes as appropriate.

During an exercise of the demand model various routines can be used. For example, tripmaker P with trip purpose K might be allocated spatially by a deterministic distribution model and might be allocated over time by an empirical model. Some other tripmaker might be allocated by other techniques.

The basic design of the demand model is modular. In the modular concept the model is organized into its logical elements, and the model is structured by independent functional blocks. Each functional block is an autonomous entity that operates independently of other functional blocks. The modular concept of model construction allows for flexibility of application, and modules can be revised without affecting other modules.

A module can consist of one or more routines that are combined to perform a designated function, so that any routine can be added or deleted from the model as desired. Each routine performs a specific function and is applied for a specific purpose in the model process. We describe several routines in a later section.

The demand model contains sets of parameter and data tables. The complete set forms the data bank from which parametric values are selected for model processing. We describe several tables in a later section.

All demands for movement are generated on the basis of rules for movement, which are implemented in the model. Given trip purpose, characteristics of tripmakers, and origins and destinations, we generate the demand for movement on the basis of specified rules. Each tripmaker is controlled by a set of movement rules that spell out procedures for spatial-temporal allocation. The rules for movement control "who-where-when" to move by tripmaker-trip purpose combination.

The demand model generates trip demands for a given trip purpose, then recycles to generate trip demands for the next trip purpose, and the next, and so on. Trip demands are cumulated as the model cycles from one trip purpose to the next. At the completion of demand model processing the demand model has cumulated total trip demands, both spatially and in increments of time. For people movements, trip demands are given by total population movement and subtotals by classification, for example, workers. For goods movement, trip demand totals are given by categories, for example, liquid bulk.

INPUT PARAMETERS AND VARIABLES

Model inputs consist of the input parameters and raw data inputs appropriate to the given problem. Demand model input parameters and variables and all the raw data inputs may be introduced in a variety of formats regarding shape, size, and general makeup. The inputs may be on punched cards or tapes, etc. The inputs include both numerical data and procedural instructions for the model. Demand model input parameters and variables are classified as follows.

Preprocessing

These are bookkeeping parameters that indicate input data formats and preprocessing procedures required to reorganize the data and construct parameter tables. These parameters flag individual data items or bodies of data in order to identify each item or body of data.

Mapping

These are the parameters that appropriately map the problem in the spatial-temporal domain. These parameters indicate boundaries and increments in space and time. The mapping parameters orient the locale of the problem in an X-Y coordinate system and indicate appropriate ΔX, ΔY, and ΔT.

Enumerative Parameters

Enumerative parameters indicate the numerical quantities by type and subtype classifications according to all other parameters, which are classified, e.g., as the number of tripmakers of type X.

Tripmakers (or Movable Items)

These parameters indicate tripmaker descriptors by types and subtypes; e.g.

1.0.0.0—people.
1.1.0.0—workers.
1.1.1.0—professional workers.
1.1.1.1—senior professional workers.

Initial X-Y locations of all tripmakers are model inputs.

Origins and Destinations

These parameters indicate origins and destinations classifications by types and subtypes; e.g.

1.0.0.0—a destination.
1.1.0.0—a destination place of employment.
1.1.1.0—employs professionals.
1.1.1.1—employs senior professionals.

Each origin and destination X-Y location is an input. O/Ds can be assigned only to the nearest grid node, and several O/D types can be assigned to the same node.

Associative Parameters

The associative parameters indicate the associations of various parameters with other parameters by types and subtypes, such as indicating what combinations of tripmaker types and origin and destination types are permissible.

Trip Regulators and Trip Generators

These parameters indicate what movement rules and allocation techniques are applicable by tripmaker type and trip purpose. These parameters include those associated with spatial and temporal allocations and trip periods by type and purpose.

Postprocessing

These parameters indicate desired model outputs in terms of detail and summary results, in which a variety of choices of output formats is possible. For example, these parameters would indicate what data to output and whether to save the data on tapes or cards.

MODEL OUTPUTS

In general the outputs give the number of trip demands for people and goods between the *i*th origin and the *j*th destination at time *T*. These demands can be given as summary totals as well as subtotal breakdowns by trip purpose or by tripmaker characteristics.

MODEL LOGIC

For a given problem we gather the appropriate inputs, which consist of raw data and parameter values. Raw input data may be in various formats and in various stages of processing. Raw inputs may be on punched cards, magnetic tapes, etc., or they may have to be transcribed from census books, maps, statistics tables, and so on.

The preprocessor is a rather flexible routine that accepts the raw data inputs (with preprocessing instructions) and manipulates the data for inputs to the demand model paper. For example, raw inputs may consist of the number of retail stores in city *A*, the gross yearly sales of each retail store, and a conversion factor to calculate wholesale goods purchases. Or the raw inputs may consist of the number of industries in city *A*, total number of employees in each industry, and the percentage of worker classifications, such as 5% managerial.

After all raw inputs are preprocessed for demand model inputs the demand model is exercised to calculate the demand for people and goods movement. The demand model consists of several routines and subroutines, which are applied as appropriate to determine "who-where-when" to move. Demands for movement are generated according to a set of movement rules. These are specific rules that relate movable items (or tripmakers) to origins and destinations and specify spatial-temporal allocation techniques for each given combination.

Normally the processing is done in three stages:

Stage 1

Spatial allocation processing is executed for tripmakers (or movable items) by type and trip purpose for a given trip period. For tripmaker type P all possible origins and destinations combinations are located. The appropriate spatial allocations technique is applied to generate trip demands for trip purpose type K from ith origin to jth destination.

The procedure cycles through all trip purpose types until every type has been spatially allocated. Every movable item must be accounted for in Stage 1. In Stage 1 data are obtained from the origins, destinations, items, distance, resistance, and spatial distribution tables.

Stage 2

In this stage temporal allocations are processed for tripmakers (or movable items) by trip purpose according to their spatial allocation

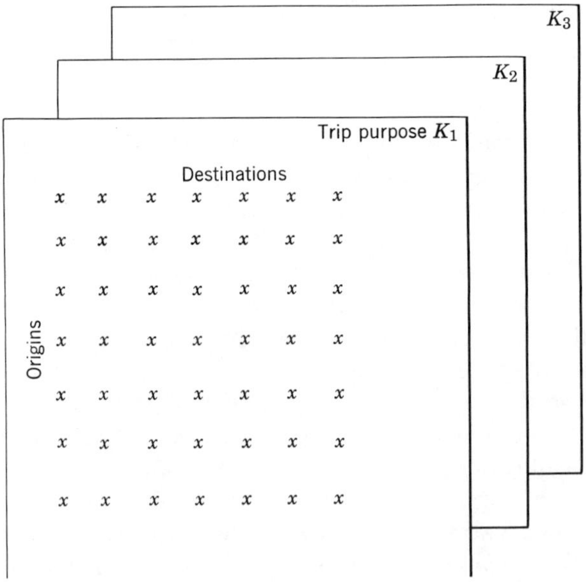

Fig. B.1 Stage 1. All trips are allocated spatially by trip purpose.

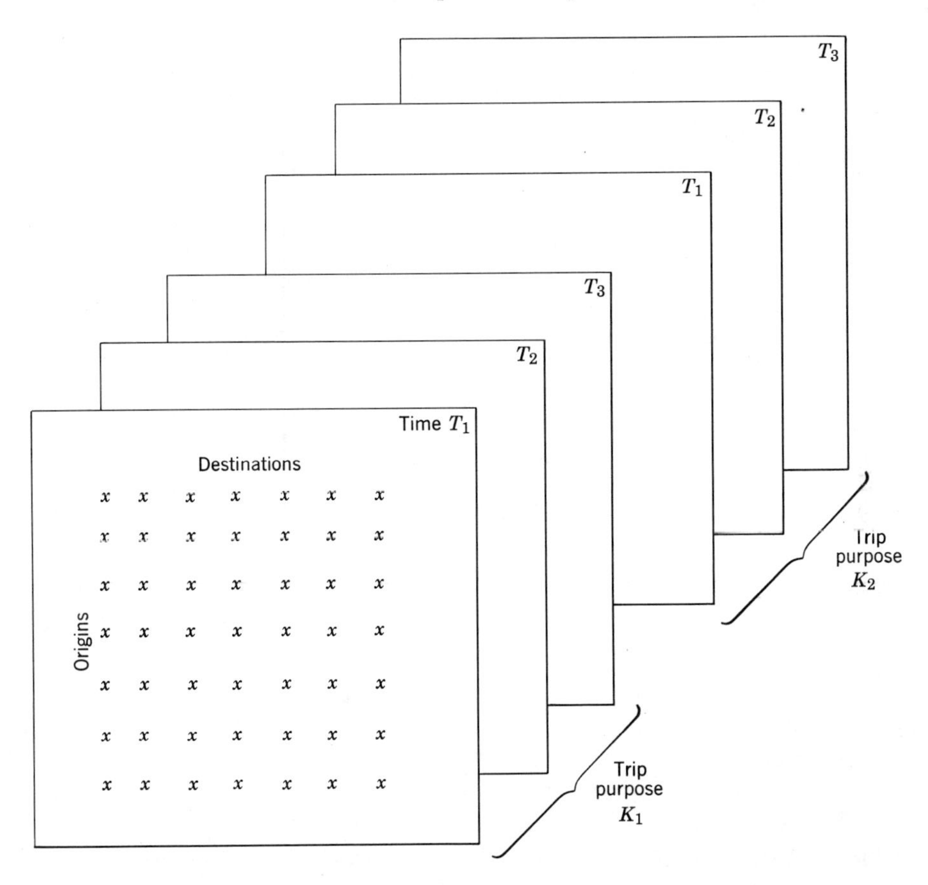

Fig. B.2 Stage 2. All trips are allocated over time by trip purpose.

in Stage 1. The appropriate temporal allocation technique is applied to allocate trip demands in time for type K from the ith origin to the jth destination. The procedure cycles through all trip purpose types over the ΔT interval.

In Stage 2 data are obtained from the time distribution tables.

Stage 3

In this stage trip demands are cumulated over the ΔT interval for all trips between the ith origin and jth destination. The processing returns to Stage 2 and cycles through until total demands over the complete trip period have been calculated. Stage 3 cumulates data from Stage 2.

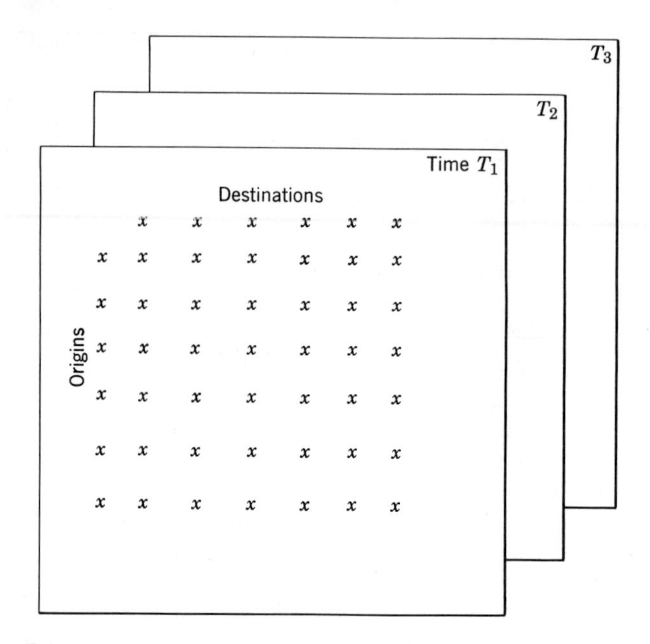

Fig. B.3 Stage 3. All trip demands are cumulated by time intervals.

The postprocessor is a rather flexible routine that operates on user requests for model outputs. The postprocessor processes output data from the demand model in the desired output format. The user may specify what summary or detail information he desires. The output format can be in tabular, in graphic, or pictorial form. The postprocessor can be tied in with automatic devices, such as graph plotters, to generate graphic or pictorial presentations.

The processing in the three stages explained above is illustrated in Figs. B.1, B.2, and B.3. A gross flow chart of the demand model is shown in Fig. B.4.

COMPUTER IMPLEMENTATION

The computer program flow represents exactly the computations and logic flow of the demand model. The basic design of the computer program is modular, in which each functional block is a separate subprogram. Each subprogram consists of computer routines and subroutines, which are called into main computer memory as required. The computer program is organized around the parameter tables and demand model

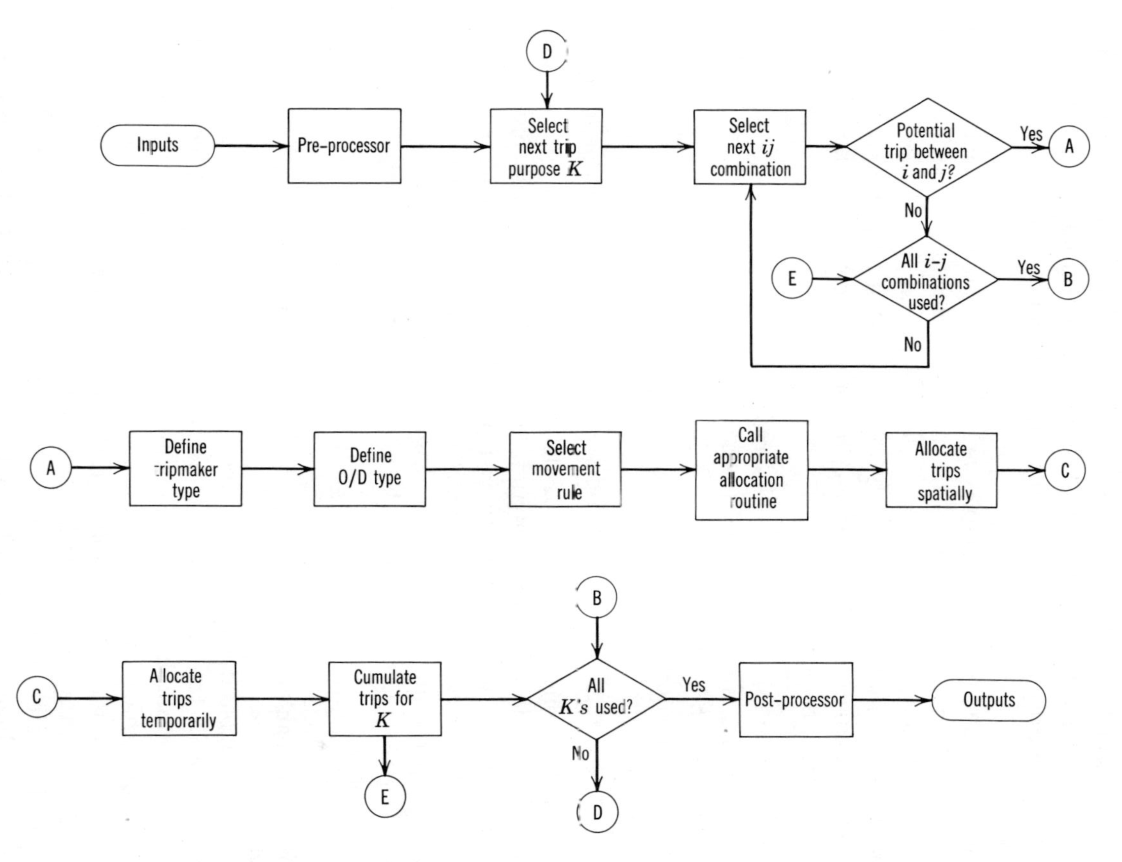

Fig. B.4 Gross flow chart of the demand model.

routines, which are described later. The over-all computer program for the demand model is controlled by the executive routine MAIN. This routine controls and monitors the entire program from beginning to end.

Routines and parameter tables are stored in auxiliary memory. The routines and parameter tables are organized for quick retrieval from magnetic tapes as required. Only relevant tabular information is called into main memory as needed during demand model processing.

During demand model processing the program consists of the following active program elements:

Main program control or MAIN routine.
Computer routine currently in process.
Applicable tabular values.
Scratch memory.
Computer monitor system.

The combined storage requirements for the above elements should never exceed one core load of 32,000 memory. Computer running time for one pass through the demand model, where one pass produces a set of outputs, should never exceed 30 min on a computer equivalent to the IBM 7094. Demand model processing places great demands on storage space and volumes of calculations. For example, one demand model pass requires thousands of data items and thousands of calculations.

Parameter Tables

Before demand model processing, several parameter and data tables are generated for model use in the preprocessor, or the tables may be input from published tables. The complete set of tables forms the data bank from which tabular values are selected for any given model application configuration. The tables are of variable size depending on the resolution and accuracy requirements for the given problem. Tables can be used to replace function generators in the model or vice versa.

The combined number of tabular values for all tables is obviously very large for a problem that contains a large number of origins and destinations. This causes a storage problem in computer implementation, and so these tables are stored on magnetic tapes. However, access to magnetic tapes is relatively slow in comparison to main memory access, such as core memory. Because of the size of the combined tables it is not feasible to call in all of the tables at one time to main memory. Therefore the parameter tables are organized for quick retrieval from tape of the tabular information for a unique origin i–destination j combination only.

Functional descriptions are given below.

Origins Tables. The origins tables are in two parts: one is static and the other is dynamic. Each part contains equivalent information. The static part contains information on the ith origin at time T_0, and the dynamic part contains information for time T. The information at time T may be retained and recorded for later output if necessary. These tables contain X-Y locations of origin i. The X-Y locations are coded in number of ΔX, ΔY intervals from the coordinate system origin, and the locations remain fixed during model processing.

The origins tables contain number of tripmakers (or movable items) by type and trip purpose for origin i at time T (see items tables). For example, a tabular value would give the number of shoppers at a given time and location.

Destinations Tables. These tables are similar to the origins tables, except that they contain information relevant to destination j. The static part contains initial capacity by tripmaker types, and the dynamic part contains the total allocation of tripmaker types from origin i at time T. This dynamic information may be recorded for later output if necessary. This information is used to cumulate trip allocations from i to j over a specified time period. This information may also be used to cumulate trip allocations from all origins to j over a specified time period, if desired. Trip allocations can be cumulated by tripmaker type only or by aggregations of tripmaker types. For example, we can cumulate trips for professional workers only, or we can cumulate for the population aggregate of workers, shoppers, etc. We can cumulate for each origin/destination combination, or we can cumulate from all origins to a given destination.

Items Table. The items table contains all information relating to tripmakers (or movable items). This table contains the number of tripmakers by types at location X-Y at time T. This table is a subset of the origins tables.

Distance Tables. The distance tables contain distance between origin i and destination j. The tables are expandable so that tabular values may contain straight line distances or over-the-road distances or both.

Resistance Tables. The resistance tables contain resistance to movement values between origin i and destination j by trip purpose. These are tabular values in which the resistance value is a function of distance and other factors. If the resistance parameter used is equated to distance only, the value does not appear in these tables, but in the distance tables.

Space Allocations Table. This table contains sets of parameter values by spatial allocation technique by trip purpose. These are the values appropriate to the given problem.

Time Allocations Table. This table contains parameter values by temporal allocation technique by trip purpose. For example, the table contains ordinate and abscissa values of the temporal allocation density function by trip purpose over a specified trip period.

Model Parameters Table. This table contains all model input constants and parameters, such as ΔX, ΔY, ΔT, and coded values that indicate model cycling procedures and spatial-temporal allocations routines by trip purpose. This table contains all the referencing and cross-referencing information required to set up a unique logic flow for a given purpose in demand model processing.

Routines

The logical and mathematical procedures in the demand model have been organized into various routines and subroutines. Each routine represents a functional subdivision of the whole model, and each routine operates independently of other functional routines. Each routine operates with a set of inputs and produces a set of outputs. Demand model processes for a given problem consist of the operations of a unique series of routines. Depending on the function, any one routine may be applied several times in the model processes.

Routines can be easily added to or deleted from the demand model as required. We describe several routines below. Others can be added as needed.

Main Control (MAIN). This routine is the executive routine, which controls and monitors the entire model process from beginning to end. MAIN calls in (during model processing) the appropriate routines to execute a specific function.

Preprocessor (PREP). This routine accepts all raw data inputs and input parameters and rearranges the data formats for compatibility with subsequent processing requirements. PREP accepts data that may be in different stages of processing and processes the data for later use in demand-for-movement computations.

Inputs. Raw input data, preprocessing parameters that tag the data to identifiers, and explicit preprocessing instructions.

Outputs. All inputs in appropriate format, stored and ready for retrieval in demand model processes.

Distance Computation (DIST). This routine computes the straight line distance between origin i and destination j.

Inputs. X-Y values of points i and j, or latitude and longitude values of points i and j, and earth radius.

Outputs. Straight line distance between i and j.

Network Allocation Model (NETAL). This routine allocates trips over a network of origins and destinations according to specified criteria or movement. NETAL combines two processes to determine the trip distributions: prenetwork and network flow routines.

Inputs. Same as prenetwork routine inputs, explained later.

Outputs. Same as network flow routine outputs, explained later.

Prenetwork (PRNET). This routine preprocesses data for the network flow routine. PRNET applies the rationale that determines the upper and lower limits of tripmakers (or movable items) permissible to flow between i and j. The rationale applied in PRNET allocates trips on the basis of specified percentages of attraction. We draw a set of contours around origin i, in which each contour specifies a given percentage of trips to allocate to all jth destinations falling inside the contour.

Inputs. ith origin and jth destination; assigned resistance between i and j; $X\%$ versus travel time t in discrete steps from time zero to maximum time; total number of tripmakers (or movable items) at the ith origin; total capacity at the jth destination; $Y\%$ of total capacity at j allowed to ith origin tripmakers.

Outputs. Same as network flow routine inputs, explained below.

Network Flow (NETFL). This routine solves the problem of trip allocations among all origins and destinations. NETFL applies an out-of-kilter method developed by Fulkerson. The routine is extremely flexible and is the most efficient if applied appropriately in the context of the problem. This routine has been programmed for the CDC 3600 computer and is written up in 1604/3600 Network Flow Routine Reference Manual, Publication No. 60130500, Control Data Corporation, 1965.

Inputs. Origins and destinations, number of tripmakers (or movable items) at ith origin, total capacity at jth destination, assigned resistance (or impedance or cost) between i and j, and upper limits (UL) and lower limits (LL) of trips permitted between i and j, where

$$0 \leq \mathrm{LL} \leq \mathrm{UL}$$

Outputs. Trip allocations between ith origin and jth destination. These are spatial allocations.

Gravity Model (GRAV). This routine solves the spatial allocation problem by the classic gravity model. Comprehensive coverage of the model is given in "Calibrating and Testing a GRAVITY MODEL for any size Urban Area," Bureau of Public Roads (BPR), 1965. This routine has been programmed for IBM 7090/7094 for BPR, reference PR-135, as well as for the CDC 3600, reference Transportation Planning System, Program No. 7, Control Data Corporation, 1965.

Inputs. Origins and destinations, travel time friction F factors, K factors, number of zones, number of districts, number of purposes, and number of F factors.

Outputs. Trip allocations between origin zone i and destination zone j.

Fratar Model (FRAT). This routine solves the spatial allocation problem by the Fratar model developed by T. J. Fratar. If the character and growth conditions of traffic zones are known (or are predictable) it is possible to estimate the total trips between origin zone i and destination zone j by using the Fratar model.

Inputs. Origins and destinations, location factors, growth factors, and base year trips between i and j.

Outputs. Future trip allocations between i and j.

Intervening Opportunities Model (INTOP). This routine solves the spatial allocation problem by the intervening opportunities model formulated by Stouffer as well as Schneider. Trip allocations are measured in terms of the number of intervening opportunities.

Inputs. (for Schneider formulation). Origins and destinations, trip origins in zone i, trip destinations considered prior to zone j, trip destinations in zone j, and probability L that a random destination will satisfy the needs of a particular trip.

Outputs. Trip allocations between zone i and zone j.

Competing Opportunities Model (COMOP). Competing opportunities model developed by A. R. Tomazinis. This method is based on probability theory and utilizes certain aspects of the gravity models. The method is described by the author in Highway Research Board, Bulletin 347, 1962.

Inputs. Origins and destinations, probability of attraction, probability of satisfaction, time bands, trip origins in zone i, time band into which zone j falls, destinations available in time bands k, last time band from origin zone i, and destinations available to zone i.

Outputs. Trip allocations between zone i and zone j.

Randomized Allocation Model (RANAL). This routine solves the allocation problem by application of randomized procedures.

Time Allocation Model (TIMAL). This routine solves the temporal allocation problem by applying a time distribution function to allocated trips between i and j.

Inputs. Number of trip allocations between i and j, trip purpose, trip period, and density function (reduced to step function) in percentage versus time interval.

Outputs. Trip allocations in time between i and j by purpose.

Trip Cumulator (TRICU). This routine cumulates outputs from TIMAL for specified time intervals.

Inputs. Outputs from TIMAL.

Outputs. Combined trips for all purposes between i and j.

Postprocessor (POSPR). This routine handles the processing of demand model outputs for any desired format.

Inputs. Demand model outputs, postprocessing parameters, and postprocessing instructions.

Outputs. Demand model outputs in specified formats.

EXPECTED RESULTS

Various methods and techniques are available and can be applied for presentation of results. The results can be presented by tabular, graphic, or pictorial methods. Presentation of results can be prepared manually, by computer output devices, or by other automated devices. For example, an automatic data plotter can be used to plot two-dimensional graphs of origin/destination flow lines on a map of the area. A Cartographatron, which consists of a cathode ray tube, can be used to display pictorially the demand for movement traces. Or the computer can be used to output the results in tabular or graphic method of presentation.

In Table B.1 we illustrate the presentation of results by tabular method. For example, between origin O3 and destination 5 there is a demand to move 45 units of movable items between 9:00 and 9:15 A.M. These movable items may be people or goods, depending on the problem.

Table B.1 Trip Demands between Origins and Destinations from 9 A.M. to 9:15 A.M.

	Destinations								
Origins	1	2	3	4	5	6	7	8	9
O1	35	46	37	58	68	73	76	53	21
O2	42	53	84	97	93	67	47	65	74
O3	9	27	34	26	45	36	29	37	44
O4	12	24	26	76	79	91	65	47	82
O5	21	34	27	25	28	31	32	29	19
O6	35	42	31	97	89	76	45	65	48
O7	42	36	19	67	86	64	43	41	39
O8	8	7	14	12	46	57	53	23	31
O9	41	38	54	37	69	78	84	67	54

Appendix C

IMPORTANT FORMULAS*

1. Arithmetic mean:

$$\bar{X} = \frac{1}{n} \sum X.$$

2. Deviation from the mean:

$$X' = X - \bar{X}.$$

3. Mean deviation:

$$\bar{X}' = \frac{1}{n} \sum |X - \bar{X}|.$$

4. Variance. Mean square deviation:

$$S^2 = \frac{1}{n} \sum (X - \bar{X})^2.$$

5. Standard deviation. Root mean square of the deviation:

$$S = \left[\frac{1}{n} \sum (X - \bar{X})^2\right]^{1/2},$$

$$S = \left[\frac{1}{n} \sum X^2 - \bar{X}^2\right]^{1/2},$$

$$S = \left\{\frac{1}{n} \sum (d^2F) - \left[\frac{1}{n} \sum (dF)\right]^2 - \frac{C^2}{12}\right\}^{1/2} . ^{**}$$

* Limits of summation and indices generally have not been included in these formulas.
** With Shephard's correction.

6. Unbiased standard deviation. Observed in the sample:

$$S = \left[\frac{1}{n-1}\sum (X - \bar{X})^2\right]^{1/2},$$

$$S = \left[\frac{1}{n-1}\left(\sum X^2 - n\bar{X}^2\right)\right]^{1/2}.$$

7. Standard error of the mean or standard deviation of the mean. The degree of accuracy of the mean:

$$S_{\bar{X}} = \frac{1}{(n)^{1/2}}\left[\frac{1}{n-1}\sum (X - \bar{X})^2\right]^{1/2}.$$

8. Standard error of the standard error:

$$\frac{S_S}{S_X} = [2(n-1)]^{-1/2}.$$

9. Simple linear regression:

$$y = \beta_0 + \beta_1 x,$$

$$\beta_1 = \frac{\Sigma X \Sigma Y - n\Sigma XY}{(\Sigma X)^2 - n\Sigma X^2},$$

$$\beta_0 = \frac{1}{n}\left(\sum Y - \beta_1 \sum X\right).$$

10. Standard error of the straight line estimate:

$$S^2 = \frac{\Sigma Z^2}{n-2},$$

where Z is the residual or the difference between *observed* and *estimated* values of a dependent variable.

11. Fitting a simple parabola:

$$y = \beta_0 + \beta_1 x + \beta_2 x^2,$$

$$\left\{\begin{aligned} n\beta_0 + (\Sigma X)\beta_1 + (\Sigma X^2)\beta_2 - \Sigma Y &= 0 \\ (\Sigma X)\beta_0 + (\Sigma X^2)\beta_1 + (\Sigma X^3)\beta_2 - \Sigma XY &= 0 \\ (\Sigma X^2)\beta_0 + (\Sigma X^3)\beta_1 + (\Sigma X^4)\beta_2 - \Sigma X^2 Y &= 0 \end{aligned}\right\}.$$

12. Standard error of the estimate. Accuracy of closeness of the estimate. Indicates how nearly the estimated values agree with the observed values:

$$S^2 = \frac{\Sigma Z^2}{n}.$$

13. Logarithmic curve fitting:

$$y = \beta_0 x^{\beta_1},$$

$$\left\{\begin{aligned} \beta_1 &= \frac{\Sigma \log X \Sigma \log Y - n\Sigma \log X \log Y}{(\Sigma \log X)^2 - n\Sigma(\log X)^2} \\ \log \beta_0 &= \frac{1}{n}\left(\sum \log Y - \beta_1 \sum \log X\right) \end{aligned}\right\}.$$

14. Exponential curve fitting:

$$y = \beta_0 e^{\beta_1 x},$$

$$\left\{\begin{aligned} \beta_1 &= \frac{\Sigma X \Sigma \log Y - n\Sigma X \log Y}{\log e[(\Sigma X)^2 - n\Sigma X^2]} \\ \log \beta_0 &= \frac{1}{n}\left(\sum \log Y - \beta_1 \log e \sum X\right) \end{aligned}\right\},$$

$(\log e = 0.4343)$.

$$y = \beta_0 \beta_1^{x},$$

$$\left\{\begin{aligned} \log \beta_1 &= \frac{\Sigma X \Sigma \log Y - n\Sigma X \log Y}{(\Sigma X)^2 - n\Sigma X^2} \\ \log \beta_0 &= \frac{1}{n}\left(\sum \log Y - \log \beta_1 \sum X\right) \end{aligned}\right\}.$$

15. Coefficient of correlation. Relative importance of the linear relationship:

$$r = \left[1 - \frac{S_{y'}^2}{S_y^2}\right]^{1/2}.$$

where $S_{y'}$ is the standard deviation of the estimated values and S_y is the standard deviation of the observed values. If $r = 1$, there is perfect correlation. If $r = 0$, there is no correlation.

16. Coefficient of correlation computed from the slopes of two lines:

$$r = (\beta_1 \beta_1')^{1/2}.$$

17. Index of correlation. Relative importance of the curvilinear relationship:

$$i = \frac{S_{y''}}{S_y}.$$

18. Coefficient of determination. Relative closeness of the linear relationship:

$$d = r^2.$$

19. Index of determination. Relative closeness of the curvilinear relationship:

$$d = i^2.$$

20. Unadjusted coefficient of correlation:

$$r = \frac{\Sigma XY - n\overline{XY}}{[(\Sigma X^2 - n\bar{X}^2)(\Sigma Y^2 - n\bar{Y}^2]^{1/2}}.$$

21. Adjusted standard error:

$$\bar{S} = \left[\frac{\Sigma Y^2 - n\bar{Y}^2}{n - 2}(1 - r^2)\right]^{1/2}.$$

22. β coefficient. Standard regression coefficient. The amount of change:

$$\beta = \beta_1\left(\frac{S_x}{S_y}\right),$$

where β_1 is the slope of the regression line.
23. Adjusted standard error of the estimate. Accuracy of the estimate:

$$\bar{S}^2 = \frac{nS_z{}^2}{n - m},$$

where n is the number of sets of observations in the sample and m is the number of constants in the regression equation.
24. Coefficient of multiple correlation. Relative importance of all the variables:

$$R = \left[1 - \frac{S_{x'}{}^2}{S_1{}^2}\right]^{1/2}.$$

25. Coefficient of multiple determination:

$$R^2 = 1 - \frac{S_{x'}{}^2}{S_1{}^2}.$$

26. Coefficient of partial correlation. Three variables:

$$r = \frac{r_1 - r_2 r_3}{[(1 - r_2)^2 (1 - r_3)^2]^{1/2}}.$$

27. Partial β coefficients. Four variables:

$$\frac{X}{S} = \beta_1 \frac{X_1}{S_1} + \beta_2 \frac{X_2}{S_2} + \beta_3 \frac{X_3}{S_3} + a',$$

$$\beta_i = b_i \frac{S_i}{S_{i-1}}.$$

28. Standard deviation of regression coefficients from one sample to another. Reliability of regression coefficients:

$$S_{byx} = \frac{\bar{S}_{yx}}{S_x (n)^{1/2}}.$$

29. Standard error of net regression coefficients. Reliability of regression coefficients:

$$S = \left[\frac{\bar{S}_1^2}{n S_2^2 (1 - R^2)}\right]^{1/2}.$$

30. Standard error of correlation coefficients. Approximation to determine reliability of correlation coefficients for large random samples:

$$S = \frac{1 - r^2}{(n - 1)^{1/2}}.$$

31. Adjusted coefficient of correlation:

$$\bar{r}_{yx} = \left[1 - \left(\frac{S_{yx}^2}{S_y^2}\right)\left(\frac{n - 1}{n - 2}\right)\right]^{1/2}.$$

32. Coefficient of autocorrelation (time series). Resulting correlation coefficient of the correlation between each item of a series and the item of the same series next following it in time:

$$r = \frac{\Sigma Z_t Z_{t+1}}{\Sigma Z_t^2}$$

where Zs are residuals.

33. Correlation ratio. Intensity of correlation between quantitative dependent factor and qualitative independent factor:

$$\eta_{yx} = \left[\frac{\Sigma(n_0\bar{Y}_0{}^2) - n\bar{Y}^2}{nS_y{}^2}\right]^{1/2}.$$

34. Ratio of a coefficient t ratio. To estimate the probability that an observed value might have been obtained by chance in random sampling from a population in which the true coefficient was zero:

$$t = \frac{\Sigma X'Y'}{\bar{S}_{YX}[\Sigma(X')^2]^{1/2}}$$

35. F ratio:

$$F = \frac{b^2\Sigma(X)^2}{\bar{S}_{yx}{}^2},$$

$$b = \frac{\Sigma X'Y'}{\Sigma(X)^2},$$

$$F = \frac{(\Sigma X'Y')^2}{\bar{S}_{yx}{}^2\Sigma(X')^2} = t^2,$$

$$F = \frac{S_1{}^2}{S_2{}^2} \qquad S_1 > S_2.$$

χ^2:

$$\chi^2 = \sum_{i=1}^{K} \frac{(\theta_i - \hat{\theta}_i)^2}{\theta_i}.$$

36. Addition law:

$$P = \sum_{i=1}^{n} p_i.$$

37. Law of compound probability. Multiplication law:

$$P = \prod_{i=1}^{n} p_i.$$

38. Permutations. The number of permutations of n things taken r at a time:

$$P_{n,r} = \frac{n!}{(n-r)!}.$$

39. Combinations. The number of combinations of n things taken r at a time:

$$C_{n,r} = \binom{n}{r} = \frac{n!}{r!(n-r)!}.$$

40. Coefficient of skewness:

$$\beta_1 = \frac{M_3}{\sigma^3}.$$

41. Coefficient of kurtosis:

$$\beta_2 = \frac{M_4}{\sigma^4}.$$

Appendix D

TABLES

Table D.1 Uniform Random Number Table

	1	2	3	4	5	6	7	8	9	10	11
1	10480	15011	01536	02011	81647	91646	69179	14194	62590	36207	20969
2	22368	46573	25595	85393	30995	89198	27982	53402	93965	34095	52666
3	24130	48360	22527	97265	76393	64809	15179	24830	49340	32081	30680
4	42167	93093	06243	61680	07856	16376	39440	53537	71341	57004	00849
5	37570	39975	81837	16656	06121	91782	60468	81305	49684	60672	14110
6	77921	06907	11008	42751	27756	53498	18602	70659	90655	15053	21916
7	99562	72905	56420	69994	98872	31016	71194	18738	44013	48840	63213
8	96301	91977	05463	07972	18876	20922	94595	56869	69014	60045	18425
9	89579	14342	63661	10281	17453	18103	57740	84378	25331	12566	58678
10	85475	36857	53342	53988	53060	59533	38867	62300	08158	17893	16439
11	28918	69578	88231	33276	70997	79936	56865	05859	90106	31595	01547
12	63553	40961	48235	03427	49626	69445	18663	72695	52180	20847	12234
13	09429	93969	52636	92737	88974	33488	36320	17617	30015	08272	84115
14	10365	61129	87529	85689	48237	52267	67689	93394	01511	26358	85104
15	07119	97336	71048	08178	77233	13916	47564	81056	97735	85977	29372
16	51085	12765	51821	51259	77452	16308	60756	92144	49442	53900	70960
17	02368	21382	52404	60268	89368	19885	55322	44819	01188	65255	64835
18	01011	54092	33362	94904	31273	04146	18594	29852	71585	85030	51132
19	52162	53916	46369	58586	23216	14513	83149	98736	23495	64350	94738
20	07056	97628	33787	09998	42698	06691	76988	13602	51851	46104	88916
21	48663	91245	85828	14346	09172	30168	90229	04734	59193	22178	30421
22	54164	58492	22421	74103	47070	25306	76468	26384	58151	06646	21524
23	32639	32363	05597	24200	13363	38005	94342	28728	35806	06912	17012
24	29334	27001	87637	87308	58731	00256	45834	15398	46557	41135	10367
25	02488	33062	28834	07351	19731	92420	60952	61280	50001	67658	32586
26	81525	72295	04839	96423	25878	82651	66566	14778	76797	14780	13300
27	29676	20591	68086	26432	46901	20849	80768	81536	86645	12659	92259
28	00742	57392	39064	66432	84673	40027	32832	61362	98947	96067	64760
29	05366	04213	25669	26422	44407	44048	37937	63904	45766	66134	75470
30	91921	26418	64117	94305	26766	25940	39972	22209	71500	64568	91402
31	00582	04711	87917	77341	42206	35126	74087	99547	81817	42607	43808
32	00725	69884	62797	56170	86324	88072	76222	36086	84637	93161	76038
33	69011	65795	95876	55293	18988	27354	26575	08625	40801	59920	29841
34	25976	57948	29888	88604	67917	48708	18912	82271	65424	69774	33611
35	09763	83473	73577	12908	30883	10317	28290	35797	05998	41688	34952
36	91567	42595	27958	30134	04024	86385	29880	99730	55536	84855	29080
37	17955	56349	90999	49127	20044	59931	06115	20542	18059	02008	73708
38	46503	18584	18845	49618	02304	51038	20655	58727	28168	15475	56942
39	92157	89634	94824	78171	84610	82834	09922	25417	44137	48413	25555
40	14577	62765	35605	81263	39667	47358	56873	56307	61607	49518	89565

Table D.2 Fractional Space under Normal, Circular Normal, and Spherical Normal Probability Density Curves

σ Interval	Normal (%)	Circular Normal (%)	Spherical Normal (%)
0–0.1	7.97	0.60	0.50
0.1–0.2	7.89	1.50	0.75
0.2–0.3	7.30	2.25	1.00
0.3–0.4	7.23	2.75	1.25
0.4–0.5	7.18	3.05	1.75
0.5–0.6	6.86	4.95	2.00
0.6–0.7	6.46	5.00	2.25
0.7–0.8	6.02	6.00	3.00
0.8–0.9	5.56	6.50	3.25
0.9–1.0	5.08	6.80	4.15
1.0–1.1	4.60	6.45	4.60
1.1–1.2	4.12	6.00	5.50
1.2–1.3	3.66	5.75	6.25
1.3–1.4	3.21	5.50	6.00
1.4–1.5	2.79	4.80	5.75
1.5–1.6	2.40	4.70	5.60
1.6–1.7	2.05	4.00	5.40
1.7–1.8	1.73	3.50	5.25
1.8–1.9	1.44	3.25	5.00
1.9–2.0	1.19	3.00	4.75
2.0–2.1	0.98	2.75	4.00
2.1–2.2	0.79	2.25	3.75
2.2–2.3	0.64	1.75	3.25
2.3–2.4	0.50	1.50	2.75
2.4 2.5	0.40	1.25	2.25
2.5–2.6	0.31	0.85	2.00
2.6–2.7	0.24	0.75	1.75
2.7–2.8	0.18	0.50	1.25
2.8–2.9	0.14	0.50	1.00
2.9–3.0	0.11	0.50	0.75

Table D.3 Cumulative of Normal, Circular Normal, and Spherical Normal Probability Distribution Functions (about the Origin)

Cumulative Probability	Normal ($\pm\sigma$)	Circular Normal (σ)	Spherical Normal (σ)
0.01	0.01	0.12	0.18
0.02	0.03	0.18	0.28
0.03	0.04	0.22	0.36
0.04	0.05	0.30	0.42
0.05	0.06	0.32	0.48
0.06	0.08	0.36	0.54
0.07	0.09	0.39	0.58
0.08	0.10	0.42	0.63
0.09	0.11	0.45	0.67
0.10	0.13	0.47	0.71
0.11	0.14	0.50	0.75
0.12	0.15	0.53	0.79
0.13	0.16	0.55	0.82
0.14	0.18	0.57	0.85
0.15	0.19	0.59	0.88
0.16	0.20	0.61	0.91
0.17	0.21	0.64	0.94
0.18	0.23	0.66	0.96
0.19	0.24	0.68	0.99 } (σ)
0.20	0.26	0.69	1.01 }
0.21	0.27	0.71	1.03
0.22	0.28	0.73	1.05
0.23	0.29	0.75	1.07
0.24	0.31	0.77	1.09
0.25	0.32	0.78	1.11
0.26	0.34	0.80	1.13
0.27	0.35	0.81	1.14
0.28	0.36	0.83	1.16
0.29	0.37	0.85	1.18
0.30	0.39	0.86	1.20
0.31	0.40	0.88	1.21
0.32	0.42	0.89	1.23
0.33	0.43	0.91	1.25
0.34	0.44	0.92	1.26
0.35	0.45	0.94	1.28

Table D.3 Cumulative of Normal, Circular Normal, and Spherical Normal Probability Distribution Functions (about the Origin) *(Continued)*

Cumulative Probability	Normal ($\pm\sigma$)	Circular Normal (σ)	Spherical Normal (σ)
0.36	0.47	0.95	1.30
0.37	0.48	0.97	1.31
0.38	0.50	0.98	1.33
0.39	0.51	0.99 } (σ)	1.35
0.40	0.53	1.01 } (σ)	1.36
0.41	0.54	1.03	1.38
0.42	0.56	1.04	1.40
0.43	0.57	1.06	1.42
0.44	0.59	1.07	1.43
0.45	0.60	1.09	1.45
0.46	0.62	1.11	1.46
0.47	0.63	1.12	1.48
0.48	0.65	1.14	1.50
0.49	0.66	1.15	1.52
0.50	0.68	1.17	1.54 (SPE)
0.51	0.69	1.18	1.55
0.52	0.71	1.20	1.57
0.53	0.72	1.22	1.59 (MSRE)
0.54	0.74	1.23 } (MRE)	1.61
0.55	0.76	1.25 } (MRE)	1.63
0.56	0.78	1.27	1.64
0.57	0.79 (MAE)	1.29	1.66
0.58	0.81	1.30	1.68
0.59	0.83	1.32	1.70
0.60	0.85	1.34	1.72
0.61	0.86	1.36	1.74
0.62	0.88	1.38	1.76
0.63	0.90	1.40	1.78
0.64	0.92	1.42	1.80
0.65	0.94	1.43	1.82
0.66	0.96	1.46	1.84
0.67	0.98	1.48	1.85
0.68	1.00 (σ)	1.50	1.87
0.69	1.02	1.52	1.89
0.70	1.04	1.54	1.91

Table D.3 Cumulative of Normal, Circular Normal, and Spherical Normal Probability Distribution Functions (about the Origin) *(Continued)*

Cumulative Probability	Normal ($\pm\sigma$)	Circular Normal (σ)	Spherical Normal (σ)
0.71	1.06	1.56	1.93
0.72	1.08	1.58	1.96
0.73	1.10	1.61	1.98
0.74	1.13	1.63	2.00
0.75	1.15	1.66	2.03
0.76	1.18	1.68	2.05
0.77	1.20	1.70	2.07
0.78	1.23	1.73	2.10
0.79	1.26	1.76	2.12
0.80	1.29	1.79	2.15
0.81	1.31	1.82	2.18
0.82	1.34	1.85	2.21
0.83	1.37	1.88	2.24
0.84	1.41	1.91	2.27
0.85	1.44	1.95	2.30
0.86	1.48	1.98	2.33
0.87	1.52	2.02	2.37
0.88	1.60	2.10	2.45
0.89	1.60	2.10	2.45
0.90	1.65	2.15	2.49
0.91	1.70	2.20	2.53
0.92	1.75	2.24	2.59
0.93	1.81	2.30	2.64
0.94	1.88	2.35	2.71
0.95	1.96	2.43	2.79
0.96	2.06	2.50	2.88
0.97	2.17	2.60	3.00
0.98	2.33	2.80	3.20
0.99	2.58	3.20	3.40

Table D.4 Table of Equivalents, Normal Distributions

Standard Normal (Gaussian)	Circular Normal (Rayleigh)	Spherical Normal
$\pm 1\sigma$ = 68.3%	1σ = 39.3%	1σ = 19.9%
$\pm 2\sigma$ = 95.5%	2σ = 86.5%	2σ = 74.0%
$\pm 3\sigma$ = 99.7%	3σ = 98.5%	3σ = 97.0%
PE = 50%	CPE = 50%	SPE = 50%
PE = 0.6745σ	CPE = 1.177σ	SPE = 1.5382σ
MAE = 57.5%	MRE = 54.6%	MSRE = 53.5%
MAE = 0.7979σ	MRE = 1.253σ	MSRE = 1.5958σ
σ = 1.4826 PE	σ = 0.8493 CPE	σ = 0.6501 SPE
σ = 1.2533 MAE	σ = 0.7979 MRE	σ = 0.6266 MSRE
MAE = 1.183 PE	MRE = 1.065 CPE	MSRE = 1.039 SPE
PE = 0.845 MAE	CPE = 0.938 MRE	SPE = 0.9639 MSRE

Table D.5 Cumulative Normal Probability Distribution Table (Octal Arguments: 128 Divisions)

Argument	Distribution*	Argument	Distribution	Argument	Distribution	Argument	Distribution
0	0	40	0.32	100	0.68	140	1.15
1	0.01	41	0.33	101	0.69	141	1.17
2	0.02	42	0.34	102	0.70	142	1.19
3	0.03	43	0.35	103	0.71	143	1.21
4	0.04	44	0.36	104	0.72	144	1.23
5	0.05	45	0.37	105	0.74	145	1.26
6	0.06	46	0.38	106	0.75	146	1.28
7	0.07	47	0.39	107	0.76	147	1.30
10	0.08	50	0.40	110	0.78	150	1.32
11	0.09	51	0.42	111	0.79	151	1.34
12	0.10	52	0.43	112	0.81	152	1.36
13	0.11	53	0.44	113	0.82	153	1.39
14	0.12	54	0.45	114	0.84	154	1.42
15	0.13	55	0.46	115	0.85	155	1.45
16	0.14	56	0.47	116	0.86	156	1.48
17	0.15	57	0.48	117	0.87	157	1.51
20	0.16	60	0.49	120	0.89	160	1.54
21	0.17	61	0.50	121	0.91	161	1.57
22	0.18	62	0.51	122	0.92	162	1.60
23	0.19	63	0.53	123	0.94	163	1.64
24	0.20	64	0.54	124	0.95	164	1.68
25	0.21	65	0.55	125	0.97	165	1.72
26	0.22	66	0.56	126	0.98	166	1.76
27	0.23	67	0.57	127	1.00	167	1.81
30	0.24	70	0.59	130	1.01	170	1.86
31	0.25	71	0.60	131	1.03	171	1.92
32	0.26	72	0.61	132	1.05	172	1.99
33	0.27	73	0.62	133	1.06	173	2.07
34	0.28	74	0.63	134	1.08	174	2.15
35	0.29	75	0.64	135	1.09	175	2.28
36	0.30	76	0.65	136	1.11	176	2.44
37	0.31	77	0.66	137	1.13	177	2.60

* Tabular values are $\pm$.

Appendix E

GRAPHS

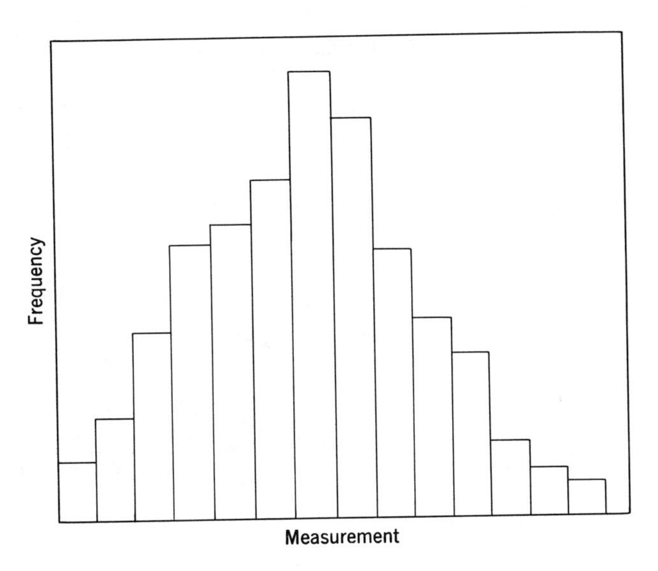

Fig. E.1 Histogram or bar graph.

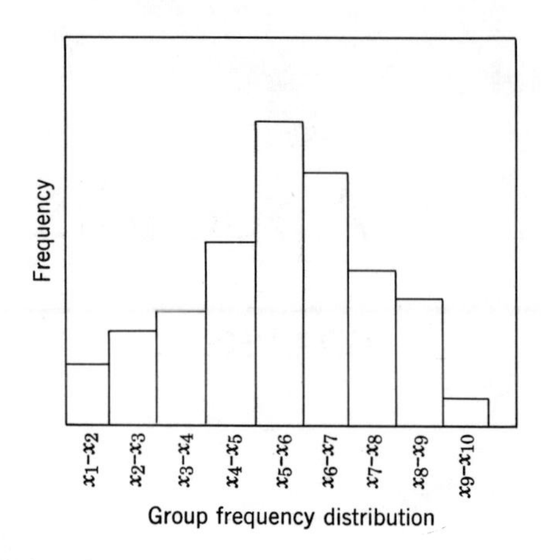

Fig. E.2 Frequency polygon.

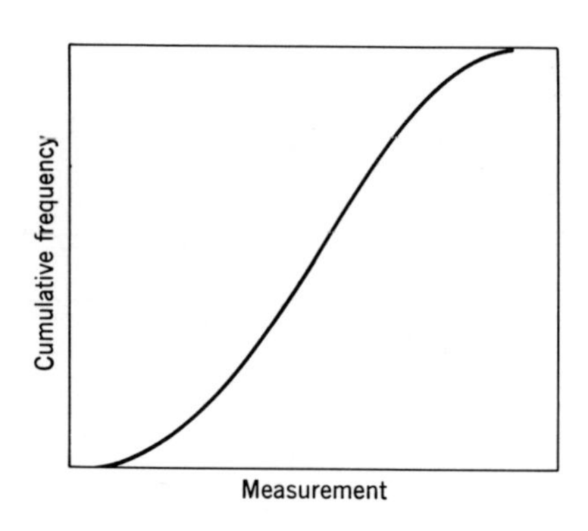

Cumulative frequency graph.

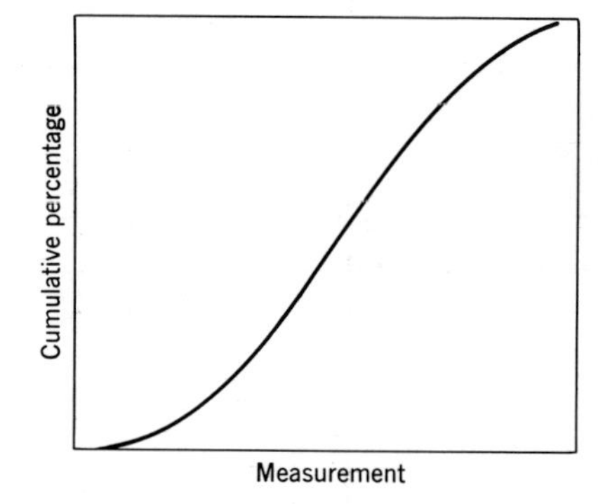

Cumulative percentage graph.

Fig. E.3

$$f(x) = \frac{(np)^s \, e^{-np}}{s!}$$

$$s = 0, 1, 2,$$

$$f(x) = \frac{1}{\sigma\sqrt{2\pi}} \exp\left[-\frac{(x-\mu)^2}{2\sigma^2}\right]$$

$$-\infty \leq x \leq \infty$$

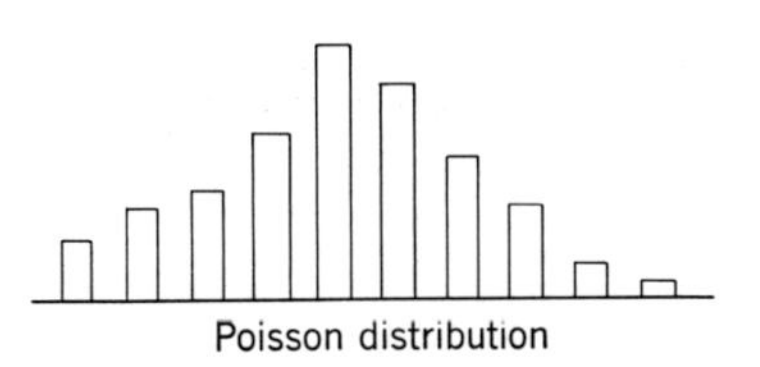

Poisson distribution

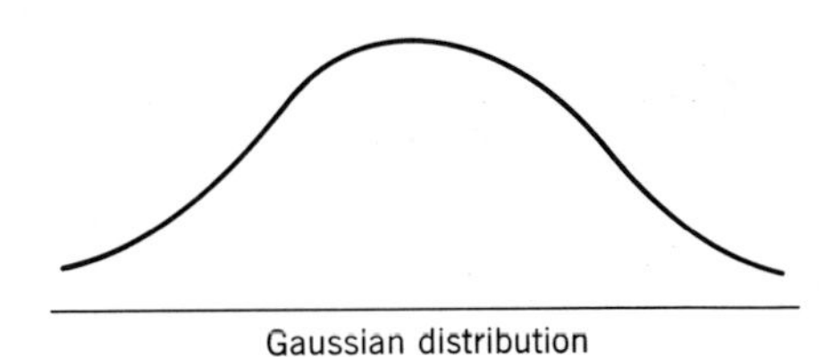

Gaussian distribution

$$f(X^2) = \left[\Gamma\left(\tfrac{r}{2}\right) 2^{r/2}\right]^{-1} (X^2)^{r/2-1} \, e^{-(x^2/2)}$$

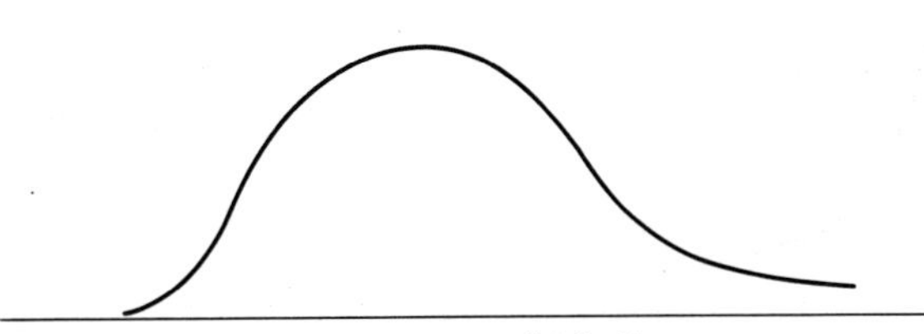

Chi square distribution

Fig. E.4

$$f(t) = \frac{1}{\theta} e^{-t/\theta}$$

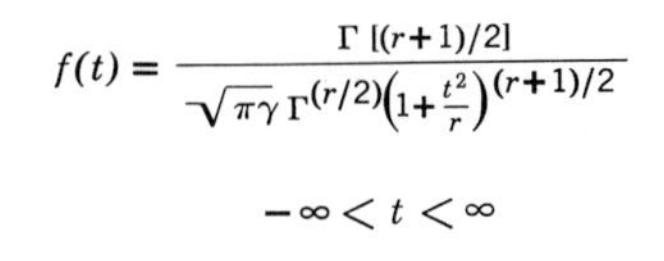

$$f(t) = \frac{\Gamma\,[(r+1)/2]}{\sqrt{\pi\gamma}\,\Gamma(r/2)\left(1+\frac{t^2}{r}\right)^{(r+1)/2}}$$

$$-\infty < t < \infty$$

Exponential distribution

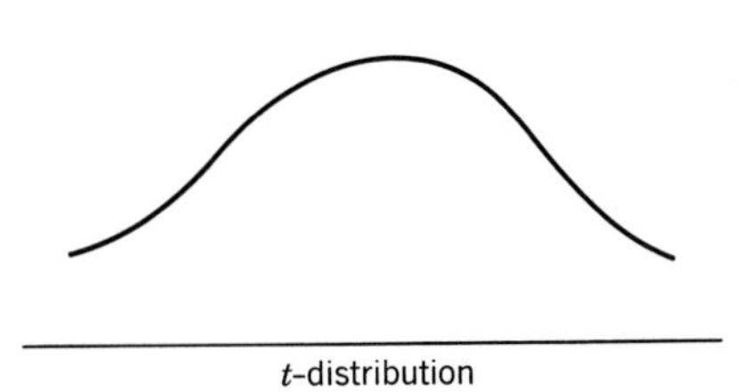

t-distribution

Fig. E.5

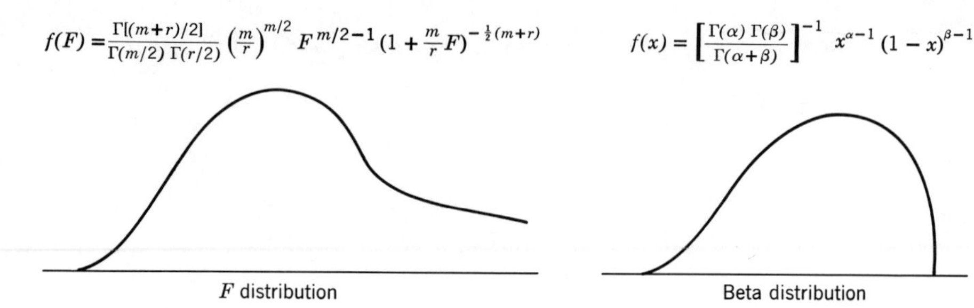

Fig. E.5a

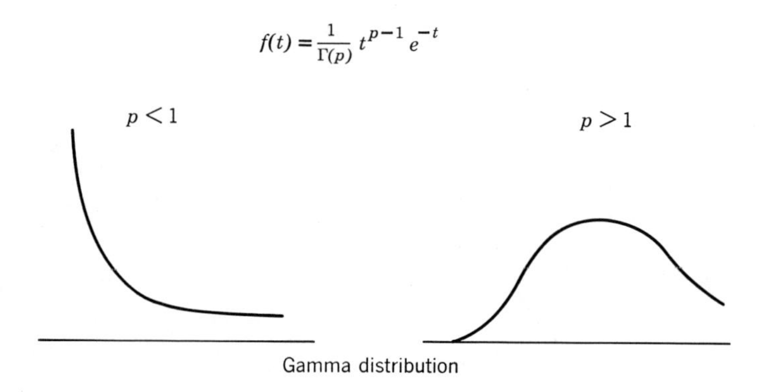

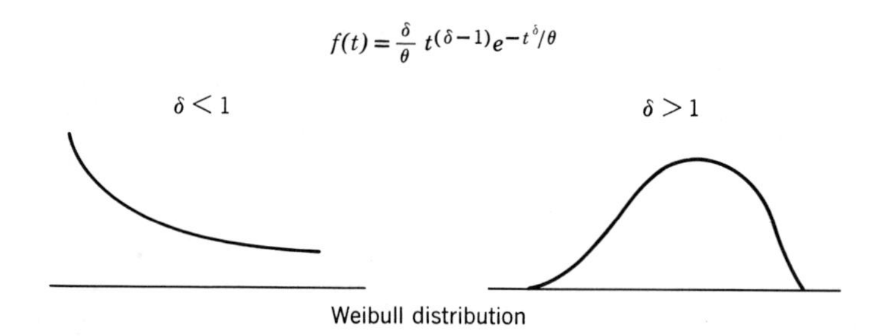

Fig. E.6

$$f(x) = \frac{x^{1/a-1}\,(-\ln x)^{n-1}}{a^n(n-1)!}$$

$0 \leq x \leq 1$

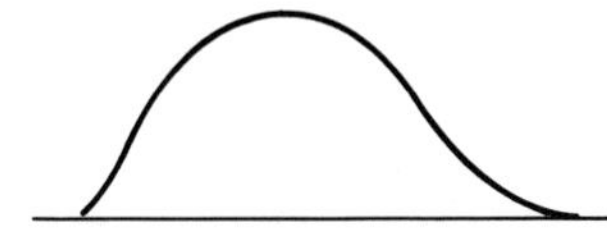

$$f(x) = \frac{-1}{a^2}\,x^{1/a-1}\ln x$$

$0 \leq x \leq 1$

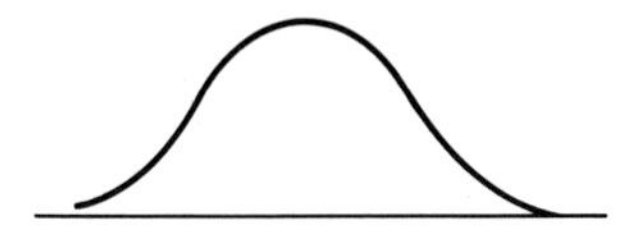

$$f(x) = ae^{-ax} + be^{-bx} - (a+b)e^{-(a+b)x}$$

$0 \leq x \leq \infty$

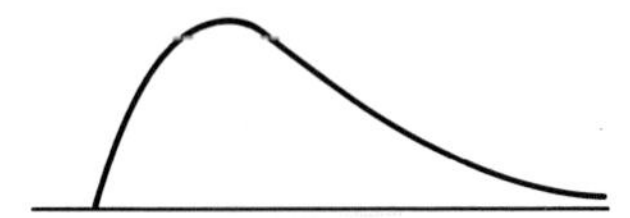

$$f(x) = \frac{ab}{b-a}\left(e^{-ax} - e^{-bx}\right)$$

$0 \leq x \leq \infty$

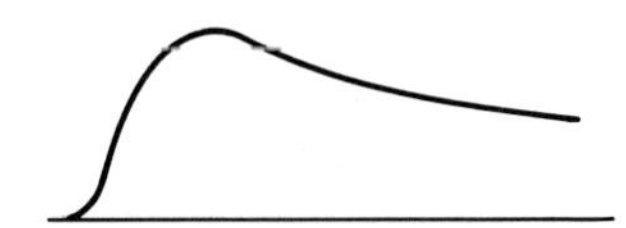

Fig. E.7

$$f(x) = \frac{X^{1/b} - X^{1/a}}{(b-a)x}$$

$$0 \le x \le 1$$

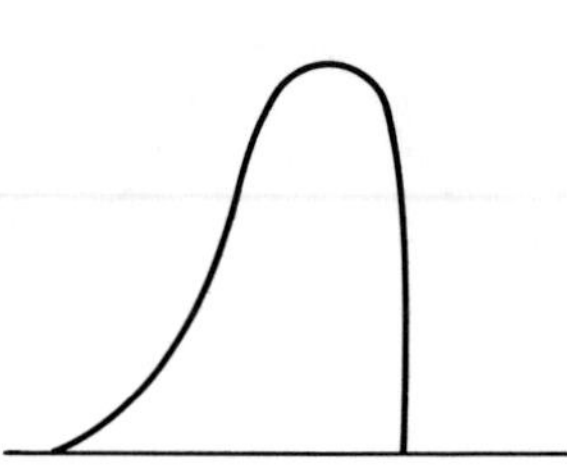

$$f(x) = 6(x - x^2)$$

$$0 \le x \le 1$$

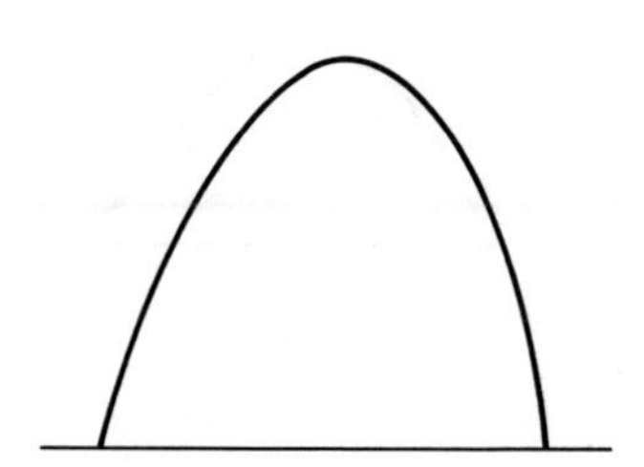

$$\begin{cases} f(x) = \frac{1}{a}\left(1 - e^{-bx}\right) \\ f(x) = \frac{1}{a}\left(e^{-b(x-a)} - e^{-bx}\right) \end{cases}$$

$$0 \le x \le a$$

$$a \le x < \infty$$

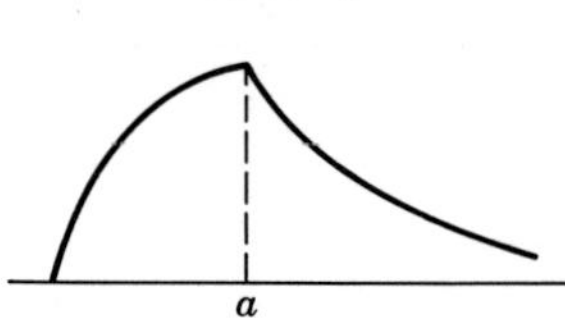

$$f(x) = \frac{e}{e-1}\, x \cosh x$$

$$0 \le x \le 1$$

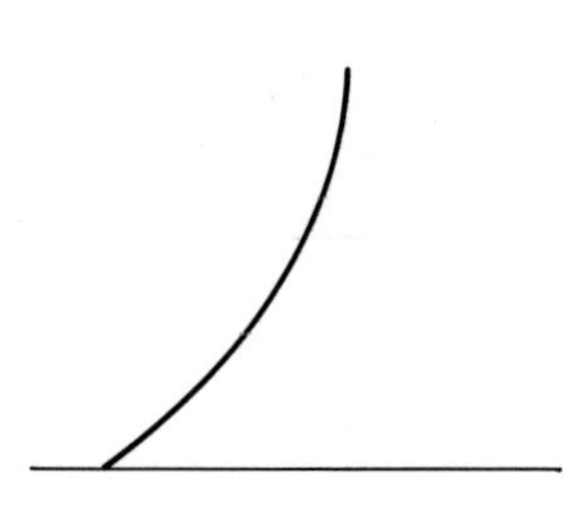

Fig. E.8

$f(x)\frac{1}{e-1}e^x$
$0 \leq x \leq 1$

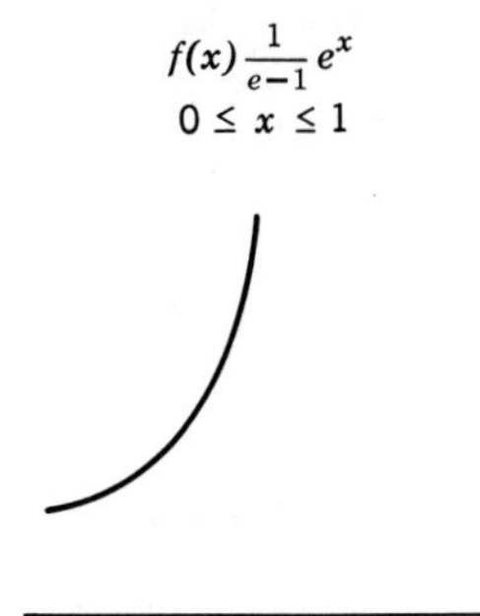

$f(x) = e^{-x}$
$0 \leq x < \infty$

$f(x) = e - e^x$
$0 \leq x \leq 1$

$f(x) = xe^x$
$0 \leq x \leq 1$

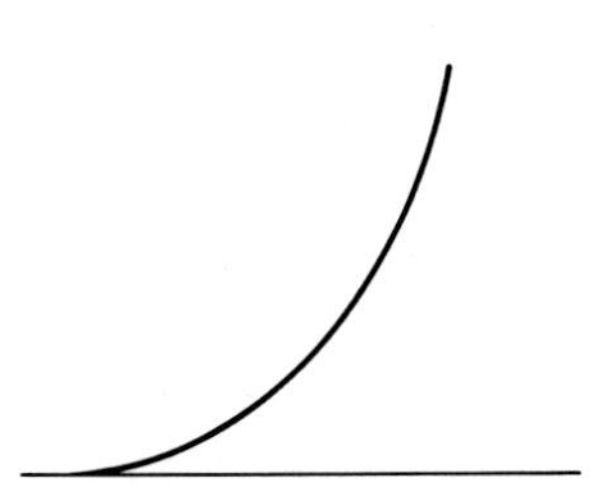

Fig. E.9

$f(x) = -\ln(1-x)$
$0 \le x \le 1$

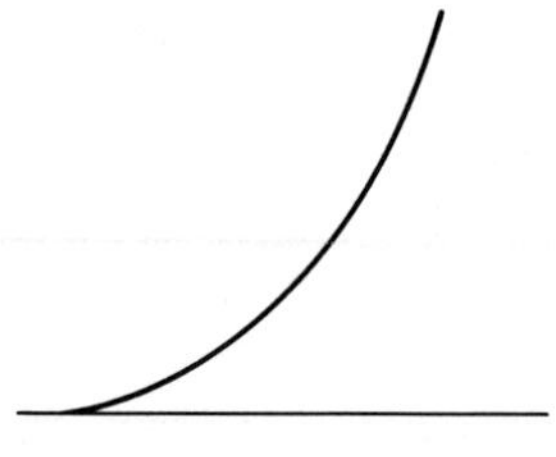

$f(x) = \frac{1}{x \ln a}$
$1 \le x \le a$

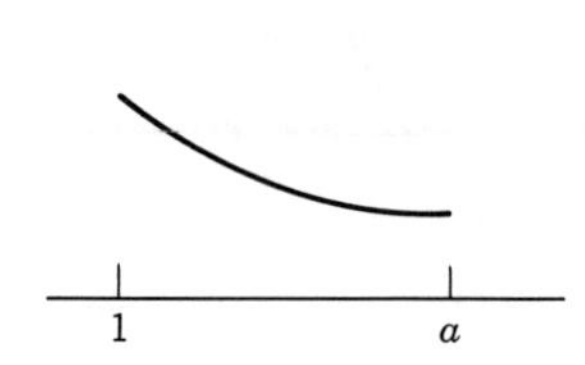

$f(x) = nx^{n-1}$
$0 \le x \le 1$

$f(x) = n(1-x)^{n-1}$
$0 \le x \le 1$

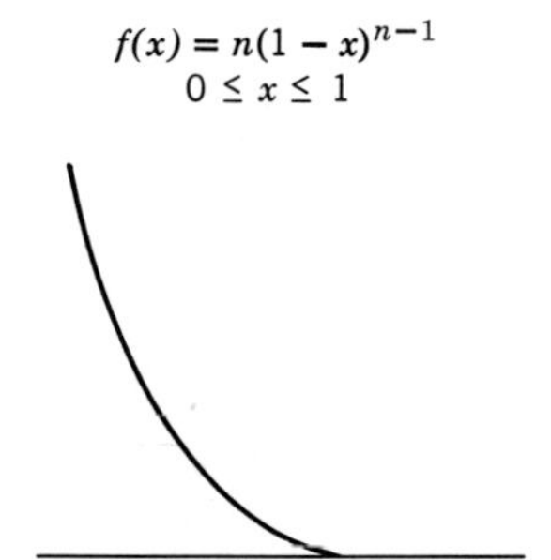

Fig. E.10

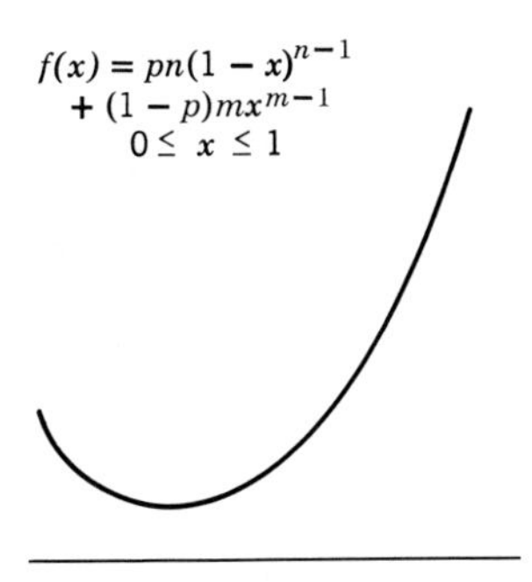

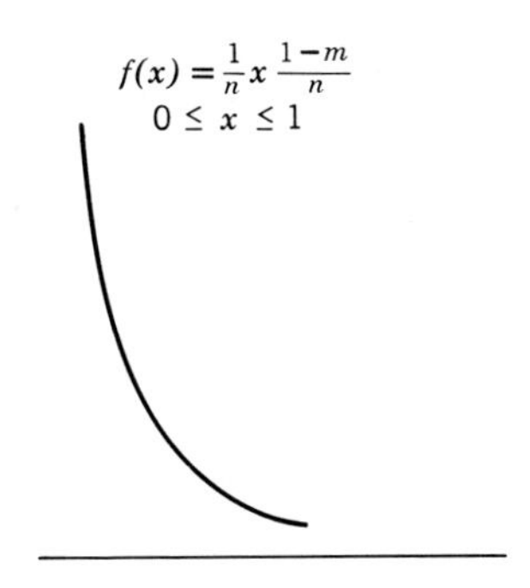

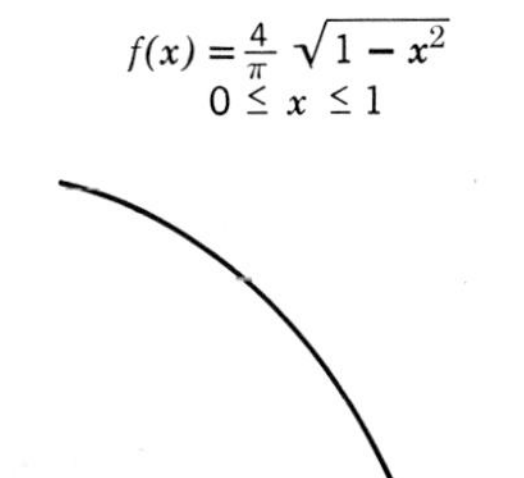

$$f(x) = \frac{1}{\pi \sqrt{1-x^2}}$$

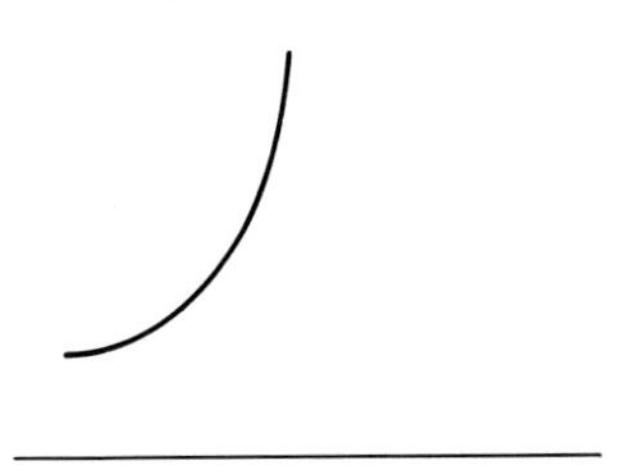

Fig. E.11

$f(x) = a + bx + cx$

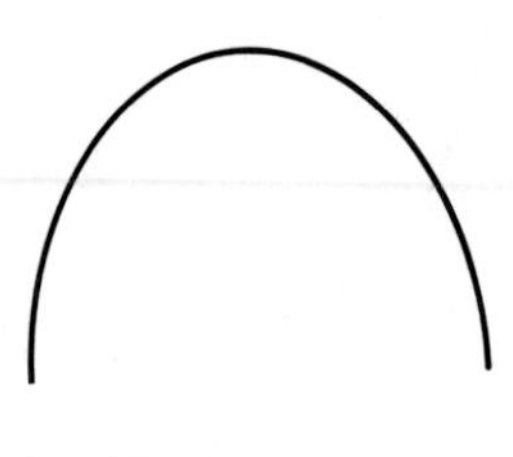

$f(x) = a + bx + cx^2 + dx^3$

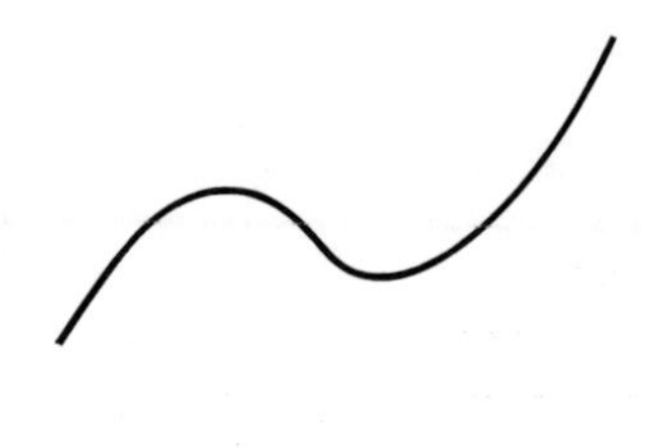

$f(\log x) = a + b \log x$

$f(x) = \frac{1}{a + bx}$

Fig. E.12

$$f(x) = \frac{1}{a + bx + cx^2}$$

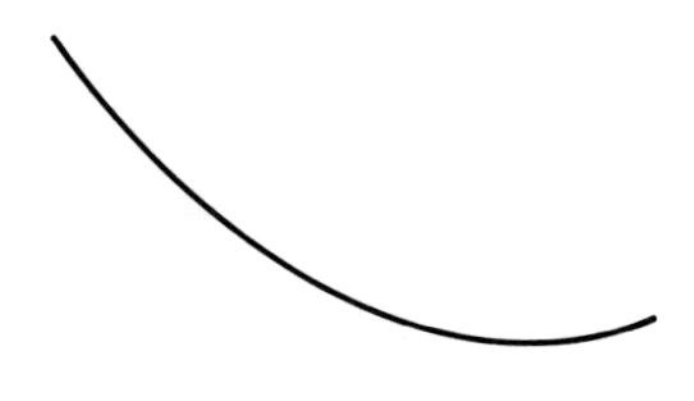

$$f(\log x) = a + b(\log x) + c(\log x)^2$$

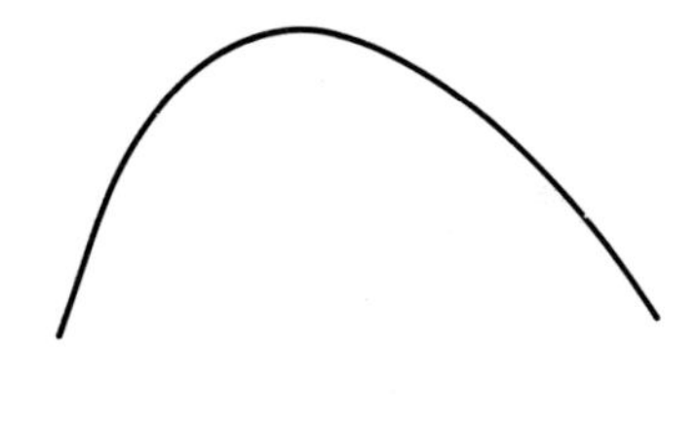

$$f(\log x) = a + b(\log x) + c(\log x)^2 + d(\log x)^3$$

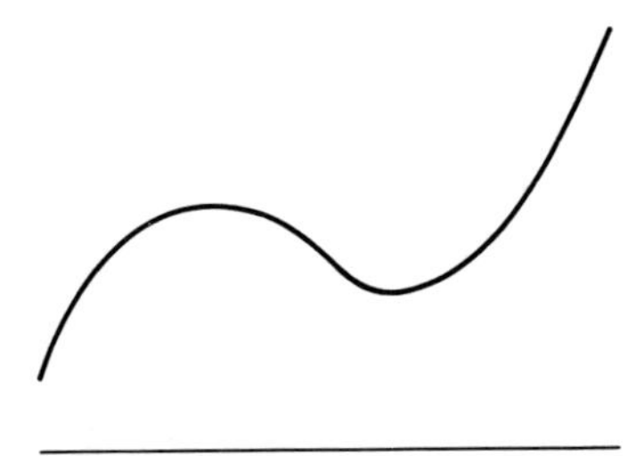

Fig. E.13

Appendix F

BIBLIOGRAPHY

The bibliography on computer modeling and simulation has been organized into various categories as shown below. Numbers appearing in brackets throughout the text refer to specific references in the bibliography. No classified documents on military and space simulation have been included even though the reference title itself may be unclassified. Documents available through Defense Documentation Center, Alexandria, Virginia, or the Office of Technical Services, U.S. Department of Commerce, Washington, D.C., are indicated by the AD number, for example, AD623145.

CATEGORIES

A. Probability and Statistics, General
B. Statistical Methods
C. Probability Distributions
D. Monte Carlo, Stochastic Processes
E. Random Numbers
F. Mathematics, Physics
G. Operations Research
H. Systems Analysis
I. Gaming, Theory of Games
J. Computers, Computer Technology
K. Programming, Programming Languages
L. Simulation Techniques
M. Simulation Languages
N. Business Simulations
O. Military and Space Simulations

P. Traffic and Transportation Simulations
Q. Communications Simulations
R. Education Simulations, Instruction
S. Human Simulations
T. Miscellaneous Simulations
U. Bibliographies
V. Dictionaries, Glossaries
W. Miscellaneous

A. PROBABILITY AND STATISTICS, GENERAL

[1] N. Arley and K. R. Buch, *Introduction to the Theory of Probability and Statistics,* Wiley, New York, 1950.
[2] R. S. Burington and D. C. May, *Handbook of Probability and Statistics with Tables,* McGraw-Hill, New York, 1953.
[3] H. Cramer, *The Elements of Probability Theory,* Wiley, New York, 1955.
[4] E. L. Crow et al., *Statistics Manual,* Dover, New York, 1960.
[5] W. J. Dixon and F. J. Massey, *Introduction to Statistical Analysis,* 2d ed., McGraw-Hill, New York, 1957.
[6] W. Feller, *Probability Theory and Its Application,* Wiley, New York, 1950.
[7] T. C. Fry, *Probability and Its Engineering Uses,* Van Nostrand, Princeton, N.J., 1928.
[8] I. Guttman and S. S. Wilks, *Introductory Engineering Statistics,* Wiley, New York, 1965.
[9] A. Hald, *Statistical Tables and Formulas,* Wiley, New York, 1952.
[10] A. Hald, *Statistical Theory with Engineering Applications,* Wiley, New York, 1955.
[11] P. G. Hoel, *Introduction to Mathematical Statistics,* 2d ed., Wiley, New York, 1954.
[12] R. V. Hogg and A. T. Craig, *Introduction to Mathematical Statistics,* Macmillan, New York, 1959.
[13] H. Jeffreys, *Theory of Probability,* Oxford University Press, New York, 1948.
[14] M. G. Kendall, *Advanced Theory of Statistics,* Hafner, New York, 1951.
[15] A. M. Mood, *Introduction to the Theory of Statistics,* McGraw-Hill, New York, 1950.
[16] M. E. Munroe, *The Theory of Probability,* McGraw-Hill, New York, 1951.
[17] D. B. Owen, *Handbook of Statistical Tables,* Addison-Wesley, Reading, Mass., 1962.
[18] L. G. Parratt, *Probability and Experimental Error in Science,* Wiley, New York, 1961.
[19] E. Parzen, *Modern Probability Theory and Its Applications,* Wiley, New York, 1960.
[20] K. Pearson, *Tables for Statistician and Biometricians,* 3d ed., Cambridge University Press, New York, 1930.
[21] C. R. Rao, *Advanced Statistical Methods in Biometric Research,* Wiley, New York, 1952.
[22] L. J. Savage, *Foundations of Statistics,* Wiley, New York, 1954.

[23] V. L. Senders, *Measurement and Statistics,* Oxford University Press, New York, 1958.
[24] G. W. Snedecor, *Statistical Methods,* Iowa State College Press, Ames, 1956.
[25] W. Volk, *Applied Statistics for Engineers,* McGraw-Hill, New York, 1958.
[26] S. S. Wilks, *Mathematical Statistics,* Princeton University Press, Princeton, N.J., 1947.

B. STATISTICAL METHODS

[27] F. S. Action, *Analysis of Straight-Line Data,* Wiley, New York, 1959.
[28] R. A. Bottenberg and J. H. Ward, *Applied Multiple Linear Regression,* Lackland Air Force Base, Tex., AD413128, 1963.
[29] G. E. P. Box, *Fitting Empirical Data,* University of Wisconsin, Madison, AD239425, 1960.
[30] R. G. Brown, *Tables of Random Sample Sizes Necessary to Estimate Mean and Aggregate Values,* Rand, Santa Monica, Calif., AD404017, 1963.
[31] H. Chernoff, *Sequential Tests for the Mean of a Normal Distribution IV (Discrete Case)*, Stanford University, Stanford, Calif., AD431814, 1964.
[32] H. Chernoff and S. Zacks, *Estimating the Current Mean of a Normal Distribution Which is Subjected to Changes in Time,* Stanford University, Stanford, Calif., AD425901, 1963.
[33] W. G. Cochran, *Sampling Techniques,* Wiley, New York, 1953.
[34] W. G. Cochran and G. M. Cox, *Experimental Design,* Wiley, New York, 1957.
[35] A. C. Cohen, *Estimation in Mixtures of Discrete Distributions,* University of Georgia, Athens, AD605128, 1963.
[36] W. S. Connor and S. Young, *Fractional Factorial Designs for Experiments with Factors at Two and Three Levels,* National Bureau of Standards, Washington, D.C., 1961.
[37] L. C. A. Corsten, "Balanced Block Design with Two Different Numbers of Replicates," Biometrics, **18**:4:499–519 (December 1962).
[38] H. Cramer, *Mathematical Methods of Statistics,* Princeton University Press, Princeton, N.J., 1963.
[39] T. Dalenius, "Recent Advances in Sample Survey Theory and Methods," *Ann. Math. Statist.,* **33**:2:325–349 (June 1962).
[40] W. E. Deming, *Some Theory of Sampling,* Wiley, New York, 1950.
[41] W. P. Elderton, *Frequency Curves and Correlation,* Harren Press, Washington, D. C., 1953.
[42] L. W. Ezekiel and K. A. Fox, *Methods of Regression and Correlation Analysis,* Wiley, New York, 1959.
[43] R. A. Fisher, *Design of Experiments,* Oliver and Boyd, Edinburgh, 1947.
[44] R. A. Fisher, *Statistical Tables,* Oliver and Boyd, Edinburgh, 1953.
[45] R. A. Fisher, *Statistical Methods,* Oliver and Boyd, Edinburgh, 1956.
[46] G. Golub and P. Businger, *Numerical Methods for Solving Linear Least Squares Problems,* Stanford University, Stanford, Calif., AD608292, 1964.
[47] W. L. Hafley and J. S. Lewis, "Analyzing Messy Data," *Ind. Eng. Chem.* **55**:4:37–39 (April 1963).
[48] B. D. Harrison, *Least-Squares Approximations in Terms of Orthogonal Polynomials,* AD236331, 1959.

[49] H. O. Hartley and J. N. K. Rao, "Sampling with Unequal P Probabilities and Without Replacement," *Ann. Math. Statist.,* **33**:2:350–374 (June 1962).
[50] W. A. Hendricks, *Estimation of the Probability That an Observation Will Fall in a Specified Class,* Research Triangle Institute, Durham, N.C., AD415969, 1963.
[51] J. E. Jacoby and S. Harrison, *Efficient Experimentation with Simulation Models,* Technical Operations, Washington, D.C., AD240118, 1960.
[52] O. Kempthorne, *The Design and Analysis of Experiments,* Wiley, New York, 1952.
[53] A. S. Levens, *Nomography,* Wiley, New York, 1959.
[54] J. Lieblein, "General Analysis of Variance Scheme," *J. Assoc. Computing Machinery,* **6**:4:469–475 (October 1959).
[55] M. R. Mickey et al., *Test Criteria for Pearson Type III Distributions,* CEIR, Beverly Hills, Calif., AD415831, 1963.
[56] S. K. Mitra, "Tables for Tolerance Limits for a Normal Population Based on Sample Mean and Range or Mean Range," *J. Am. Statist. Assoc.* **52**:277:88–94 (March 1957).
[57] M. N. Murthy, "Recent Advances in Sampling Theory," *J. Am. Statist. Assoc.* **58**:303:737–755 (September 1963). (Contains large list of references.)
[58] J. R. Newman, *Application of Factor Analysis to Large Scale Test and Evaluation Programs,* Hughes Aircraft Company, Fullerton, Calif., 1958.
[59] D. B. Owen, "The Power of Student's *t*-Test," *J. Am. Statist. Assoc.,* **60**:309:320–333 (March, 1965).
[60] E. Parzen, "An Estimation of a Probability Density Function and Mode," *Ann. Math. Statist.,* **33**:3:1065–1076 (September 1962).
[61] J. F. Price and R. H. Simonsen, *Various Methods and Computer Routines for Approximation, Curve Fitting, and Interpolation,* Boeing Scientific Research Laboratories, Seattle, AD418385, 1963.
[62] P. R. Rider, "Sampling from a Triangular Distribution," *J. Am. Statist. Assoc.,* **58**:302, 509–512 (June 1963).
[63] H. Scheffe, *Analysis of Variance,* Wiley, New York, 1959.
[64] R. B. Schnell, *Fitting Empirical Particle Size to the Log Normal Distribution,* Army Chemical Center, Md., AD291553, 1962.
[65] M. J. Slakter, "A Comparison of the Pearson Chi-Square and Kolmogorov Goodness-of-Fit Tests with Respect of Validity," *J. Am. Statist. Assoc.,* **60**:311, 854–858 (September 1965).
[66] R. A. Sparks, *Comparison of Various Least Squares Refinement Techniques,* University of California at Los Angeles, AD237762, 1960.
[67] R. Steel and J. Torrie, *Principles and Procedures of Statistics,* McGraw-Hill New York, 1960.
[68] E. Taft, *Sampling from a Rayleigh Distribution,* Institute of Science and Technology, University of Michigan, Ann Arbor, AD266355, 1961.
[69] M. Toda, *Measurement of Subjective Probability Distributions,* L. G. Hanscom Field, Bedford, Mass., AD416405, 1963.
[70] A. Wald, *Sequential Analysis,* Wiley, New York, 1947.
[71] J. E. Walsh, *Handbook of Nonparametric Statistics,* Van Nostrand, Princeton, N.J., 1962.
[72] E. J. Williams, *Regression Analysis,* Wiley, New York, 1959.
[73] A. Worthing and G. Joseph, *Treatment of Experimental Data,* Wiley, New York, 1943.

[74] Y. Yao, *On the Comparison of the Means of Two Populations with Unknown Variances,* Carnegie Institute of Technology, Pittsburgh, AD415002, 1963.
[75] H. D. Young, *Statistical Treatment of Experimental Data,* McGraw-Hill, New York, 1962.

C. PROBABILITY DISTRIBUTIONS

[76] J. Aitchison and J. A. C. Brown, *The Lognormal Distribution,* University Press, Cambridge, 1957.
[77] C. Asano, *Runs Test for a Circular Distribution and a Table of Probabilities,* Catholic University, Washington, D.C., AD415018, 1962.
[78] J. N. Berrettoni, "Practical Applications of the Weibull Distribution," *Ind. Quality Control,* **21**:2:71–79 (August 1964).
[79] W. C. Boyd, "A Nomogram for Chi-Square," *J. Am. Statist. Assoc.,* **60**:309:344–346 (March 1965).
[80] A. R. DiDonato and M. P. Jarnagin, *Integration of the General Bivariate Gaussian Distribution over An Offset Ellipse,* Naval Weapons Laboratory, Dahlgren, Va., AD242185, 1960.
[81] T. S. Ferguson, "A Characterization of the Exponential Distribution," *Ann. Math. Statist.,* **35**:3:1199–1208 (September 1964).
[82] E. J. Gumbel, "Applications of the Circular Normal Probability Distribution," *J. Am. Statist. Assoc.,* **49**:266:267–297 (June 1954).
[83] H. L. Harter, "Circular Error Probabilities," *J. Am. Statist. Assoc.,* **55**:723–731 (December 1960).
[84] M. Kamins, *Two Notes on the Lognormal Distribution,* Rand, Santa Monica, Calif., AD415360, 1963.
[85] A. G. Laurent, "The Lognormal Distribution and the Translation Method: Description and Estimation Problems," *J. Am. Statist. Assoc.,* **58**:301:231–235 (March 1963).
[86] F. C. Leone et al., *Order Statistics and Estimators for the Weibull Distribution,* Case Institute of Technology, Cleveland, AD237042, 1960.
[87] Z. N. Loh, *Some Applications of the Poisson Distribution,* Aeronautical Research Laboratoies, Wright-Patterson Air Force Base, Ohio, AD246334, 1960.
[88] E. Lukacs, "A Characterization of the Gamma Distribution," *Ann. Math. Statist.,* **26**:319–324, 1955.
[89] G. Marsaglia, *Elementary Relations between Uniform and Normal Distributions in the Plane,* Boeing Scientific Research Laboratories, Seattle, 1962.
[90] M. V. Menon, "A Characterization of the Cauchy Distribution," *Ann. Math. Statist.,* **33**:4:1267–1271 (December 1962).
[91] A. J. Truelove, *A Nomogram for Lognormal Distribution Functions,* Rand Santa Monica, Calif., AD608992, 1964.
[92] M. B. Wilk, "Probability Plots for the Gamma Distribution," *Technometrics,* **4**:1:1–20 (February 1962).

D. MONTE CARLO, STOCHASTIC PROCESSES

[93] M. S. Bartlett, *An Introduction to Stochastic Processes,* Cambridge University Press, New York, 1955.

[94] A. Blumstein, "A Monte Carlo Analysis of the Ground Controlled Approach System," *J. Operations Res. Soc. America,* **5**:3:397–408 (June 1957).

[95] E. D. Cashwell and C. J. Everett, *Practical Manual on the Monte Carlo Method for Random Walk Problems,* Pergamon Press, New York, 1959.

[96] C. E. Clark, *Importance Sampling in Monte Carlo Analysis,* System Development Corporation, Santa Monica, Calif., AD297456, 1960.

[97] J. G. Cragg, *The Results of Some Monte Carlo Experiments,* Princeton University, Princeton, N.J., AD610085, 1964.

[98] K. M. Curtin, "A Monte Carlo Approach to Evaluate Multimoded System Reliability," *J. Operations Res. Soc. America,* **7**:6:721–727, (November–December 1959).

[99] L. W. Ehrlich, "Monte Carlo Solutions to Boundary Value Problems," *J. Assoc. Computing Machinery,* **6**:2:204 (April 1959).

[100] M. M. Everett et al., "Monte Carlo Techniques to Evaluate Experimental Design Analysis," *Proc. Conf. Design Exp.,* **65**:3:731–745, 1965.

[101] D. A. Freedman, "Poisson Processes with Random Arrival Rate," *Ann. Math. Statist.,* **33**:3:924–929 (September 1962).

[102] J. M. Hammersley and D. C. Handscomb, *Monte Carlo Method,* Wiley, New York, 1964.

[103] H. Kahn, *Applications of Monte Carlo,* Rand, Santa Monica, Calif., AD94552, 1954.

[104] H. Kahn and A. W. Marshall, "Methods of Reducing Sample Size in Monte Carlo Computations," *Operations Res.,* **1**:263–278, 1953.

[105] G. W. King, "The Monte Carlo Method as a Natural Mode of Expression in Operations Research," *J. Operations Res. Soc. America,* **1**:2:46–51 (February 1953).

[106] H. A. Meyer (ed.), *Symposium on Monte Carlo Methods,* Wiley, New York, 1956.

[107] R. Morey, *Stochastic Wear Processes,* University of California, Berkeley, AD619875, 1965.

[108] National Bureau of Standards, *Monte Carlo Methods,* U.S. Department of Commerce, Washington, D.C., 1951.

[109] E. S. Page, "On Monte Carlo Methods in Congestion," *J. Operations Res. Soc. America,* **13**:2:291–305 (March–April 1965).

[110] A. L. Schrieber, *Monte Carlo Methods as Tools for Systems Research,* Human Sciences Research, Arlington, Va., AD229926, 1959.

[111] Y. A. Shreider, *The Monte Carlo Method,* Pergamon Press, New York, 1965.

[112] R. M. Van Slyke, *Monte Carlo Methods and the PERT Problem,* University of California, Richmond, 1963.

[113] J. E. Walsh, "Use of Linearized Nonlinear Regression for Simulations Involving Monte Carlo," *J. Operations Res. Soc. America,* **11**:2:228–235 (March–April 1963).

[114] White Sands Proving Ground, *Stochastic Processes in Engineering Problems,* White Sands, New Mexico, AD48063, 1953.

E. RANDOM NUMBERS

[115] V. D. Barnett, "The Behavior of Pseudo-random Sequences Generated on Computers by the Multiplicative Congruential Method," *Math. Computations,* **16**:77:63–69 (January 1962).

[116] D. D. Bishop, *A Comparison of Two Random Number Generators,* Wright-Patterson Air Force Base, Ohio, AD425962, 1963.

[117] J. Certaine, "On Sequences of Pseudo-random Members of Maximal Length," *J. Assoc. Computing Machinery,* **5**:353–356 (1958).

[118] C. E. Clark, "The Utility of Statistics of Random Numbers," *J. Operations Res. Society America,* **8**:2:185–195 (March–April 1960).

[119] R. R. Coverou, "Serial Correlation in the Generation of Pseudo-random Numbers; Monte Carlo Calculation," *J. Assoc. Computing Machinery,* **7**:72–74 (January 1960).

[120] R. Eisen, *An Alogrithm for Generating Pseudo-random Permutations,* Northwestern Technological Institute, Evanston, Ill., AD431536, 1964.

[121] D. J. Ellis and P. C. Ryan, *Tests on the Multiplicative Congruence Method of Generating Pseudo-random Numbers on the NAREC Computer,* U.S. Naval Research Laboratory, Washington, D.C., 1965.

[122] E. C. Fieller et al., *Correlated Random Normal Variates,* Cambridge University Press, New York, 1955.

[123] T. E. Hull and A. R. Dobell, "Random Number Generators," *Soc. Ind. Appl. Math.,* **4**:230–254, 1962.

[124] T. E. Hull and A. R. Dobell, "Mixed Congruential Random Number Generators for Binary Machines," *J. Assoc. Computing Machinery,* **11**:1:31–40 (January 1964).

[125] IBM, *Random Number Generation and Testing,* IBM, White Plains, N.Y., 1959.

[126] M. L. Juncosa, *Random Number Generation on the BRL High Speed Computing Machines,* Ballistics Research Laboratories, Aberdeen, Md., 1953.

[127] M. D. MacLaren, *A Note on Generating Chi Random Numbers,* Boeing Scientific Research Laboratories, Seattle, AD288929, 1962.

[128] M. D. MacLaren and G. Marsaglia, *Uniform Random Number Generators,* Boeing Scientific Research Laboratories, Seattle, 1964.

[129] M. D. MacLaren et al., *A Fast Procedure for Generating Exponential Random Variables,* Boeing Scientific Research Laboratories, Seattle, 1964.

[130] G. Marsaglia, *On Generating Exponentially Distributed Random Variables,* Boeing Scientific Research Laboratories, Seattle, 1960.

[131] G. Marsaglia, *Uniform Distributions over a Simplex,* Boeing Scientific Research Laboratories, Seattle, AD273207, 1961.

[132] G. Marsaglia, *Improving the Polar Method for Generating a Pair of Normal Random Variables,* Boeing Scientific Research Laboratories, Seattle, 1962.

[133] G. Marsaglia, *Random Variables and Computers,* Boeing Scientific Research Laboratories, Seattle, AD278358, 1962.

[134] G. Marsaglia, *Generating a Variable from the Tail of the Normal Distribution,* Boeing Scientific Research Laboratories, Seattle, AD423993, 1963.

[135] G. Marsaglia, *A Method for Producing Random Variables on a Computer,* Boeing Scientific Research Laboratories, Seattle, 1964.

[136] G. Marsaglia, *Still Another Method for Producing Normal Variables in a Computer,* Boeing Scientific Research Laboratories, Seattle, AD612430, 1965.

[137] G. Marsaglia and T. A. Bray, *A Small Procedure for Generating Normal Random Variables,* Boeing Scientific Research Laboratories, Seattle, 1962.

[138] G. Marsaglia et al., *A Fast Procedure for Generating Normal Random Variables,* Boeing Scientific Research Laboratories, Seattle, 1962.

[139] M. E. Muller, "Comparison of Methods for Generating Normal Deviates on Digital Computers," *J. Assoc. Computing Machinery,* **6**:3:376–383 (July 1959).

[140] R. K. Pathria, "A Statistical Study of Randomness among the First 100,000 Digits of Pi," *Math. Computations,* **16:**78:188–197 (April 1962).
[141] Rand Corporation, *One Million Random Digits and 100,000 Normal Deviates,* Free Press, Glencoe, Ill., 1955.
[142] F. Stockmal, "Calculations with Pseudo-random Numbers," *J. Assoc. Computing Machinery,* **11:**1:4–52 (January 1964).

F. MATHEMATICS, PHYSICS

[143] M. Abramowitz and I. A. Stegun (eds.), *Handbook of Mathematical Functions with Formulas, Graphs, and Mathematical Tables,* National Bureau of Standards, Washington, D.C., 1964.
[144] H. Arkin and R. R. Colton, *Graphs—How to Make Them and Use Them,* Harper, New York, 1940.
[145] J. Bass, *Calculus of Probabilities,* Academic Press, New York, 1966.
[146] C. Berge, *The Theory of Graphs and Its Application,* Wiley, New York, 1962.
[147] R. A. Buckingham, *Numerical Methods,* Pitman, New York, 1957.
[148] R. S. Burington, *Handbook of Mathematical Tables and Formulas,* 4th ed., McGraw-Hill, New York, 1965.
[149] H. B. Dwight, *Tables of Integrals and Other Mathematical Data,* Macmillan, New York, 1961.
[150] J. L. Kennedy, *Uses and Limitations of Mathematical Models,* Rand, Santa Monica, Calif., 1952.
[151] G. A. Korn, *Mathematical Handbook for Scientists and Engineers,* McGraw-Hill, New York, 1961.
[152] D. H. Menzel, *Fundamental Formulas of Physics,* Prentice-Hall, Englewood Cliffs, N.J., 1955.
[153] J. B. Scarborough, *Numerical Mathematical Analysis,* Johns Hopkins Press, Baltimore, 1955.

G. OPERATIONS RESEARCH

[154] R. Ackoff, *Progress in Operations Research,* Wiley, New York, 1961.
[155] B. S. Albert, *Probability Applications in Military Operations Research,* Ohio State University, Columbus, AD235191, 1959.
[156] F. L. Bagby et al., *A Feasibility Study of Techniques for Measuring and Predicting the State of the Art,* Battelle Memorial Institute, Columbus, Ohio, AD233350, 1959.
[157] C. W. Churchman et al., *Introduction to Operations Research,* Wiley, New York, 1957.
[158] C. D. Flagle et al., *Operations Research and Systems Engineering,* Johns Hopkins Press, Baltimore, 1960.
[159] J. Harling, "Simulation Techniques in Operations Research," *J. Operations Res. Soc. America,* **6:**3:307–319 (May–June 1958).
[160] A. Kaufmann, *Methods and Models of Operations Research,* Prentice-Hall, Englewood Cliffs, N.J., 1963.

[161] M. L. Leibowitz, "The Role of Computer Simulation in Military Operations Research," *Bull. Operations Res. Soc. America,* **8:** Suppl. 2:**B**-98 (Fall 1960).
[162] A. S. Locke, *Guidance,* Van Nostrand, Princeton, N.J., 1955.
[163] Massachusetts Institute of Technology, *Notes from MIT Summer Course on Operations Research,* Massachusetts Institute of Technology, Cambridge, AD21105, 1953.
[164] J. E. McGrath and P. G. Nordlie, *Synthesis and Comparison of System Research Methods,* Human Sciences Research, Arlington, Va., AD234463, 1960.
[165] P. M. Morse and G. E. Kimball, *Methods of Operations Research,* Wiley, New York, 1958.
[166] K. J. Radford, "Simulation Techniques in Operational Research," *Bull. Operations Res. Soc. America,* **8:** Suppl. 1:**B**-36 (Spring 1960).
[167] G. M. F. di Roccaferrera, *Operations Research Models for Business and Industry,* South-Western Publishing Co., Cincinnati, 1964.
[168] M. Sasieni et al., *Operations Research—Methods and Problems,* Wiley, New York, 1959.

H. SYSTEMS ANALYSIS

[169] C. R. Arnold et al., *The Characterization and Identification of Systems,* Cruft Laboratory, Harvard University, Cambridge, AD623145, 1965.
[170] C. W. Carroll, "The Created Response Surface Technique for Optimizing Nonlinear Restrained Systems," *J. Operations Res. Soc. America,* **9:**2:169–184 (March–April 1961).
[171] H. Chestnut, *Systems Engineering Tools,* Wiley, New York, 1965.
[172] H. Kahn, *Techniques of Systems Analysis,* Rand, Santa Monica, Calif., AD123512, 1957.
[173] L. D. Krull, *Mathematical Models for Systems Analysis,* Wright-Patterson Air Force Base, Ohio, AD419609, 1963.
[174] C. McMillan and R. F. Gonzalez, *Systems Analysis: A Computer Approach to Decision Models,* R. D. Irwin, Homewood, Ill., 1965.
[175] D. J. Wilde, *Optimum Seeking Methods,* Prentice-Hall, Englewood Cliffs, N.J., 1964.

I. GAMING, THEORY OF GAMES

[176] D. Blackwell, *Game Theory for War Gaming,* Operations Research Office, Johns Hopkins University, Bethesda, Md., AD236152, 1957.
[177] E. Burger, *Introduction to the Theory of Games,* Prentice-Hall, Englewood Cliffs, N.J., 1963.
[178] N. C. Dalkey, *Games and Simulation,* Rand, Santa Monica, AD601138, 1964.
[179] S. Eilon, "Management Games," *Operational Res. Quart.,* **14:**2:137–149 (June 1963).
[180] T. A. Goldman, *War Gaming the War on Poverty,* Philco Corporation, Fort Washington, Pa., 1966.
[181] O. Gross, *A Mechanical Proof of the Min-Max Theory,* Rand, Santa Monica, Calif., AD225228, 1959.

[182] R. Isaacs, *Differential Games: A Mathematical Theory with Applications to Warfare and Pursuit, Control and Optimization,* Wiley, New York, 1965.
[183] Joint War Games Agency, *Catalog of War Gaming Models,* Joint Chiefs of Staff, Washington, D.C., 1967.
[184] H. L. Toothman, *A Table of Probability Distributions Useful in War Games and Other Competitive Situations,* U.S. Naval Research Laboratories, Washington, D.C., AD238398, 1960.
[185] J. von Neumann and O. Morgenstern, *Theory of Games and Economic Behavior,* Wiley, New York, 1964.
[186] B. J. Voosen, *MISSLOGS: A Game of Missile Logistics,* Rand, Santa Monica, Calif., AD232507, 1959.
[187] M. G. Weiner, *An Introduction to War Games,* Rand, Santa Monica, Calif., AD221676, 1959.

J. COMPUTERS, COMPUTER TECHNOLOGY

[188] F. L. Alt, *Electronic Digital Computers,* Academic Press, New York, 1958.
[189] T. C. Bartee, *Digital Computer Fundamentals,* McGraw-Hill, New York, 1960.
[190] A. D. Booth, *Digital Computers in Action,* Pergamon Press, New York, 1965.
[191] N. A. Crowder, *The Arithmetic of Computers,* Doubleday, Garden City, N.Y., 1960.
[192] C. Fanwick, *Trends in Computer Hardware,* System Development Corporation, Santa Monica, Calif., AD632477, 1966.
[193] A. G. Favret, *Introduction to Digital Computer Applications,* Reinhold, New York, 1965.
[194] I. H. Gould and F. S. Ellis, *Digital Computing Technology,* Reinhold, New York, 1962.
[195] F. Gruenberger and G. Jeffray, *Problems for Computer Solution,* Wiley, New York, 1965.
[196] S. S. Kuo, *Numerical Methods and Computers,* Addison-Wesley, Reading, Mass., 1965.
[197] Office of Technical Services, *Computers,* U.S. Department of Commerce, Washington, D.C., 1963.
[198] Office of Technical Services, *Computer Related Research,* U.S. Department of Commerce, Washington, D.C., 1963.
[199] K. C. Parton, *The Digital Computer,* Pergamon Press, New York, 1964.
[200] R. L. Petruschell, *Sixty Years of Growth in Computing and Data Processing Capability,* Rand, Santa Monica, Calif., AD616579, 1960.
[201] M. Phister, *Logical Design of Digital Computers,* Wiley, New York, 1958.
[202] R. K. Richards, *Arithmetic Operations in Digital Computers,* Van Nostrand, Princeton, N.J., 1958.
[203] P. Siegel, *Understanding Digital Computers,* Wiley, New York, 1961.
[204] W. H. Ware, *Digital Computer Technology and Design,* vol. I, Wiley, New York, 1963.
[205] W. H. Ware, *Future Computer Technology and Its Impact,* Rand, Santa Monica, Calif., 1966.
[206] W. H. Weik, *A Fourth Survey of Domestic Electronic Digital Computing Systems,* Ballistics Research Laboratories, Aberdeen, Md., AD429000, 1964.

[207] S. M. Weinstein and A. Keim, *Fundamentals of Digital Computers,* Holt, Rinehart and Winston, New York, 1965.

K. PROGRAMMING, PROGRAMMING LANGUAGES

[208] Electronic Systems Division, *Advanced Programming Developments: A Survey,* Air Force Systems Command, Bedford, Mass., AD614704, 1965.
[209] I. Flores, *Computer Software,* Prentice-Hall, Englewood Cliffs, N.J., 1965.
[210] I. Flores, *Computer Programming,* Prentice-Hall, Englewood Cliffs, N.J., 1966.
[211] M. A. Goetz, *Automated Program Documentation,* Applied Data Research, Princeton, N.J., 1965.
[212] C. Hastings, *Approximations for Digital Computers,* Princeton University Press, Princeton, N.J., 1955.
[213] D. D. McCracken, *A Guide to FORTRAN IV Programming,* Wiley, New York, 1965.
[214] R. Nathan and E. Hanes, *Computer Programming Handbook: Guide for Beginners,* Prentice-Hall, Englewood Cliffs, N.J., 1961.
[215] E. I. Organick, *A FORTRAN IV Primer,* Addison-Wesley, Reading, Mass., 1966.
[216] A. Ralston and H. S. Wilf (eds.), *Mathematical Methods for Digital Computers,* Wiley, New York, 1960.
[217] M. R. Rosenthal, *Numerical Methods in Computer Programming,* R. D. Irwin, Homewood, Ill., 1966.
[218] P. M. Sherman, "FLOWTRACE" A Computer Program for Flow Charting Programs," *Commun. Assoc. Computer Machinery,* **9**:12:845–854 (December 1966).
[219] M. L. Stein and W. D. Munro, *Computer Programming: A Mixed Language Approach,* Academic Press, New York, 1964.

L. SIMULATION TECHNIQUES

[220] R. W. Conway, "Some Tactical Problems in Digital Simulation," *Management Sci.,* **10**:1:47–61 (October 1963).
[221] J. R. Crawford, *Simulation Methods and Model Design,* System Development Corporation, Santa Monica, Calif., AD411963, 1963.
[222] M. Davidson and E. Scott, *Simulation Techniques and Their Applications,* System Development Corporation, Santa Monica, Calif., AD630148, 1963.
[223] E. Feigenbaum and J. Feldman (eds.), *Computers and Thought,* McGraw-Hill, New York, 1963.
[224] O. J. Feorene, "The Gentle Art of Simulation," *Proc. Ann. Ind. Eng. Inst., 12th,* University of California, Berkeley–Los Angeles, 1960.
[225] A. V. Gafarian and C. J. Ancker, *Mean Value Estimation from Digital Computer Simulation,* System Development Corporation, Santa Monica, Calif., AD613272, 1965.
[226] M. A. Geisler, *Statistical Approach to Simulation,* Rand, Santa Monica, Calif., AD606872, 1962.
[227] M. Greenberger, *A New Methodology for Computer Simulation,* Massachusetts Institute of Technology, Cambridge, AD609288, 1964.

[228] M. Greenberger, *Incremental Simulation,* University of California, Berkeley, 1966.
[229] G. B. Hawthorne, *Digital Simulation and Modeling,* Mitre, Bedford, Mass., AD615831, 1964.
[230] R. F. Iuorno, *Simulation Using the Monte Carlo Method,* Griffiss Air Force Base, N.Y., AD410290, 1963.
[231] J. G. Laski, "On Time Structure in Monte Carlo, Simulations," *Operational Res. Quart.,* **6**:3:329–339 (September 1965).
[232] W. W. Leutert, *Simulation of a Battle on High Speed Digital Computers,* Ballistics Research Laboratories, Aberdeen, Md., AD39337, 1954.
[233] T. H. Naylor et al., *Computer Simulation Techniques,* Wiley, New York, 1966.
[234] R. I. Ribler, *System Simulation: A Conceptual Approach,* System Development Corporation, Santa Monica, Calif., AD606173, 1964.
[235] R. P. Rich, "Simulation as an Aid to Model Building," *J. Operations Res. Soc. America,* **3**:1:15–19 (February 1955).
[236] E. H. Shuford, *The Decision Sciences Laboratory Program of Techniques and Facilities for Automating Research,* Air Force Systems Command, Bedford, Mass., AD608421, 1964.
[237] W. W. Soroka, "Simulation in Science and Technology," *Am. Soc. Naval Engineers J.,* **73**:109–113 (February 1961).
[238] K. D. Tocher, *The Art of Simulation,* Van Nostrand, Princeton, N.J., 1963.
[239] S. H. Walker, *Computer Simulation and Gaming in Logistics Research,* Research Analysis Corporation, McLean, Va., 1962.

M. SIMULATION LANGUAGES

[240] G. W. Armerding *GQS: General Single-Server Queue-Simulation Compiler,* Massachusetts Institute of Technology, Cambridge, AD243492, 1960.
[241] J. N. Buxton and J. G. Laski, "Control and Simulation Language," *Computer J.,* **5**:3:194–199 (October 1962).
[242] M. A. Geisler and H. M. Markowitz, *A Brief Review of SIMSCRIPT as a Simulating Technique,* Rand, Santa Monica, Calif., AD411324, 1963.
[243] A. S. Ginsberg, *Simulation Programming and Analysis of Results,* Rand, Santa Monica, AD615303, 1965.
[244] G. Gordon, "A General Purpose Systems Simulator" *IBM Systems J.* (September 1962).
[245] M. Greenberger et al., *On-Line Computation and Simulation: The OPS-3 System,* Massachusetts Institute of Technology, Cambridge, 1965.
[246] P. R. Hills, *SIMON—A Computer Simulation Language in ALGOL,* Bristol College of Science and Technology, England, 1964.
[247] IBM, *General Purpose System Simulator II, Reference Manual,* IBM Data Processing Division, 1963.
[248] D. H. Kelly and J. N. Buxton, "MONTECODE—An Interpretive Program for Monte Carlo Simulations," *Computer J.,* **5**:2:88–93 (July 1962).
[249] H. W. Karr, *A Quick Look at SIMSCRIPT,* Rand, Santa Monica, Calif., AD604818, 1962.
[250] P. J. Kiviat, *Simulator Language Report Generators,* Rand, Santa Monica, Calif., AD631940, 1966.

[251] P. J. Kiviat, *Development of New Digital Simulation Languages,* Rand, Santa Monica, Calif., AD631961, 1966.
[252] H. S. Krasnow and R. A. Merikallio, "The Past, Present, and Future of General Simulation Languages," *Management Sci.,* **11:**2:236–267 (November 1964).
[253] C. A. Kribs, *Building a Model Using SIMPAC,* System Development Corporation, Santa Monica, Calif., 1962.
[254] H. M. Markowitz, *Simulating with SIMSCRIPT,* Rand, Santa Monica, Calif., AD423695, 1963.
[255] H. M. Markowitz and R. C. Steorts, *Modify and Restart Routines for SIMSCRIPT Games and Simulation Experiments,* Rand, Santa Monica, Calif., AD616240, 1965.
[256] H. M. Markowitz et al., *SIMSCRIPT: A Simulation Programming Language,* Prentice-Hall, Englewood Cliffs, N.J., 1962.
[257] A. L. Pugh, *DYNAMO User's Manual,* Massachusetts Institute of Technology Press, Cambridge, 1961.
[258] K. D. Tocher, "Review of Simulation Languages," *Operational Res. Quart.,* **6:**2:189–217 (June 1965).
[259] J. W. J. Williams, "ESP the Elliott Simulator Package," *Computer J.,* **6:**4:328–331 (January 1964).

N. BUSINESS SIMULATIONS

[260] G. C. Armour and E. S. Buffa, "A Heuristic Algorithm and Simulation Approach to Relative Location of Facilities," *Management Sci.* **9:**2:294–309 (January 1963).
[261] E. S. Buffa, *Models for Production and Operations Management,* Wiley, New York, 1963.
[262] K. Chu and T. H. Naylor, "A Dynamic Model of the Firm," *Management Sci.,* **11:**7:736–750 (May 1965).
[263] J. W. Colin, *Forecasting Financial Needs of a Business: A Computer Simulation,* Hughes Dynamics, Los Angeles, 1963.
[264] R. L. Day, "Simulation of Consumer Preference," *J. Advertising Res.,* **5:**3:6–10 (September 1965).
[265] M. A. Geisler, "Integration of Modeling and Simulation in Organizational Studies," in *Management Sciences, Models and Techniques,* C. W. Churchman, (ed.), Vol. 1, Pergamon Press, New York, 1960, pp. 139–147.
[266] P. S. Greenlaw et al., *Business Simulation,* Prentice-Hall, Englewood Cliffs, N.J., 1962.
[267] T. R. Hoffmann, "Programmed Heuristics and the Concept of Par in Business Games," *Behavioral Sci.,* **10:**2:169–172 (April 1965).
[268] A. Y. Lewin, *Productivity Simulation of Production Personnel,* University of California at Los Angeles, 1963.
[269] T. H. Naylor et al., *Computer Simulation Techniques for Business and Economics,* Wiley, New York, 1965.
[270] R. Neate and W. J. Dacey, "A Simulation of Melting Shop Operations by Means of a Computer," *Process Control and Automation,* **5:**7:264–272 (July 1958).
[271] G. H. Orcutt, "Simulation of Economic Systems," *Am. Economic Rev.,* **50:**5:893–907 (December 1960).

[272] T. R. Roby, *Computer Simulation Models for Organization Theory,* Tufts University, Medford, Mass., AD611870, 1964.
[273] H. N. Shycon and R. B. Maffei, "Simulation—Tool for Better Distribution," *Harvard Bus. Rev.,* **38**:6:65–75 (November–December, 1960).
[274] E. Sussna, *Computer Simulation of Commercial Bank Response to Federal Reserve Open Market,* University of Pittsburgh, Pittsburgh, Pa., 1963.
[275] H. Weitz, *Simulation Models in Marketing,* IBM, Yorktown Heights, N.Y., 1966.

O. MILITARY AND SPACE SIMULATIONS

[276] R. H. Adams and J. L. Jenkins, "Simulation of Air Operations with the Air Battle Model," *J. Operations Res. Soc. America,* **8**:5:600–615 (September–October 1960).
[277] F. C. Brooks, *The Stochastic Processes of Large Battle Models,* Technical Operations, Burlington, Mass., 1963.
[278] C. E. Clark et al., *War Gaming, COSMAGON and ZIGSPIEL,* Operations Research Office, Johns Hopkins University, Bethesda, Md., AD235892, 1960.
[279] D. K. Clark, et al., *HUTSPIEL, A Theater War Game,* Operations Research Office, Johns Hopkins University, Bethesda, Md., AD216717, 1959.
[280] R. Dion, *The Organization of a Large Model,* Technical Operations, Washington, D.C., 1960.
[281] L. Feldman, *Summary Description of STAGE,* Technical Operations, Washington, D.C., 1963.
[282] R. J. Freeman et al., "A Mathematical Model of Supply Support for Space Operations," *J. Operations Res. Soc. America,* **14**:1:1–15 (January–February 1966).
[283] J. B. Friedman, *Data Requirements for the Air Battle Model,* Technical Operations, Washington, D.C., AD240456, 1958.
[284] S. I. Gass, "Computer Simulation Techniques in Project Mercury," *Bull. Operations Res. Soc. America,* **8**: Suppl. 2:B-96, B-97 (Fall 1960).
[285] H. J. Gawlik, *On the Use of a Digital Computer for Playing War Games,* Fort Halstead, Kent, England, AD226539, 1959.
[286] J. O. Harrison and E. M. Lee, *The STRATSPIEL Pilot Model,* Operations Research Office, Johns Hopkins University, Bethesda, Md., AD243663, 1960.
[287] S. H. Howe and P. W. McCree, *Model and Computer Program for Calculating the Kill Probabilities for Certain ASW Tactics,* Office of Naval Operations, Washington, D.C., AD402265, 1962.
[288] J. I. Keenan and Q. B. Morrison, *Computer Simulation and Logistics Management,* Wright-Patterson Air Force Base, Ohio, AD424440, 1963.
[289] W. J. Kenneally, *The Role of Large-Scale Simulation in the Program Definition Phase Environment,* Army Electronics Laboratory, Fort Monmouth, N.J., AD618273, 1964.
[290] Operations Simulation Group, *Air Defense Model,* Hughes Aircraft Company, Fullerton, Calif., 1961.
[291] L. F. Page, *A Dynamic Computer Model for Simulating Military Command Systems,* System Development Corporation, Santa Monica, Calif., AD612939, 1964.
[292] J. Pappas, *Mathematical Modeling for Missile Systems,* White Sands Missile Range, N.M., AD213761, 1959.

[293] J. E. Walsh, "General Simulation Model for Logistics Operations in a Randomly Damaged System," *Naval Res. Logistics Quart.*, **7**:4:453–470 (December 1960).
[294] D. F. Wilson et al.. *A Mathematical Model for Evaluating Tactical Decisions in Fleet Air Defense Games,* Naval Research Laboratories, Washington, D.C., AD241241, 1960.

P. TRAFFIC AND TRANSPORTATION SIMULATIONS

[295] C. M. Bennett, *Computer Simulation of Ship Tracks,* Navy Mine Defense Laboratories, Panama City, Fla., AD470156, 1965.
[296] P. B. Billing and J. E. Walsh, *A Model for Maritime Transportation Systems,* System Development Corporation, Santa Monica, Calif., AD407320, 1963.
[297] R. T. Coupal et al., "Digital Computer Simulation of Single-Track Railroad Operation," *Elect. Eng.,* **79**:8:648–653 (August 1960).
[298] I. M. Datz et al., "A Description of the Maritime Administration Mathematical Simulation of Ship Operations," *Trans. Soc. Naval Architects Marine Engineers,* **72**:493–513 (1965).
[299] D. A. D'Esopo et al., "Model for Simulating an Air Transportation System," *Naval Res. Logistics Quart.,* **7**:3:213–220 (September 1960).
[300] A. V. Gafarian et al., *The Development and Validation of a Digital Simulation Model for Design of Freeway Diamond Interchanges,* System Development Corporation, Santa Monica, Calif., 1966.
[301] H. H. Goode, "The Application of a High Speed Computer to the Definition and Solution of the Vehicular Traffic Problem," *J. Operations Res. Soc. America,* **5**:6:775–793 (December 1957).
[302] R. S. Grubmeyer, *Operations Analysis and Simulation Applied to Air Traffic Control,* Franklin Institute Laboratories for Research and Development, Philadelphia, 1961.
[303] W. A. Gunn, "Airline System Simulation," *J. Operations Res. Soc. America,* **12**:2:206–229 (March–April 1964).
[304] J. H. Katz, "Simulation of a Traffic Network," *Commun. Assoc. Computing Machinery,* **6**:8:480–486 (August 1963).
[305] J. H. Kell, "Intersection Delay Obtained by Simulating Traffic on a Computer," *Highway Res. Rec.,* **15**:73–97 (1963).
[306] R. M. Lewis and H. L. Michael, "Simulation of Traffic Flow to Obtain Volume Warrants for Intersection Control," *Highway Res. Rec.,* **15**:1–43 (1963).
[307] D. N. Madge, "Simulation of Truck Movements in an Open Pit Mining Operation," *J. Can. Operational Res. Soc.,* **2**:1:32–41 (June 1964).
[308] B. L. Marks, "Digital Simulations of Runway Utilization," *Operational Res. Quart.,* **15**:3:249–259 (September 1964).
[309] E. R. Ruiter and P. W. Shuldiner, "Operating Costs at Intersections Obtained from the Simulation of Traffic Flow," *Highway Res. Rec.,* **89**:26–38 (1965).
[310] R. P. Shumate and J. R. Dirksen, "A Simulation Study of Traffic Flow Behavior," *Highway Res. Rec.,* **72**:19–39 (1965).
[311] T. Thedeen, "A Note on the Poisson Tendency in Traffic Distribution," *Ann. Math. Statist.,* **35**:4:1823–1824 (December 1964).
[312] P. I. Welding, "Simulation of Underground Railway Operations," *Railway Gazette,* **121**:11:438–441 (June 1965).

Q. COMMUNICATIONS SIMULATIONS

[313] B. Backhaut, *Problems in Simulating Communications Networks,* General Services Administration, Washington, D.C., 1966.

[314] L. Brotman and J. Minker, "Digital Simulation of Complex Traffic Problems in Communications Systems." *J. Operations Res. Soc. America,* **5**:5:670–679 (October 1957).

[315] E. E. David, "Digital Simulation in Research on Human Communication," *Inst. Radio Engineers Proc.,* **49**:1:319–329 (January 1961).

[316] R. R. Legault et al., *Four Papers Concerning the Modeling of Communications Systems,* Institute of Science and Technology, University of Michigan, Ann Arbor, 1961.

[317] I. Shear, *An Airborne Communication Simulation (COMSIMP),* Mitre, Bedford, Mass., AD431200, 1964.

R. EDUCATION SIMULATIONS, INSTRUCTION

[318] D. D. Bushnell, *The Effects of Electronic Data Processing in Future Instructional Systems,* System Development Corporation, Santa Monica, Calif., AD402646, 1963.

[319] J. F. Cogswell et al., *Purpose and Strategy of the School Simulation Project,* System Development Corporation, Santa Monica, Calif., AD427752, 1963.

[320] J. E. Coulson, "Teaching Machine Simulated by Computer," *Computers Automation,* **9**:10:9–16 (October 1960).

[321] J. Csisma and C. C. Gotlieb, "Tests on a Computer Method for Constructing School Timetables," *Commun. Assoc. Computing Machinery,* **7**:3:160–163 (March 1964).

[322] W. J. Pelton and J. Staudhammer, *Computer Assistance in Teaching Engineering Mathematics,* System Development Corporation, Santa Monica. Calif., AD618953, 1965.

[323] I. R. Sternlicht and T. C. Rowan, *Computer Technology and Applications to Education,* System Development Corporation, Santa Monica, Calif., AD611057, 1964.

[324] L. M. Stolurow, *Computer-Based Instruction,* University of Illinois, Urbana, AD619155, 1965.

[325] J. A. Swets et al., *The Socratic System: A Computer System to Aid in Teaching Complex Concepts,* Bolt Beranek and Newman, Cambridge, AD421792, 1963.

S. HUMAN SIMULATIONS

[326] G. P. E. Clarkson and H. A. Simon, "Simulation of Individual and Group Behavior," *Am. Economic Rev.,* **50**:5:920–932 (December 1960).

[327] E. E. David, "Digital Simulation in Perceptual Research," *Nat. Electronic Conf.,* **15**:322–328 (1959).

[328] M. Davidson, *The Use of Simulation in the Development of Man-Machine Systems,* System Development Corporation, Santa Monica, Calif., AD630149, 1963.

[329] E. A. Feigenbaum, *Computer Simulation of Human Behavior,* Rand, Santa Monica, Calif., AD601075, 1964.
[330] J. T. Gullahorn and J. E. Gullahorn, "A Computer Model of Elementary Social Behavior," *Behavioral Sci.,* **8**:4:354–362 (October 1963).
[331] J. T. Gullahorn and J. E. Gullahorn, *Computer Simulation of Role Conflict Resolution,* System Development Corporation, Santa Monica, Calif., AD624941, 1965.
[332] E. P. Hanavan, *A Mathematical Model of the Human Body,* Wright-Patterson Air Force Base, Ohio, AD608463, 1964.
[333] A. P. Hare, "Computer Simulation of Interaction in Small Groups," *Behavioral Sci.,* **6**:3:261–265 (July 1961).
[334] A. Hormann, "GAKU: An Artificial Student," *Behavioral Sci.,* **10:1**:88–107 (January 1965).
[335] C. I. Hovland, "Computer Simulation of Concept Attainment," *Behavorial* Sci., **5**:3:265–267 (July 1960).
[336] E. B. Hunt, *Simulation and Analytical Models of Memory,* University of California at Los Angeles, AD400136, 1962.
[337] K. R. Laughery, "Simulation of Human Problem-Solving Behavior," *Psychometrika,* **27**:3:265–282 (September 1962).
[338] F. N. Marzocco, *Computer Models for Human Behavior,* System Development Corporation, Santa Monica, Calif., 1963.
[339] A. Newell and H. A. Simon, *The Simulation of Human Thought,* Rand, Santa Monica, Calif., 1959.
[340] N. Reid, "Aping Man on Computers; Human Simulation," *Control Eng.,* **7**:8:38–39 (August 1960).
[341] R. F. Reiss, "Digital Simulation of Neuro-muscular Organisms," *Behavioral Sci.,* **5**:4:343–358 (October 1960).
[342] F. Rosenblatt, "Perception Simulation Experiments," *Inst. Radio Engineering Proc.,* **48**:3:301–309 (March 1960).
[343] A. I. Seigel, "Computer Simulation of Man's Performance," *Naval Res. Rev.* (June 1961).
[344] H. A. Simon, "Computer Simulation of Human Thinking and Problem Solving," *Computers Automation* **10**:4:18–24 (April 1961).
[345] I. de Sola Pool, "Simulating Social Systems," *Intern Sci. Technol.,* **23**:27:62–70 (March 1964).
[346] R. W. Stacy and N. A. Coulter, "Simulation of Human Psychological System," *Am. Soc. Mechanical Engineers,* Paper 60-AV-38 (June 1960).

T. MISCELLANEOUS SIMULATIONS

[347] W. A. Badlong, "Simulating Electronic Switching with a Computer," *Bell Labs Rec.,* **38**:9:328–333 (September 1960).
[348] C. T. Baker and B. P. Dzielinski, "Simulation of a Simplified Job Shop," *Management Sci.,* **6**:3:311–323 (April 1960).
[349] R. C. Brigham, "Generalized Simulation of Post Office Systems," *J. Assoc. Computing Machinery,* **8**:252–259 (April 1961).
[350] R. B. Fetter and J. D. Thompson, "The Simulation of Hospital Systems," *J. Operations Res. Soc. America,* **13**:5:689–711 (September–October 1965).

[351] L. R. Ford et al., "Computer Terrain Simulation for Line-of-Sight Calculations," *J. Operations Res. Soc. America,* **7**:4:478–482 (July–August 1959).
[352] F. G. Foster and I. Elce, "A Simulation Programme for Machine Maintenance, Telephone Traffic and Stock Models," *Operational Res. Quart.,* **14**:3:333–342 (September 1963).
[353] A. V. Gafarian and J. E. Walsh, *Statistical Approach for Validating Simulation Models by Comparison with Operational Systems—Illustrated for Traffic Flow,* System Development Corporation, Santa Monica, Calif., AD632478, 1966.
[354] B. E. Goetz, "Monte Carlo Solution of Waiting-Line Problems," *Management Technol.,* Monograph, No. 1:2–11 (January 1960).
[355] C. S. Gromme, *Digital Computer Programs for Paleomagnetic Research,* University of California, Berkeley, AD616358, 1964.
[356] D. Gross and J. L. Ray, "A General Purpose Forecast Simulator," *Management Sci.,* **11**:6:B-119-135 (April 1965).
[357] J. Gyr et al., "Computer Simulation of a Model of Cognitive Organization," *Behavioral Sci.,* **7**:1:111–116 (January 1962).
[358] S. W. Hess et al., "Nonpartisan Political Redistricting by Computer," *J. Operations Res. Soc. America,* **13**:6:998–1006 (November –December 1965).
[359] C. G. Hilton, *The SPADATS Mathematical Model,* Ford Motor Company, Newport Beach, Calif., AD415001, 1963.
[360] S. Klein, *Dynamic Simulation of Historical Change in Language Using Monte Carlo Techniques,* System Development Corporation, Santa Monica, Calif., AD610695, 1964.
[361] R. S. Ledley and L. B. Lusted, "Computers in Medical Data Processing," *J. Operations Res. Soc. America,* **8**:3:299–310 (May–June 1960).
[362] H. Ozhaptan and R. Gettig, "Computer Simulation of Man-Integrated Systems," *Behavioral Sci.,* **8**:3:259–266 (July 1963).
[363] M. N. Palley and W. G. O'Regan, "A Computer Technique for the Study of Forest Sampling Methods," *Forest Sci.,* **7**:3:282–294 (September 1961).
[364] E. B. Roberts, "Simulation Techniques for Understanding R and D Mangement," *IRE Nat. Convention Rec.,* **7**:10:38–43 (1959).
[365] H. Schenck, "Simulation of the Evolution of Drainage-Basin Networks with a Digital Computer," *J. Geophys. Res.,* **68**:20:5739–5745 (October 1963).
[366] D. R. Schurz and E. Persson, *Computer Programs for the Reduction of Photogrammetric Cloud Data,* Massachusetts Institute of Technology, Cambridge, AD616386, 1964.
[367] A. K. Wolf et al., *The Baseball Game: An Automatic Question-Answerer,* Massachusetts Institute of Technology, Lexington, Mass., AD432038, 1963.

U. BIBLIOGRAPHIES

[368] J. H. Batchelor, *Operations Research—An Annotated Bibliography,* vols. 1–3, St. Louis University Press, St. Louis, Mo., 1959, 1962, 1963.
[369] L. S. Deming, "Selected Bibliography of Statistical Literature 1930 to 1957," *Nat. Bur. Standards J. Res.,* **64B**:55–76 (January–March 1960); **64B**:175–192 (July–September 1960); **65B**:61–93 (January–March 1961); **66B**:15–28 (January–March 1962); **66B**:109–151 (July–September 1962).
[370] L. S. Deming, "Selected Bibliography of Statistical Literature: Supplement, 1958–1960," *Nat. Bur. Standards J. Res.,* **67B**:91–133 (April–June 1963).

[371] W. T. Federer, *Literature Review of Experimental Design Through 1949,* University of Wisconsin, Madison, AD433913, 1964.
[372] E. E. Graziano, *Medical Diagnosis with Electronic Computers: An Annotated Bibliography,* Lockheed Aircraft Corporation, Sunnyvale, Calif., AD407945, 1963.
[373] D. G. Malcolm, "Bibliography on the Use of Simulation in Management Analysis," *J. Operations Res. Soc. America,* **8**:2:169–177 (March–Arpil 1960); also see AD297445.
[374] Mathematics and Computations Laboratory, *Bibliography of Publications,* National Resource Evaluation Center, Washington, D.C., AD457358, 1965.
[375] H. W. Miles, *Operations Research—An ASTIA Report Bibliography,* Department of Commerce, Washington, D.C., AD269750, 1962.
[376] F. E. Murfree and W. L. Hercules, *Operations Research (Supplement), A DDC Report Bibliography,* Defense Documentation Center, Alexandria, Va., AD426275, 1964.
[377] Operations Research Group of Case Institute of Technology, *A Comprehensive Bibliography on Operations Research, 1957–1958,* Wiley, New York, 1963.
[378] N. G. Parke, *Guide to the Literature of Mathematics and Physics,* Dover, New York, 1958.
[379] M. F. Ronayne (ed.), *An Annotated Bibliography for the Systems Professional,* Systems and Procedures Association, Detroit, 1962.
[380] H. S. Schloss, *A Bibliography of Publications in the Theory of Games,* Northeastern University, Boston, Mass., AD234153, 1959.
[381] M. Shubik, "Bibliography on Simulation, Gaming, Artificial Intelligence and Other Topics," *J. Am. Statist. Assoc.,* **LV**:736–751 (1969).
[382] R. L. Thayne et al., *Computers and Data Processing Systems (Bibliography),* Department of Commerce, Washington, D.C., AD291850, 1962.

V. DICTIONARIES, GLOSSARIES

[383] H. Breuer, *Dictionary for Computer Languages,* Academic Press, New York, 1966.
[384] W. B. Fritz, "Selected Definitions," *Commun. Assoc. Computing Machinery,* **6**:4:152–158 (April 1963).
[385] M. G. Kendall and W. R. Buckland, *Dictionary of Statistical Terms,* Oliver and Boyd, Edinburgh, 1957.
[386] J. W. Mayne, "Glossary of Terms Used in Gaming and Simulation," *J. Can. Operational Res. Soc.,* **4**:2:114–118 (July 1966).
[387] C. J. Sippl, *Computer Dictionary and Handbook,* Howard W. Sams, Indianapolis, 1966.
[388] R. Taylor, *Glossary—Computer Technology, Conversion Tables,* Autonetics, Downey, Calif., AD459708, 1962.

W. MISCELLANEOUS

[389] H. Borko (ed.), *Computer Applications in the Behavioral Sciences,* Prentice-Hall, Englewood Cliffs, N.J., 1962.
[390] S. H. Brooks, "A Discussion of Random Methods for Seeking Maxima," *J. Operations Res. Soc. America,* **6**:2:244–251 (March–April 1958).

[391] G. W. Brown, *Computation in Decision Making,* McGraw-Hill, New York, 1960.

[392] R. L. Chapman, *Data for Testing a Model of Organizational Behavior,* Rand, Santa Monica, Calif., AD237789, 1960.

[393] C. W. Churchman, *Measurement—Definitions and Theory,* Wiley, New York, 1959.

[394] A. Hillier, *A Program for Computing Probabilities over Rectangular Regions under the Multivariate Normal Distribution,* Stanford University, Stanford, Calif., AD261283, 1961.

[395] F. McNolty, "Kill Probabilities When the Weapon Bias Is Randomly Distributed," *J. Operations Res,. Soc. America,* **10**:5:693–707 (September–October 1962).

[396] R. W. Metzger, *Elementary Mathematical Programming,* Wiley, New York, 1958.

[397] Navy Department, *The Nature of Random Demand,* Navy Department, Washington, D.C., AD414725, 1961.

[398] W. Richardson, *RAWS II: A Multiple Regression Analysis Program,* Institute of Science and Technology, University of Michigan, Ann Arbor, AD414967, 1963.

[399] M. Rosenblatt, *Independence and Dependence,* Brown University, Providence, R.I., AD240011, 1960.

[400] T. L. Saaty, *Elements of Queueing Theory,* McGraw-Hill, New York, 1961.

[401] C. H. Springer et al., *Advanced Methods and Models,* vol. 2, R. D. Irwin, Homewood, Ill., 1965).

[402] J. W. Taylor and N. J. Dean, "Managing to Manage the Computer," *Harvard Bus. Rev.,* **44**:5:98–110 (September–October 1966).

[403] J. W. Tukey, "The Future of Data Analysis," *Ann. Math. Statist.,* **33**:1:1–67, (March 1962).

[404] R. G. West and J. R. Reynolds, *FORTRAN Program for Plotting Two Dimensional Graphs,* Naval Missile Center, Point Mugu, Calif., AD616730, 1965.

[405] D. R. J. White, et al., "POED—A Method of Evaluating System Performance," *IEEE Trans. Engineering Management,* **EM-10**:4:177–182 (December 1963).

INDEX